WORLD® AIR POWER

J O U R N A L

Aerospace Publishing Ltd

Airtime Publishing Inc.

Published quarterly by
Aerospace Publishing Ltd
179 Dalling Road
London W6 0ES
UK

Copyright © 1992 Aerospace
Publishing Ltd

Cutaway drawings
copyright © 1992 Greenborough
Associates Ltd

ISSN 0959-7050

Aerospace ISBN 1 874023 17 4
            (softback)
            1 874023 18 2
            (hardback)
Airtime ISBN   1-880588-07-2
            (hardback)

Published under licence in USA and
Canada by Airtime Publishing Inc.,
10 Bay Street, Westport,
CT 06880, USA

Editorial Offices:
WORLD AIR POWER JOURNAL
Aerospace Publishing Ltd
179 Dalling Road
London W6 0ES
UK

Publisher: Stan Morse
Editors: David Donald
        Jon Lake
Production Editors:
    Karen Leverington
    Trisha Palmer
Design: Barry Savage
        Robert Hewson
Typesetting: SX Composing Ltd
Origination and printing by
    Imago Publishing Ltd
Printed in Italy

Europe Correspondent:
    Paul Jackson
Washington Correspondent:
    Robert F. Dorr
USA West Coast Correspondent:
    René J. Francillon
Asia Correspondent:
    Pushpindar Singh

The editors of WORLD AIR
POWER JOURNAL welcome
photographs for possible
publication, but cannot accept any
responsibility for loss or damage to
unsolicited material.

World Air Power Journal is a
registered trademark in the
United States of America of
Airtime Publishing Inc.

World Air Power Journal
is published quarterly
and is available by
subscription

SUBSCRIPTION AND BACK
NUMBERS:

UK and World (except USA and
Canada) write to:
Aerospace Publishing Ltd
FREEPOST
PO Box 2822
W6 0BR
UK

(No stamp required if posted
within the UK)

USA and Canada, write to:
Airtime Publishing Inc.
Subscription Dept
10 Bay Street
Westport, CT 06880
USA

Prevailing subscription rates are
available on request.
For single and back issues of the
soft-cover edition (subject to
availability):
$17.95 each for delivery within
mainland USA, Alaska and
Hawaii. $21 (Can) each for
delivery to Canada. $21 (US)
each for delivery overseas.
Please enclose payment with
your order. Visa and MasterCard
accepted. Include your card
number, expiration date and
signature.
Hard-cover subscription rates
available on request.

Publisher, North America:
    Melvyn Williams
Subscription Director:
    Linda DeAngelis
Charter Member Services Managers:
    Jill Brooks

WORLD AIR POWER®

J O U R N A L

CONTENTS

Military Aviation Review

International

Harrier II-Plus production

In signing an agreement on 7 February 1992, Italy became the first to commit itself to production of the Harrier II-Plus radar-equipped version of the AV-8B. Similar action by Spain and the US Marine Corps was expected to be a formality in view of the September 1990 memorandum committing all three to integration of AN/APG-65 in the Harrier II airframe. The prototype, converted on the production line, is 164128, and is scheduled to fly in October 1992. Delivery of 24 to the USMC will begin with 164542 in the second quarter of 1993. Spain plans to buy eight new Plus aircraft as well as converting its 11 surviving AV-8Bs to the same standard and obtaining a TAV-8B trainer. Italy, which has already taken delivery of two TAV-8Bs for its operating unit, the Gruppo Aerei Imbarcati (Embarked Aircraft Squadron) at Taranto/Grottaglie, wants 16 and has options on a further eight. A first batch of three II-Plus aircraft was ordered for Italy in 1991, comprising aircraft from the USMC batch of 24.

Western Europe

BELGIUM:

Agustas conditionally accepted

Delayed acceptance took place on 13 January of the first of 46 Agusta A 109CM helicopters armed with BGM-71 TOW anti-tank missiles. Assembled by SABCA at Charleroi for the Belgian army, the helicopters were due to be delivered from June 1991 but were rejected when found to be 123 kg (270 lb) above the specified weight. Measures such as introduction of Kevlar components in the undercarriage and re-positioning of avionics to shorten wiring runs will solve the problem by reducing the empty weight to 1191 kg (2,626 lb), allowing the last A 109 to be delivered in June 1993. However, the first 10 A 109s are being accepted in overweight condition and will be modified later. Initial operator is 18 Squadron at Merzbrück, Germany. Plans to integrate the Belgian and Netherlands armies will assist Agusta in its aim of selling A 109s to meet the latter's anti-tank helicopter requirements.

FRANCE:

Naval Rafale's first flight

Naval deployment of the Dassault Rafale – due in 1998 – was brought a step nearer with the first flight of prototype M01 on 12 December. Airborne from the company's test airfield at Istres, M01 achieved Mach 1.4 and an altitude of 42,000 ft (412802 m) during its maiden outing in the hands of Yves Kerherve. Later in 1992 it will go to the US Navy experimental base at Patux-ent River for catapult trials, after which it is to make its first carrier landings and take-offs in 1993, aboard the *Foch*. This will be the first time a French naval aircraft has been tested in the USA. France used to use the catapult at the UK's Royal Aircraft Establishment, Bedford, for its naval air-craft development, but that was scrapped with the advent of the Sea Harrier.

Front-line cuts

Following a 2.3-per cent cut in defence spending, the Armée de l'Air will suffer a 13 per cent reduction in its front-line strength – from 450 to 390 aircraft – according to information released in Paris during February. Before the end of 1993, the 13ᵉ Escadre de Chasse will disband its three squadrons of Mirage IIIs and Mirage 5Fs. Its place at Colmar/Mayenheim will be taken by the 33ᵉ Escadre de Recon-naissance, which is to move from Stras-bourg/Entzheim. At Reims/Champagne, EC 30 will relinquish air defence duties for ground attack when it begins to receive Mirage F1CTs in 1994. The air force is con-verting 55 F1Cs into F1CTs to re-equip the wing's three squadrons, and received the first at Colmar in January.

EC 11 at Toul/Rosières is expected to begin Rafale conversion in 1998, although only one of its three squadrons will have completed the process by 2000. The other Jaguar wing, EC 7 at St Dizier/Robinson, expects no new equipment before the end of the century, and must be regarded as prime subject for any cuts to be made in the coming years. Two squadrons of Mirage IVPs armed with ASMP missiles are to be withdrawn in 1996, to be replaced by simi-larly-equipped Mirage 2000Ns of the type already deployed by EC 4 at Luxeuil/St Sauveur. The conventional attack Mirage 2000D will remain in EC 3 at Nancy/Essey. (The wing's first squadron – EC 2/3 – converted from Mirage IIIEs on 1 Sep-tember 1991, but is using Mirage 2000Ns until the 2000D becomes available at the end of 1993.)

Cuts have been made in the Mirage 2000 programme, however. The final 24 planned 2000Cs will not be funded, leav-ing the interceptor version's order book at 146 2000Cs and 22 2000Bs to serve with EC 2 at Dijon/Longvic (completed), EC 5 at Orange/Caritat (completed) and EC 12 at Cambrai/Epinoy (beginning conver-sion). Firm orders for the attack versions comprise all 75 planned Mirage 2000Ns and 75 of the intended 105 2000Ds. It now appears that no more 2000Ds will be ordered.

In its 1992 budget, the air force ordered 20 EMBRAER EMB-312 Tucanos and the last 14 Mirage F1CT conversions. It will take delivery of 16 Mirage 2000Cs and the final six 2000Ns, following which Mirage 2000D deliveries will begin in 1993 at the rate of 15 per year, accompanied by a mere six 2000Cs annually. A significant omis-sion from funding was the first production batch of Dassault Rafales, making the planned July 1996 delivery date impossible to meet. The Tucanos follow two aircraft authorised in September 1991 and are part of a requirement for 50 to equip the Ecole de l'Air at Salon de Provence. A further 30 Tucanos, required to replace Fouga Magis-ters in several base flights, are unlikely to be funded.

Fennecs for ALAT

French army aviation, ALAT, took de-livery on 7 February of its first Aérospatiale AS 355UN Fennec training helicopter, equipped with a 'glass' cockpit compatible with night vision goggles. The first four Fennecs were ordered in 1990 as a cheaper operating alternative to the Pumas pre-viously used for night training, and the total has now increased to 10, all to be de-livered by May 1993. User will be the Ecole d'Application at Luc/Le Cannet des Maures.

Second-hand Alpha Jets

Plans became known during February for a purchase from Germany of 30 surplus attack-configured Dassault/Dornier Alpha Jet Es to replace some of the 40 Alpha Jet A trainers with 8ᵉ Escadre de Chasse at Cazaux. EC 8 is the French fighter weapons school, and hard use of its aircraft in combat training has resulted in flight restrictions, including a 5g manoeuvring limit and a ban on low-level dogfighting. The ex-German machines are destined for the wing's second squadron, Escadrille 2/8 'Nice'.

Atlantique production cut

The Aéronavale appears unlikely to order more than the 30 Dassault Atlantique 2 maritime patrollers to which it is currently committed, despite earlier plans to acquire 42. Funding for three in the 1992 budget is expected to be the last, and deliveries will now end in 1998. By the end of 1992, the navy will have received 15 Atlantique 2s to complete replacement of Atlantic 1s with 23 and 24 Flottilles at Lann-Bihoué. Next to re-equip are 21F and 22F at Nimes-Garons.

Mercy missions

Transall C.160Fs of the 61ᵉ Escadre de Transport from Orléans were unusually active abroad in the closing months of 1991. During December, Operation Baumier was completed in Zaïre with the evacu-ation since 23 September of 2,300 Euro-pean refugees from civil disorder. The air-craft flew some 250 hours, operating from nearby Chad and the Central African Re-public. An overall white C.160F, No. 44, was operating in Cambodia on behalf of the UN observer force, following the end-ing of the civil war. The C.160 deployed on 25 October and was soon joined by four army Pumas.

This venerable Sud-Est SE 210 Caravelle continues to serve the French government as a VIP transport, based at Paris-Orly with GLAM.

The Luftwaffe is to sell many of its Alpha Jets to France to equip EC 8 at Cazaux, whose own aircraft are reaching the end of their fatigue lives.

GERMANY:

Tornado deliveries complete

Germany's 357th and final production Panavia Tornado was accepted by the Luftwaffe on 28 January. Serial number 4657 was also the last of 35 Tornado ECR electronic combat and reconnaissance aircraft bought as a follow-on to the 322 (and two refurbished pre-series aircraft) which formed the original commitment to the tri-national programme. A third batch of 35 had been planned, but was abandoned. The air force received 245 production Tornados (excluding six prototype/pre-series machines), of which 55 have dual controls, but are fully combat-capable. The balance of 112, including 12 with a second stick, has been supplied to the Marineflieger.

All 35 ECRs have initially gone to form 2 Staffel of JBG 38 at Jever, where the first was received on 21 May 1990. The initial 18 are being transferred (from mid-1991 onwards) to 1 Staffel of JBG 32 at Lechfeld, its strike Tornados going to other units as attrition replacements. Development problems have been reported with the ECR's Texas Instruments emitter-locator, resulting in a delay to this version being declared operational.

Meanwhile, the Luftwaffe is looking at reconnaissance systems to be installed in some 40 Tornados which it will receive from the navy when MFG 1 disbands at Schleswig. The aircraft will remain at the base and re-form AG 51, which is due to disband as an RF-4E Phantom unit (with AG 52) before 1994 and pass at least some of its old equipment to Turkey. The RAF's infra-red video system installed in Tornado GR.Mk 1As is one potential reconnaissance fit being examined by Germany.

Alpha's omega

At Oldenburg, 1 Staffel of JBG 43 began running down late in 1991 prior to disbandment before April. Known to NATO as 431 Squadron, the Alpha Jet unit was an honorary 'Tiger' although its badge depicted a fox's mask. JBG 43 was to have continued as a one-squadron wing for a year or more, but Germany is now planning to relinquish all 166 remaining (from 175) Alpha Jets during 1992. The Alpha's role in support of the NATO ACE Mobile Force will be assumed by RF-4E Phantoms (until they, also, are withdrawn) and Tornados. France plans to buy 30 Alpha Jets and Portugal is interested in 50, which will probably be received as German military aid.

Twenty of Hungary's MiG-21bis aircraft are scheduled to receive an avionics upgrade, including Western radar, and the other 23 will follow if this is judged a success.

More VIP jets required

Provision of communications between Bonn and Berlin has forced the Luftwaffe to consider purchasing additional executive transport aircraft. The air force already has seven Canadair Challengers and three ageing VFW-614s, but the commander of its transport force indicated in February that three more Challengers and up to four of the forthcoming Canadair Regional Jets are needed. There could also be a requirement for a stretched version of the new Dornier 328 twin-turboprop. Some loss of capacity will follow conversion of the Luftwaffe's four Boeing 707s to tankers, although the three Airbus A310s recently added to the fleet will be useful replacements: two in VIP fit and the other as a combi. Two VIP A340s will be bought in 1996-97.

Below: Mirage 2000s of EC 3/4 are shown carrying three different Escadrille badges. 'Le Gauloise' is nearest, the Eagle next, and the Desert Fox nearest the C-135. The same badge is on each side of the fin.

Eastern retentions announced

Only at the turn of the year did the Luftwaffe announce officially which former East German aircraft would be retained – although basic intentions had been apparent for some time. In this category are the 24 MiG-29s, plus seven Mil Mi-2 'Hoplites', 26 Mil Mi-8 'Hips', four Let L-410 Turbolets, eight Antonov An-26 'Curls', two Tupolev Tu-154 'Careless' and three Ilyushin Il-62 'Candids'. In an intermediate classification are 49 Mil Mi-24 'Hinds' which will be used for a short time before disposal. Some other types of aircraft, including Antonov An-2 'Colts' and Zlin 43s, were disposed of almost immediately after unification. Additionally, the navy is to discard 16 Mil Mi-14 'Hazes'.

In all, new serial numbers were allocated to 671 former East German aircraft, which were three Airbus A310s of the civil airline, Interflug; two Tu-154Ms; two Tu-134As; three Il-62Ms; 63 'Floggers' comprising nine MiG-23MFs, 28 -23MLs, 18 -23BNs and eight -23UB trainers; 251 'Fishbeds' comprising 45 MiG-21SPSs, 56 -21Ms, 47 -21MFs, 41 -21bis variants and training equipment of 36 -21UMs, 13 -21Us and 13 -21USs; 54 'Fitters' comprising 46 Su-22M-4s and eight two-seat -22M-3UKs; 52 Albatrosses comprising 50 L-30ZOs and two -39Vs; 24 'Fulcrums' comprising 20 MiG-29s and four trainer MiG-29UBs; 12 An-26s; 12 L-410UVPs; 101 'Hips' comprising 23 Mi-8Ss, 70 Mi-8Ts and eight Mi-9s; 25 Mi-2Ss; 16 'Hazes' comprising 10 Mi-14PLs and six -14BTs; and 51 'Hinds' comprising 39 Mi-24Ds and 12 -24Ps. During 1991, some surplus aircraft were delivered to allied countries for evaluation, including three MiG-23MLs, two Su-22M-4s, an Mi-8T, an Mi-24D and an Mi-24P to the USA, and one Su-22M-4 to the United Kingdom.

Left and below: The contest to fulfil Finland's fighter requirement is hotting up. This F/A-18 has been evaluated in-country, and Dassault have even designed a promotional Mirage 2000-5 zap.

Military Aviation Review

Upgraded helicopters enter service

Re-delivery began in 1991 of the first army MBB PAH-1 anti-tank helicopters to have undergone conversion to PAH-1-A1 standard. The helicopters have upgraded engines and rotor blades, but the most obvious recognition feature is re-positioning of the three HOT anti-tank missile launch tubes. These are now angled downwards at 45° instead of being mounted horizontally. The Heeresflieger is modifying 155 of its 207 remaining PAH-1s to this standard, while a further 52 are to receive Stinger SAMs in place of HOT for armed escort duties, changing their designation to BSH (Begleitschutzhübschrauber).

GREECE:

Armed helicopters planned

A significant upgrading of army aviation in Greece was timetabled in the 1992-96 defence plan in the shape of at least 12 attack helicopters. Greece is to choose between US offers of up to 20 McDonnell Douglas AH-64 Apaches equipped with 446 Rockwell AGM-114 Hellfire anti-tank missiles and the TADS/PNVS infra-red system for night flying and target-finding; and 12 Bell AH-1W SuperCobras also with Hellfire. Apache is understood to be the preferred helicopter. The proposed order would apparently be separate to the 15 Bell AH-1F Cobras promised by the US in October 1991.

Seahawk successful

Following a protracted battle against the Aérospatiale AS 532CS Cougar, Sikorsky's Seahawk was chosen for deployment aboard four MEKO 2000G frigates on order for the Hellenic Navy. The contract includes five S-70B-6 versions of the anti-submarine Seahawk, plus options on three more, deliveries to take place in 1995-96. Equipment fitted to the helicopters will include Bendix AN/AQS-18(V)-3 dipping sonar, Eaton AN/APS-143 search radar and Litton/General Instrument AN/ALR-66(V)-2 radar warning receiver.

Chinook upgrade plans

It was revealed in December that nine Greek army Boeing Vertol CH-47C Chinooks are to be upgraded to CH-47D standard. An associated contract to Textron Lycoming covers the helicopters' 3,750-shp T55-L11 turboshaft engines which will be raised to T55-L-712 configuration, in which each will deliver 4,378 shp. The army received 10 Chinooks, five of them transferred from the air force in 1988, one of which has been lost. Shipments to the US for re-work at Boeing's Ridley plant began in March 1992, and re-deliveries are expected between October 1993 and 1995. Three will return in 1993, four in 1994 and two in 1995.

Mirage 2000 deliveries resume

Following resolution of a dispute with Thomson-CSF, makers of the RDM multi-role radar, Greece agreed on 21 February to continue taking delivery of Dassault Mirage 2000s. All are expected to be in service with 331 and 332 Mire, components of 114ᵃ Pterix Mahis at Tanagra, by the end of 1992. Supply of 36 Mirage 2000EGs and four 2000BG two-seat trainers began in March 1988 but was halted on Greek instructions in October 1989 when 12 of the single-seat aircraft remained to be delivered. Greece alleged that RDM did not meet its specifications, but no further details of the shortcoming have been revealed.

RAF Phantom interest

An announcement in Athens on 20 February brought news that the HAF was sending assessors to the United Kingdom to examine McDonnell Douglas F-4M Phantom FGR.Mk 2s of the RAF, with a view to buying 32 when they are withdrawn from service later in 1992. This move is somewhat surprising, in that the British Phantom is a very different aircraft to the remainder of its fellows, with Rolls-Royce Spey turbofans (in place of GE J79s) and a high proportion of UK avionics.

Above: This Dutch Lynx wears a red, white and blue tricolour and fuselage badge to commemorate 75 years of naval aviation in the Netherlands.

Below: Two No. 14 Squadron Tornados. The aircraft in desert pink wears No. 617 Squadron tail markings, being earmarked for rapid deployment to Turkey. The other fought (as 'Buddha') in the war.

Below and below left: These are two of the Yugoslav government VIP aircraft that have visited Valkenburg in connection with the European peace initiatives. They are a Learjet 35B and a Dassault Falcon 50.

Above: This Tu-134 serves with the former Soviet air force as a VIP transport aircraft, and has visited Western Europe on a number of occasions.

Left: This Dutch Orion is one of at least two that has been specially decorated to celebrate the 75th anniversary of Dutch naval aviation.

ITALY:
Defence cuts planned

Five squadrons and four air bases of the Aeronautica Militare Italiana are scheduled to disappear as the result of defence cuts presented to parliament for approval late in 1991. The AMI will be reduced from 76,460 to 63,100 personnel and slim down to six F-104S-ASA Starfighter squadrons (including one mostly equipped with TF-104Gs); three interdictor squadrons, all with Tornados; five attack/reconnaissance squadrons (eventually all equipped with AMX); and one maritime patrol squadron combining the 16 Atlantics formerly operated by two squadrons. Additionally, a new squadron will be formed with two AEW aircraft of a type yet to be decided. Bases nominated for closure are Grazzanise (home of 10 Squadron and its F-104S-ASAs); Treviso/San Angelo (14 Squadron, G91R); Brindisi (13 Squadron, G91Y); and Cagliari/Elmas (86 Squadron, Atlantic).

The new plan reduces single-seat AMX procurement from 187 to 135 and limits the Eurofighter programme to 130 aircraft instead of 165 – the latter as Starfighter replacements. On the positive side, the army is to get 30 more scout-configured Agusta A 129 Mangustas to augment 60 in anti-tank roles, while the navy is to receive a second V/STOL carrier and more AV-8B Harrier II-Plus attack aircraft.

Army aviation additions

Italian Army Light Aviation (ALE – Aviazione Leggera dell'Esercito) took delivery in November 1991 of the first four Agusta-Bell AB 412SP helicopters from a follow-on batch of six – plus six Meridionali-Boeing CH-47C-Plus Chinooks also on order – which it will operate for the National Civil Protection Agency (SNPC – Servizio Nazionale Protezione Civile). On completion of deliveries, SNPC will have six Canadair CL-215s, one Lockheed C-130H Hercules, three Alenia G 222s, nine CH-47s, six AB 412s and two AB 212s. With the exception of the civil-registered CL-215s, the other aircraft are normally operated by the Italian armed forces and made available (with crews) to the SNPC when required.

ALE also took delivery of the first of eight Dornier 228-212 light twin transports (including two with survey equipment for the Istituto Geografico). The three major helicopter wings of the Italian army have been retitled from Raggruppamenti to Regimenti and are now 1° Regimento 'Antares' at Viterbo; 4° Regimento 'Altair' at Bolzano; and 5° Regimento 'Rigel' at Casarsa.

Para-military Piaggios

Italy's paramilitary customs service, the Guardia di Finanza, received the first of 10 new Piaggio P.166DL-3/SEM surveillance aircraft on 23 January. Two more will be transferred from the Alitalia airline training school. Initial operating unit is the 1° Gruppo Osservazione Aeromarittima.

NETHERLANDS:
Combat helicopter plans

Plans were revealed late in 1991 to re-form 302 Squadron of the Royal Netherlands Air Force with combat helicopters at Gilze-Rijen later in the 1990s. This will be the second part of a procurement programme which initially requires 298 Squadron (with Alouette IIIs at Soesterberg) to move to Gilze and re-equip with 20 leased attack helicopters in 1994. During 1997-98, these will be returned in favour of 40 new helicopters of a more advanced type, allowing a second unit to be established. Currently, 301 and 302 Squadrons are 'shadow' reservist units which would form in wartime with Alouette IIIs and BO 105s.

Last Fokker F-16

Almost 13 years of General Dynamics F-16 Fighting Falcon production came to an end on 27 February when Fokker's Schiphol plant delivered its 300th and final aircraft. Serialled J-021 (89-0021), this was also the last of 213 for the home air force, comprising 177 F-16As and 36 F-16Bs. Remaining aircraft have been built for export: 60 F-16As and 12 F-16Bs for Norway; eight F-16As and four F-16Bs in Denmark's follow-up batch; two F-16As for the USAF; and one attrition replacement F-16B for Egypt. The KLu lost its 25th F-16 on 11 February, but the premier Fokker-built aircraft, J-259 (78-0259), remains in service, having first flown on 3 May 1979.

NORWAY:
Second Coast Guard Orion

Redelivery took place in February of the second of two Lockheed P-3B Orions converted for maritime surveillance duties with the Kystvakt (Coast Guard). Replaced in 1989 by delivery of four new P-3Cs, the two aircraft have been converted to P-3N standard by removal of their submarine detection equipment. VIP transport is a secondary duty.

SPAIN:
Upgrade programmes cut

Phase-out of the Dassault Mirage III before the end of 1992 was one result of funding reductions confirmed early in the year. The 18 IIIEs and five IIIDE trainers were to have received a comprehensive upgrade by CESELSA and CASA, but operating wing Ala 11 at Manises will now be disbanded. Two squadrons totalling 23 CASA/Northrop SF-5s have also had refurbishment of their equipment – this time by CASA with new wings from Bristol Aerospace of Canada – abandoned. They will continue to fly with Ala 21 at Morón despite reports that they are in generally poor state. Finance for modernising the seven Lockheed P-3A/B Orions of Ala 22 at Jerez has been halved, with the result that their upgrade will probably be restricted to improving the AN/APS-80 radar for better surface surveillance and leaving anti-submarine sensors as they stand.

SWEDEN:
Disbandments planned

Four squadrons of Sweden's Flygvapen were set to disband in the spring after parliament debated the proposed 1992-97 five-year defence plan. The units – not yet named – will represent the first half of a two-stage reduction which will see four wings disbanded by the end of 1997. More positively, the SIG Gripen programme, including 25 two-seat JAS 39Bs, will proceed with priority, as will the PS 890 AEW radar, which is being tested aboard a Swearingen Metro.

Elint equipment upgraded

A late-1991 announcement revealed that the two veteran Tp 85 Caravelles operated by F 13M at Malmslätt on electronic intelligence (Elint) gathering missions are to be replaced. The Swedish air force expects to be able to announce the successor aircraft later in 1992 and is currently examining the McDonnell Douglas MD-87, Gulfstream IV, Fokker 100 and Canadair Challenger.

SWITZERLAND:
Hunter squadrons disband

Two of a previous nine Hawker Hunter squadrons were stood down on 1 January when Fliegerstaffeln 3 at Ambri and 4 at Raron relinquished their equipment. The squadrons' number-plates have not disappeared, however, as they have been allocated to two flights of four Dassault Mirage IIIRS reconnaissance fighters stationed at Sion and Payerne, having previously been detachments of Dübendorf-based Fliegerstaffel 10. Switzerland currently has 106 Hunter F58/As and seven T68s, flown by Militia squadrons 2, 5, 7, 15, 20, 21 and 24.

TURKEY:
New transports arrive

Delivery was anticipated early in the new year of the first two of 52 Airtech CN.235 medium transports ordered for the air force in 1990. These will be the sole aircraft manufactured by the Spanish component of Airtech, CASA. The remaining 50 will be built locally by TUSAS at Mürted as replacements for the air force's venerable Douglas C-47s. In late 1991/early 1992 the THK also received two ex-USAF Lockheed C-130Bs and the army gained five Beech Super King Air 200s.

UNITED KINGDOM:

New military orders

UK forces had a welcome break from long lists of closures and amalgamations on 19 February when Parliament was told of new equipment orders. Most significant was a contract for six Westland Sea King HAR.Mk 3s to begin replacement of Wessexes with No. 22 Squadron in the SAR role. It is anticipated that the helicopters will be equipped with improved avionics, including digital radar and GPS and that these features will be incorporated in the 18 remaining HAR.Mk 3s which have served No. 202 Squadron since 1978. Some Royal Navy Sea King HAS.Mk 5s may be passed to the RAF and modified for SAR to complete phase-out of Wessexes with No. 22's four dispersed flights and the SAR Training Squadron at Valley. On 1 October 1992, the UK SAR headquarters at Finningley will be split, with HQ No. 22 Squadron moving to St Mawgan and HQ 202 to Boulmer. St Mawgan will also gain the SAR Engineering Squadron, SAR Aircraft Engineering & Development Investigation Team and Sea King Maintenance School from Finningley, plus – on 1 April 1993 – the formerly Navy-administered Sea King Training Unit which operates two RAF HAR.Mk 3s at RNAS Culdrose.

Westland also gained a contract for conversion of the first seven Lynx HAS.Mk 3s to full HAS.Mk 8 standard with Racal's Central Tactical System and nose-mounted GEC Sea Owl infra-red sensor (displacing the Ferranti Sea Spray Mk 1 radar to an underfuselage radome). Remaining conversions are expected to be undertaken by the Navy's own workshops at Fleetlands. Also for the Fleet Air Arm, go-ahead was given to convert five BAe Harrier trainers to T.Mk 8 standard with cockpits and systems reflecting the forthcoming Sea Harrier FRS.Mk 2 – apart from radar, training in which is undertaken in Hunter T.Mk 8Ms. The FAA currently has seven two-seat Harriers, comprising two navalised T.Mk 8Ns and five T.Mk 4/4As in RAF configuration.

RAF Harrier training will in future be conducted in T.Mk 10s to be newly built by BAe. The February announcement of an order for 13 was dressed up as a new contract for political reasons but was, in fact, a reduction of one in the announcement made two years earlier (28 February 1990). Although based on the TAV-8B, the Harrier T.Mk 10 will have the full eight underwing pylons and complete combat avionics, including Marconi Zeus ECM and GEC FLIR. BAe orders also included 200 ALARM anti-radiation missiles to replace 121 launched in the Gulf War, while Vinten received a contract to equip Tornado F.Mk 3s with VICON 78 Srs 210 flare dispensers under the rear fuselage, plus chaff/flare management systems. The source of chaff dispensers has not been disclosed, but may be the same Bofors BOL system as earmarked for the Harrier, which is installed in the rear of the LAU-7 Sidewinder launch rails.

Finally, options were taken up for addition of Flight Refuelling Ltd Mk 32 pods beneath the wings of five more VC10 C.Mk 1 strategic transports of No. 10 Squadron. These will join eight conversions authorised in 1990 and increase the RAF's VC10 tanker force to 27: 13 C.Mk 1Ks, five K.Mk 2s, four K.Mk 3s and (under conversion) five K.Mk 4s. Mks 1 and 4 have no additional fuel tanks.

RAF Germany runs down

Withdrawal of Panavia Tornado GR.Mk 1s from RAF Germany continued in December 1991 with two more of Laarbruch's four squadrons. Following No. 16, which had disbanded on 11 September, No. XV held its final parade on 18 December, but was due to emerge once more on 1 April 1992 as the new 'shadow' identity (replacing No. 45) of the Tornado Weapons Conversion Unit at Honington. No. 2 Squadron, equipped with tactical reconnaissance Tornado GR.Mk 1As, moved from Laarbruch to Marham on 3 December, leaving only No. 20 at the German base until its disbandment on 31 May.

At Wildenrath, McDonnell Douglas Phantom FGR.Mk 2 air defence operations came to an end on 31 December when No. 19 Squadron was relieved of its commitment. The unit disbanded on 9 January, leaving the RAF with only two Phantom squadrons based in the UK (Nos 56 and 74) and a section of four (No. 1435 Flight) in the Falkland Islands. The last-mentioned was due to re-equip with Tornado F.Mk 3s in June 1992, while the last two UK squadrons will both disband in October.

ASRAAM victorious

A much-needed financial boost for British Aerospace was delivered on 3 March when defence minister, Tom King, announced to Parliament that Dynamics Division had been awarded a contract to produce the AIM-132 ASRAAM (Advanced Short-Range Air-to-Air Missile) for the RAF in collaboration with Hughes of the USA. Intended as an AIM-9 Sidewinder replacement, AIM-132 was to have been a pan-NATO venture until the US decided to concentrate on further development of the venerable 'Winder. Losing contender was MICASRAAM, offered by a GEC/MATRA consortium and combining a British seeker with the body of the French MICA missile. ASRAAM is of the new generation of highly agile weapons with only four small fins at the rear, but its procurement plans have been reduced by deletion of the Tornado F.Mk 3 and Sea Harrier requirements, leaving only the Harrier GR.Mk 7 and Eurofighter EFA.

Pilot training course modified

Changes in RAF pilot training were announced in February, involving disbandment of BAe Hawk-equipped No. 1 Tactical Weapons Unit at Brawdy on 31 August 1992 and redesignation on 1 April of Chivenor-based No. 2 TWU as a Flying Training School. Formerly, fast-jet students received 75 hours of advanced flying on Hawks at No. 4 FTS, Valley, to achieve their 'wings', followed by 54 hours of weapons instruction at one of the two TWUs. In the new scheme, both Valley and Chivenor are taking students from the Tucano-equipped schools (Nos 1 and 3 FTSs) and giving them identical courses of advanced flying and weaponry lasting 100 hours. Only then do they receive pilot's brevets. Savings for RAF Support Command are 30 flying hours per student, 20 fewer Hawks and 28 fewer instructors for the same output of 65 fast-jet pilots per year posted to an OCU.

Radar-equipped Hawk flies

Transformation of the BAe Hawk from an advanced trainer to a potent light fighter was completed on 13 February when the first of the type fitted with Westinghouse AN/APG-66H radar made an initial flight at Warton, piloted by Phil Dye. Serialled ZJ201, Hawk 200RDA (indicating Radar Development Aircraft) is the second single-seat Hawk to fly and the 358th built, excluding US T-45 Goshawk production. Firm orders for Hawk 200s comprise 18 Mk 208s for Malaysia and 12 Mk 203s for Oman, but Saudi Arabia is also considering up to 60 Mk 205s. Hawk production has just transferred from Kingston and Dunsfold to Brough and Warton, and the second new aircraft to fly from the last-mentioned will be the first fully representative 100 Series demonstrator, Mk 102D ZJ100. Orders for this version have been placed by Abu Dhabi (18 Mk 102s), Malaysia (10 Mk 108s) and Oman (four Mk 103s). Overall projected sales of the Hawk have slipped slightly, however, following changes in the US Navy requirement for McDonnell Douglas/BAe T-45As. Originally 302, this has been reduced to 270, including the two YT-45s.

Above: Delivered as long ago as November 1991 but not previously illustrated in these pages, this smart-looking Airbus A310 was procured by the Royal Thai Air Force for VIP transport duties. The Airbus remains something of a military rarity.

Left: The South Korean Super Lynx Mk 99 is pictured during flight tests at Westland's Yeovil base. Twelve were ordered with Seaspray 360 radar, Sea Skua and Racal Doppler 71/TANS N nav system for operation from 'Sumner'- and 'Gearing'-class destroyers. Similar aircraft (with US Bendix radar and other US systems) have more recently been delivered to Portugal. These export orders, in the face of stiff competition from Sikorsky's Seahawk, are a great achievement.

Eastern Europe

COMMONWEALTH OF INDEPENDENT STATES:

Air forces for all

Unprecedented in the history of aviation has been the nominal creation of a dozen new air forces – most of them with confused organisation and of limited effectiveness. The Soviet Union dissolved itself on 21 December, producing a Commonwealth of Independent States (CIS) containing 11 republics – plus a 12th, Georgia, which has yet to decide its future. All are claiming the former Soviet forces on their territory, including tactical air forces. Of the two major constituents of the CIS, Russia is demanding complete control of strategic nuclear forces, although Ukraine has also lodged a claim. The newly created states are Armenia, Azerbaijan, Byelorussia, Georgia, Kazakhstan, Kyrgyzstan, Moldavia, Russia, Tajakistan, Turkmenistan, Ukraine and Uzbekistan, but the distribution of air assets in their territory is far from balanced.

Ukrainian air force

Strength estimates of the newly-established Ukrainian air force, formed by decree of the president on 12 December, suggest an inventory of 850 aircraft, including 620 with combat capability. Additionally, the Ukraine hosts 21 Tu-95MS strategic bombers (and their 168 cruise missiles) based at Uzin-Chepelevka, near Kiev and nominally under central control (36th Air Army), but which were taken over by Ukrainian decree on 17 February. This was only four days after six Su-24M 'Fencers' were lost when their crews defected from the Ukrainian base of Starokonstantinov (formerly 24th Air Army) to Shatalovo in Russia.

Still under central command is the sole Tu-160 'Blackjack' regiment of two squadrons, totalling some 20 aircraft, together with their RK-55 (AS-15 'Kent') cruise missiles and a few Tupolev Tu-134UBL systems trainer versions of the 'Crusty' transport. Previously reported at Dolon, Turkestan, the Tu-160s are now known to be at Priluki, Ukraine, but will be relocated to Russia as soon as an airfield is available. Ukraine also is the base of 20 per cent of CIS ICBMs in sites near Pervomaisk and Khmelnitskiy.

HUNGARY:

MiG-21s upgraded

Unable for financial reasons to buy new MiG-29 'Fulcrums' from the CIS at hard-currency rates, Hungary decided early in 1992 to proceed with a trial upgrade of 20 MiG-21bis 'Fishbed-Ns' with Western (including consideration of Israeli) radar and IFF. The remaining 23 such aircraft may follow if the conversion is judged successful, these serving three squadrons at Pápa and Taszár. A further two squadrons of older MiG-21MF 'Fishbed-Js' at Kecskemét may not be worth modification.

YUGOSLAVIA:

Croatia and Slovenia recognised

Pressed by Germany, the EEC agreed to recognise Croatia and Slovenia, the two north-west provinces of Yugoslavia, as independent states, from 15 January. This has not been reflected by the United Nations, which – for the purposes of its peacekeeping force – continues to treat Yugoslavia as a nation undergoing civil war. The UN observer force was expected to be deployed during March, supported by a liaison element of 26 helicopters and four aeroplanes. A further fracture in the map of old Yugoslavia appeared on 2 March when Bosnia-Herzegovina became the third region to declare its independence from the Serbian-dominated federation.

Croatia and northernmost Slovenia were making efforts to form air forces during the early part of 1992. Speaking in February, Brigadier General Milan Macek, commander of the Croatian air force, claimed that his embryonic air arm would soon have combat aircraft contesting the air supremacy previously enjoyed by the Serb-controlled federal air force, the JRV.

UN observers killed

Five UN personnel in an Italian army Agusta-Bell AB 205A-1, painted white for conspicuity, were killed on 7 January when their helicopter was shot down near Novi Marof by a federal MiG-21 'Fishbed' shortly after entering Croatia from Hungary. The MiG pilot was reportedly Lieutenant Emir Sesic, who was operating from Bihac, just inside Bosnia-Herzegovina. An accompanying Italian AB 206 was damaged in the same attack and force-landed.

Middle East

KUWAIT:

Iraq returns captured equipment

Rebuilding of the KAF has continued in an unexpected manner with the release by Baghdad of aircraft captured in its August 1990 invasion and flown to Iraq. At least six McDonnell Douglas A-4KU Skyhawks were returned in February, increasing the fleet to 23, plus two TA-4KUs. Shortly before, Kuwait regained four BAe Hawk Mk 64s to add to the six remaining examples, plus a few Aérospatiale Puma, Super Puma and Gazelle helicopters, while a Lockheed Hercules was due to follow despite having been holed by a rocket-propelled grenade. Much of the other equipment – especially the Hawks, which were left in the open – is in poor condition.

Hornets delivered

The first three of 40 McDonnell Douglas F/A-18 Hornets arrived in Kuwait on 25 January and the remainder will be received by September 1993. Six Hornets had been delivered to Kuwait in time for participation in a 25 February flypast of approximately 60 aircraft from some of the coalition air arms which liberated Kuwait City exactly one year before.

Left: A recent customer for the Pilatus PC-9 is the Royal Thai Air Force, which uses the aircraft for advanced training. Other users include Australia, Saudi Arabia, Myanmar (Burma), and Germany (which uses the aircraft target towing).

Left: This rarely photographed South African Air Force C-54 bristles with extra aerials and is used for Elint and other electronic warfare tasks.

Left: South Africa's Mirage F1s are to receive a major upgrade, perhaps including the installation of Isotov RD-33 turbojets (as used by the MiG-29). A fuselage has already been shipped to Moscow for installation trials, and examples of the Soviet engine have been sent to South Africa. This aircraft retains camouflaged top surfaces over its grey colour scheme, and has toned-down, low-vis national insignia.

Right: Bophuthatswana's tiny air arm operates a variety of aircraft, from ex-SAAF Alouettes to PC-7s and this CASA C.212-300, used for light transport duties. This versatile transport is picking up customers rapidly, with orders pending from many more customers, including the US Army National Guard.

ISRAEL:

Helicopter upgrade begins

Life extension of the Sikorsky CH-53 Yas'ur (Albatross) took a step forward on 8 January when the prototype's new systems were powered up for their first ground test – although the helicopter will not make its first flight until late in 1992. Upgrading involves 92 systems, including avionics, cockpit displays and navigation equipment, the prototype having arrived at IAI's MATA helicopter plant for conversion as long ago as 13 June 1990. All the IDF/AF's 40 CH-53s will be modified.

SAUDIA ARABIA:

Eagle request renewed

Having only a few months previously floated a request for 72 McDonnell Douglas F-15 Eagles and quickly withdrawn it in the face of US Congressional opposition, Saudi Arabia entered a formal application on 18 February. The requirement is for 24 F-15H air superiority aircraft and – more contentiously – 48 F-15E Strike Eagles. Prospects for the acquisition of such an attack aircraft by an Arab nation would previously have been rated as zero, but recent weakening of the notorious pro-Israeli lobby in Washington and an urgent need for new work in the US defence industries could tip the balance. Saudi Arabia has hinted that it will order Eurofighter EFAs if it is denied more F-15s.

Far East

MALAYSIA:

Patrol aircraft ordered

Replacement of three Lockheed C-130H-MP patrol aircraft of No. 4 Squadron at Subang has been organised in the form of four Beech King Air 200Ts equipped for maritime surveillance. One will be supplied in 1993, the remainder in 1994.

S-61 helicopters upgraded

Having abandoned plans to replace its 34 remaining Sikorsky S-61A-4 helicopters, the RMAF took delivery in December of the first to have undergone modernisation by Aerod in Kuala Lumpur. Named 'Nuri' after a local jungle bird, the S-61s are being fitted with weather radar, Doppler navigation and a radar altimeter under a contract awarded in March 1991. The last will be returned to service in mid-1993.

TAIWAN:

Kiowa Warrior and SuperCobra contracts

An early-1992 contract with Bell covered 12 OH-58D Kiowa Warrior observation helicopters, delivery to begin in July 1993.

A further 14 options are held. Warrior is the armed version of OH-58D, production deliveries of which began to the US Army in 1991 after 207 unarmed helicopters (rebuilt OH-58As) had been received. Early OH-58Ds are being given provision for armament from 1992 onwards, but the Army has yet to issue weapons to operating units.

Underground base completed

Construction was completed in December of what is claimed to be the largest underground air base in the Far East. Built partly under a mountain – identified only as somewhere in the eastern province of Hualien, on the Pacific seaboard – the base has accommodation for 200 fighter aircraft as well as troops and tanks. Facilities include a hospital, ammunition depot and other storage facilities.

Trainer plans

Government approval was being sought during February for a fleet of 50 Aero L-39 Albatros advanced trainers to be equipped with Garrett TPE731 engines and Western avionics. First deliveries are planned in 1995 to replace Cessna T-37s and Lockheed T-33A in the RTAF. One stage lower in the training programme, the last of 20 Pilatus PC-9s was expected in March, completing replacement of the comparatively new RFB Fantrainers with which Thailand is displeased. Approval has been requested by the RTAF for a further 10 PC-9s. The air force took delivery of an additional five Pacific Aerospace CT-4B Airtrainers early in 1992, augmenting 24 CT-4As with the FTS at Kamphaeng Saen.

Hawkeye request

Approval was requested from Washington in February for an order covering three Grumman E-2C Hawkeye AEW aircraft for land-based operation. The RTAF had earlier hoped to acquire four.

PHILIPPINES:

Air force expansion

Plans revealed in February for continuation of the air force modernisation programme begun in 1989 include purchase of 16 SIAI-Marchetti SF.260TP basic trainer/COIN aircraft and 18 Aero L-39 Albatros armed trainers. A further eight MD 500 Defender-armed helicopters were ordered in February, increasing procurement to 30. Deliveries of all three types are due to begin before the end of 1992. The PhilAF has 26 piston-engined SF.260MP/WPs, but only six are airworthy. Recent arrivals have comprised the first of 24 ex-US Rockwell OV-10 Broncos for light attack and observation and five more Bell UH-1H utility helicopters, a similar quantity to follow in 1993. Under negotiation is a prospective order for 18 IAI Kfirs to replace a dozen Northrop F-5A/Bs.

Africa

SOUTH AFRICA:

Mirage re-engine studies

In an unusual development, the SAAF has considered installation of a Sargisov/Klimov RD-33 reheated turbofan (two of which power the MiG-29 'Fulcrum') in its remaining 15 Dassault Mirage F1CZs and 30 F1AZs. This would offer 10 per cent

additional thrust, compared with a SNECMA Atar 09K50. A Mirage F1 fuselage was despatched to Moscow on 25 April 1991 for installation tests and two RD-33s travelled in the opposite direction for further examination. Assessment was continuing early in 1992, but the question of the long-standing UN arms embargo has yet to be resolved.

Below: This Cessna A-37 Dragonfly of Chile's newly formed Grupo de Aviación No. 3 is based at Maquehue. The A-37 already served with Grupo 1 at Iquique and Grupo 12 at Punta Arenas.

Below: This Venezuelan air force Boeing 707 visited the Netherlands to refuel and escort ex-KLu NF-5As being ferried to Venezuela.

South America

ARGENTINA:

US to aid FAA expansion?

Requests by the Fuerza Aérea Argentina for 20 General Dynamics F-16A/B Fighting Falcons are likely to receive a favourable hearing in Washington 10 years after the arms embargo imposed when Argentina invaded the Falkland Islands (and was soon afterwards ejected). Earlier attempts to modernise the FAA have been thwarted by the US embargo and financial problems but, even now, it is probable that Argentina's Dassault Mirage IIIs and 5Ps and Super Etendards will have to be sold to provide finance. US controls prevented the FAA from obtaining replacement McDonnell Douglas A-4 Skyhawks from Israel, although a request for surplus USMC A-4Ms has now been made. Having received two ex-USAF Lockheed C-130B Hercules in 1991, the FAA will ask for a pair of C-130Es from the same source in 1992 and seek to augment its support helicopter force.

CHILE:

Dragonflies for No. 3 Aviation Group

The Chilean air force (Fuerza Aérea de Chile) has re-activated, at the end of March, the No. 3 Aviation Group (Grupo de Aviación N° 3). The unit will be equipped with the Cessna A-37B Dragonfly, and will be based at Maquehue Airport.

Mirage update

The modernisation of the Chilean Mirage 50 fighters continues, although the programme is going ahead at a slow pace. Four aircraft have already been updated (three single-seaters and one two-seater). The modernisation includes the installation of canards, a flight-refuelling probe, a head-up display and a radar of Israeli origin. The refurbished Mirage 50 is known locally as the Pantera (Panther).

Left: Apparently designated YE-8B, this new-build Boeing 707 closely resembles a Navy E-6A (and may have been ordered as such), but was reportedly allocated to become a third J-STARS airframe at one time. Still in primer, the aircraft is being shown to potential civilian buyers at Davis-Monthan's AMARC facility.

Below: The very first F-15E for RAF Lakenheath's 48th Fighter Wing touches down at its new home on 21 February 1992. The aircraft wears the colours of both of the wing's squadrons, the 492nd and 494th Fighter Squadrons, and is 'owned' by wing commander Colonel Mike Guth.

North America

UNITED STATES:

Boeing 707 for sale – maybe

In January 1992, the US Air Force was offering guided tours to prospective buyers of its sole Boeing YE-8B aircraft (88-0322), an apparent new-build Boeing 707 with four 24,000-lb (10,886-kg) thrust General Electric/SNECMA F108-CF-100 (CFM56) engines. The YE-8B was being shown by appointment at Davis-Monthan AFB, Arizona. If not purchased by a civilian buyer, it was scheduled to be preserved at the base's AMARC facility.

A brilliant gold in colour because of preservative applied to its natural-metal fuselage, the YE-8B is not necessarily a bargain. It has no airline-style windows, no seats, and no cargo pallets.

The aircraft also does not exist, according to most sources. It was not to be found in the Official USAF Inventory, in the central maintenance records for Boeing aircraft kept at Tinker AFB, Oklahoma, or in any official reference source. The reason the USAF acquired this 707, and the reason it is for sale, remain as obscure as the exact identity of the aircraft.

According to Lee Williams at Davis-Monthan, the aircraft began life as one of the E-6A Hermes TACAMO (Take Charge and Move Out) strategic communications aircraft ordered by the US Navy in the late 1980s. The YE-8B does have the distinctive wingtip antennas associated only with the E-6A. An order for four E-6As was cancelled only after Navy bureau numbers (163532/163534) were assigned. The USAF apparently purchased the aircraft with the intention of making it the third airframe for the Grumman Joint STARS (Joint Surveillance Target Attack Radar System) programme, a USAF/US Army system for a battlefield management system which will detect, locate, track and classify enemy ground formations at long range, and which proved successful in the Persian Gulf.

However, the two E-8A aircraft used in initial testing of the Joint STARS (and deployed during Operation Desert Storm) are significantly different from 88-0322. Both are powered by four 19,000-lb (8,618-kg) thrust Pratt & Whitney JT3D-7 turbofan engines almost identical to military TF33 turbofans.

A Pentagon source has indicated that 88-0322 is not a former E-6A, but was purchased as a new-build 707 under the designation YE-8B from the beginning. USAF public affairs officers refuse to discuss the aircraft, or to offer any explanation as to why the service is selling a new aeroplane.

No replacements for Hunters

The Commander-in-Chief of the Chilean air force, General Ramón Vega Hidalgo, has declared in March that at the moment the FACh (Fuerza Aérea de Chile) has no plans to replace its fleet of ageing Hawker Hunter fighter-bombers. It has also been reported by air force sources that Chile will receive from the USA 12 A-7H Corsair IIs, 30 Cessna A-37B Dragonflies and 20 Bell UH-1 helicopters.

PERU:
More Tucanos

With surplus airframes in stock, EMBRAER was able to respond rapidly to a Peruvian request in November 1991 for an additional 10 EMB-312 Tucano turbo-prop trainers, all of which were delivered in December, increasing the inventory to 30. Tucano sales up to January thus totalled 576, comprising Argentina 30, Brazil 128, Egypt 54, France 22 (plus 28 planned), Honduras 12, Iran 25, Iraq 80, Kenya 12, Kuwait 16, Paraguay six, Peru 30, United Kingdom 130 and Venezuela 31. Egypt assembled those built for Iraq and itself,

Above: Despite the disbandment of the Aggressor squadrons, a handful of F-16s at Nellis continues to serve in this vital role under the auspices of the 57th FWW.

while Shorts produced the aircraft for the UK, Kenya and Kuwait – the last-mentioned held in storage awaiting the re-start of pilot training.

VENEZUELA:
Netherlands F-5 deliveries

Long-awaited supply of six ex-Netherlands Canadair/Northrop NF-5s came closer in February when the first aircraft to have undergone refurbishment by Fokker began flight-testing at Woensdrecht, Netherlands. All other KLu NF-5s, the last of which was withdrawn in May 1991, have long been scrapped, sold or passed to Greece and Turkey. Venezuela is to receive five NF-5B trainers and a single NF-5A.

Right: Already wearing a new 'SF' (Shaw FAC) tailcode, one of Alconbury's A-10 Thunderbolt IIs taxis out for the long ferry flight to its new home at Shaw AFB with the 502nd ACW.

Left: One of the YF-22s strains against tethering chains as its engines are run up into the afterburner range. One YF-22 prototype was grounded to serve as a training aircraft, and the other suffered a major accident on 28 April 1992.

Below: The high-tech cockpit of the YF-22 is based around four-colour multi-function displays. A sidestick is visible far right.

C-135 news

Airborne command post operations on behalf of the Commander-in-Chief European Command ended after 26 years on 21 January 1992 when EC-135H 61-0286 departed RAF Mildenhall for Offutt AFB, Nebraska. 1-0286 was accompanied by 10th ACCS WC-135B 61-2667 and 92nd Wing KC-135R 58-0056, probably to provide a final air-to-air photo opportunity and for the tanker to refuel the EC-135 for the final journey home.

A continuous airborne alert was maintained for many years with one aircraft on station for eight hours before being relieved by a second example. In addition, a back-up aircraft was available on the ground as a replacement in the event of the airborne aircraft being unable to complete its mission. However, budgetary constraints halted the airborne relay during the 1970s, with a full-time ground alert and frequent routine flights performed instead. Gradually, the ground alert was relaxed until the role was no longer required. During early 1991 it was announced that the role would be withdrawn, with 61-0291 returning to the USA on 28 May 1991, followed by 61-0282 on 12 November and 61-0286 in January 1992. The fourth aircraft, 61-0285, was already in the USA, having been at Waco, Texas, since May 1990 for modification and did not return to the unit. The 10th ACCS WC-135B, 61-2667, was therefore the last aircraft to be operated from Mildenhall and was flown back to the USA on 7 February.

The Air Force announced during the late 1980s that two RC-135s were to be retired as part of an economy measure, although in reality no aircraft have been withdrawn and the success of the RC-135V and W 'Rivet Joint' versions during Desert Shield and Desert Storm look set to result in additional RC-135s joining the 55th Wing. C-135Bs 62-4125 and 62-4127 were delivered to Offutt AFB during 1991, having previously served with the 58th MAS at Ramstein AB, Germany, and 89th MAW (now 89th AW) at Andrews AFB, Maryland respectively. The two aircraft joined the Command Support Aircraft detachment (CSA) and were joined briefly by 62-4130 from Andrews AFB although the latter was loaned to Hickam AFB, for service with det 1 of the 89th AW. The CSA detachment has recently disbanded and the two C-135Bs are contenders for the airframes to be converted to RC-135s, pre-sumably the W model. Another report suggests the Air Force is considering re-engining the RC-135V and W models with General Electric/SNECMA F108-CF-100 powerplants (licence-built CFM56s) if funds can be made available. If the modification is adopted it will probably be carried out as part of an extension programme incorporating other improvements.

The Air Force has announced plans to re-engine 54 KC-135Qs with the F108-CF-100, beginning with 35 aircraft which will be redesignated as KC-135Ts. This will be the second time the latter designation has been used, as 55-3121 was assigned as a KC-135R (for reconnaissance training rather than a tanker fitted with the F108-CF-100) before changing to a KC-135T and finally an RC-135T, prior to it being destroyed when it crashed into a mountain near Valdez, Alaska, on 25 February 1985. Some, if not all, of the aircraft being converted to KC-135T standard will be fitted with air-refuelling receivers removed from various EC-135s being retired from service.

Finally, US Southern Command (SOUTHCOM) acquired a Boeing 707-355C during the latter half of 1991, with the designation EC-137E applied. The aircraft has been allocated a USAF serial number which incorporates its constructor's number (19417) as its external identity with fiscal year 67. The aircraft has been assigned to the 19th Wing at Robins AFB, Georgia, and will operate alongside the EC-135N and EC-135Y of US Central Command (CENTCOM). The EC-137E was formerly N525EJ, G-AYEX and N707HL before assuming its military career.

48th FW begins transition to F-15E

The 48th Fighter Wing at Lakenheath began conversion to the F-15E when it received its first example on 21 February. 90-0248 was marked with tail code 'LN' and was displaying a red and blue tail stripe. The aircraft was ferried from the McDonnell Douglas plant at St Louis to Bitburg on 19 February, and remained in Germany until midday on 21 February when it departed for Lakenheath and the official acceptance ceremony. The aircraft was piloted by Captain Mike Stansby with 48th FW Commanding Officer Colonel Mike Guth in the rear seat; however, once the aircraft landed, the two swapped places to enable the 'boss' to taxi the new Eagle to the reception area. The solitary Eagle spent the first three weeks as a maintenance trainer being dismantled and rebuilt prior to commencing flight operations on 9 March.

In readiness for the transition from the F-111 to the F-15, the 495th FS inactivated on 13 December 1991, with their aircraft being redistributed to the other three squadrons. The 492nd and 494th Fighter Squadrons will be the two units which will operate the F-15E, with the 493rd FS due to inactivate later this year. The wing expects to have approximately 20 of their eventual complement of 55 Eagles by August 1992, and complete the conversion process during 1993. The F-111Fs began returning to the USA on 15 January when eight aircraft flew to Cannon AFB, New Mexico. This was only a staging flight, however, as the F-111s were in transit to an Air Warrior exercise at Nellis AFB, Nevada, and were not officially delivered to the 27th FW until 15 February. The remainder of the 48th FW F-111s should all have been returned to the USA by the end of 1992.

'Stealth Fighters' on the move

The 49th Fighter Wing at Holloman AFB, New Mexico, has begun preparations to receive the first examples of the F-117A 'Stealth Fighter' during April 1992. The 37th Fighter Wing at Tonopah Test Range, Nevada, has been involved in the planning and transfer of personnel and equipment, as the wing has an ongoing commitment in the Middle East which will be maintained, despite the upheaval at home. The 49th FW will operate three squadrons of F-117As, with the 7th, 8th and 9th Fighter Squadrons converting to the type from the F-15A. The 7th TFS inactivated at Holloman AFB on 13 September 1991, passing its F-15As to other units, with the majority joining the 122nd FS Louisiana ANG at NAS New Orleans. However, the 7th FS will reform during 1992 and begin converting to the F-117 later in the year. Operational F-117s have displayed tail code 'TR' for Tonopah Range, although this will change to 'HO' once they are transferred to Holloman AFB.

The 37th TFW, which was redesignated 37th FW on 1 October 1991, was assigned all operational F-117s of Tactical Air Command, although a number of other examples have been based elsewhere for test and evaluation work. As stated earlier, a Middle East commitment has involved approximately a dozen 37th FW F-117s being deployed to Khamis Mushait AB, Saudi Arabia, and rotated on a regular basis with fresh aircraft and crews.

U-2R designation replaces TR-1

The Air Force has decided there is no longer any need to differentiate between the U-2R and TR-1A and withdrew the latter designation during December 1991.

The first U-2R batch was composed of a dozen aircraft serials, 68-10329 to 10340, although U-2s displaying bogus identities 10342 and 10345 were noted on occasion. As the entire rear fuselage and tail assembly were removable it is conceivable the Air Force had more 'rear ends' than it did whole aircraft, although this suggestion is far too dull and it is much more in keeping with the clandestine nature of U-2 operations for the serials to have been 'modified'. The general secrecy surrounding the 'Dragon Lady' family has often been extended to include the physical changing of serial numbers randomly between airframes. Four U-2Rs are known to have been lost in accidents, consisting of 10330 (7 December 1977), 10334 (15 August 1975), 10335 (date unknown) and 10336 (date unknown), so the remainder are all presumed to be still in service.

The requirement for a tactical reconnaissance platform with a long loiter time close to the forward edge of battle resulted in the third-generation 'Dragon Lady' being ordered, with 37 aircraft purchased from 1980 onwards and consisting of two aircraft for NASA designated ER-2, a pair of twin-seater TR-1Bs and a solitary U-2R(T) trainer. The remainder were all given the designation U-2R or TR-1A. Despite orders being placed over several consecutive years, all were given fiscal year 1980 serials, with the batch extending from 80-1063 to 1099. The two NASA ER-2s were N706NA/80-1063 and N709NA/80-1097 and have been joined by former

USAF TR-1A 80-1069 as N708NA. The two TR-1Bs were 80-1064 and 80-1065, while the U-2R(T) was 80-1091. The former pair have changed their designation to U-2R(T). All the rest were assigned the designation TR-1A apart from 80-1066, 1070, 1071, 1076, 1095 1096 and 1098, all constructed as U-2Rs. Two TR-1As have been lost in accidents, consisting of 80-1072 and 1075, although the details remain unknown. The remaining 23 aircraft have changed their designations to U-2R.

Air Force command structure reorganisation update

Additional information has been made available concerning the radical overhaul of the Air Force structure which is due for implementation during the current financial year. MAC, SAC and TAC will officially cease to exist on 1 June 1992 when Air Combat Command (ACC) and Air Mobility Command (AMC) form, although both of the new commands have

Above: The new AAC Penetrator is based on the proven power train and dynamic system of the UH-1 Iroquois.

Above: The 2,000th C-130 Hercules is rolled out of final assembly prior to being painted and finished.

existed in provisional format since 15 January 1992 to enable the transition to be as smooth as possible. The two new commands will receive most of the responsibilities, personnel and equipment of the three outgoing bodies. The former director of Strategic, Special Operations Forces, and Airlift Programs, Major General Stephen Croker, took command of the provisional ACC, while Major General Walter Kross, the former Director of Operations, was appointed commander of the provisional AMC. Permanent commanders for the new commands have not yet been named.

ACC Headquarters will be located in the building presently occupied by HQ TAC at Langley AFB, Virginia, while headquarters AMC will function from Scott

AFB, IL, from what is currently the HQ MAC complex. ACC will acquire three dozen bases including one from MAC, 18 from SAC and 17 formerly under TAC control, while the remaining four SAC bases and 12 MAC facilities will be assigned to AMC. The prime duty of Air Mobility Command will be global airlift and air refuelling, with a central tanker and airlift control facility established to co-ordinate activities. At present, SAC tankers, particularly KC-10As, frequently perform resupply flights on behalf of MAC while on intercontinental missions. The accompanying table lists those bases due to change assignment and includes some which are scheduled for closure, together with types due for retirement.

Bases to be transferred to Air Combat Command on 1 June

Base	Present Major Unit	Current Primary Aircraft Types
Barksdale AFB, LA	2nd Wg	B-52G, KC-135A (ex SAC)
Beale AFB, CA	9th Wg	KC-135Q, U-2R (ex SAC)
Bergstrom AFB, TX	67th RW	RF-4C (ex TAC)
Cannon AFB, NM	27th FW	F-111D/E/F/G (ex TAC)
Carswell AFB, TX	7th Wg	KC-135A, B-52H (ex SAC)
Castle AFB, CA	93rd Wg	B-52G, KC-135A/R (ex SAC)
Davis-Monthan AFB, AZ	355th FW	A-10A, OA-10A (ex TAC)
Dyess AFB, TX	96th Wg	B-1B, KC-135A (ex SAC)
	463rd AW	C-130H (ex MAC)
Eaker AFB, AR	97th Wg	B-52G, KC-135A (ex SAC)
Ellsworth AFB, SD	28th Wg	B-1B, KC-135R, EC-135A/C/G/L (ex SAC)
	44th SMW	LGM-30F (ex SAC)
England AFB, LA	23rd FW	A-10A (ex TAC)
Fairchild AFB, WA	92nd Wg	B-52H, KC-135R (ex SAC)
Francis E. Warren AFB, WY	90th SMW	LGM-30G/118A (ex SAC)
George AFB, CA	35th FW	F-4E/G (ex TAC)
Grand Forks AFB, ND	319th Wg	B-1B, KC-135R (ex SAC)
	321st SMW	LGM-30G (ex SAC)
Griffiss AFB, NY	416th Wg	B-52G, KC-135R (ex SAC)
Holloman AFB, NM	49th FW	F-15A/B to F-117A (ex TAC)
Homestead AFB, FL	31st FW	F-16C/D (ex TAC)
K.I. Sawyer AFB, MI	410th Wg	B-52H, KC-135A (ex SAC)
Langley AFB, VA	1st FW	F-15C/D (ex TAC)
Loring AFB, ME	42nd Wg	B-52G, KC-135R (ex SAC)
Luke AFB, AZ	58th FW	F-15E, F-16C/D (ex TAC)
MacDill AFB, FL	56th FW	F-16C/D (ex TAC)
McConnell AFB, KS	384th Wg	B-1B, KC-135R (ex SAC)
Minot AFB, ND	5th Wg	B-52H, KC-135A (ex SAC)
	91st SMW	LGM-30G (ex SAC)
Moody AFB, GA	347th FW	F-16C/D (ex TAC)
Mountain Home, ID	366th Wg	F-111A, EF-111A (ex TAC)
Myrtle Beach AFB, SC	354th FW	A-10A (ex TAC)
Nellis AFB, NV	57th FW	A-10A, F-15C/D/E, F-16C/D (ex TAC)
Offutt AFB, NE	55th Wg	EC-135C, RC-135U/V/W (ex SAC)
Pope AFB, NC	317th AW	C-130E (ex MAC)
		to become 23rd Wing in June 1992
Seymour Johnson AFB, NC	4th Wg	KC-10A, F-15E (ex TAC)
Shaw AFB, SC	363rd FW	A-10A, OA-10A (ex TAC)
Tyndall AFB, FL	325th FW	F-15A/B (ex TAC)
Whiteman AFB, MO	351st SMW	LGM-30F (ex SAC)
Wurtsmith AFB, MI	379th Wg	B-52G, KC-135A (ex SAC)

Bases to be transferred to Air Mobility Command on 1 June

Altus AFB, OK	443rd AW	C-5B, C-141B (ex MAC)
	340th Wg	KC-135R (ex SAC)
Andrews AFB, MD	89th AW	various VIP types (ex MAC)
Charleston AFB, SC	437th AW	C-141B (ex MAC)
Dover AFB, DE	436th AW	C-5A/B (ex MAC)
Grissom AFB, IN	305th Wg	KC-135R, EC-135G/L (ex SAC)
Hurlburt Field, FL	1st SOW	AC-130H, MC-130E/H, MH-53J

(Note: the unit/aircraft are operated by AFSOC and will not be part of the reorganisation.)

Kirtland AFB, NM	542nd CTW	HC-130N/P, MH-53J, MH-60G (ex MAC)
Little Rock AFB, AR	314th AW	C-130E (ex MAC)
Malmstrom AFB, MT	301st Wg	KC-135R (ex SAC)
	341st SMW	LGM-30G (ex SAC)
March AFB, CA	22nd Wg	KC-10A (ex SAC)
McChord AFB, WA	62nd AW	C-141B (ex MAC)
McGuire AFB, NJ	438th AW	C-141B (ex MAC)
Norton AFB, CA	63rd AW	C-141B (ex MAC)
Plattsburgh AFB, NY	380th Wg	KC-135A/Q (ex-SAC)
Scott AFB, IL	375th AW	C-9A, C-12F, C-21A (ex MAC)
Travis AFB, CA	60th AW	C-5A/B, C-141B (ex-MAC)

Below: The AS 365M Panther prototype is seen in flight, in company with a Coast Guard HH-65. The Panther has now matured into the Panther 800.

Base and wing level reorganisation

Following hard on the heels of the reorganisation of the major commands will be a change in the composition at base and wing level. At present, a typical wing is commanded by a full colonel and includes several other posts of similar rank including the vice commander, combat support group commander, and deputy commanders for operations, maintenance and resource management. However, under changes to be implemented in due course, the wing commander will be the rank of brigadier general, with the wing composed of an operations group, a logistics group and a support group, each of which will be commanded by a full colonel. These groups will concentrate on their own staff functions which, in the case of the operations group, will be responsible for a number of flying squadrons and an operations support squadron (OSS). The latter will provide services which are currently the responsibility of the wing director of operations, including weapons and tactics, scheduling and operations training. In addition, the OSS will be responsible for base operations, air traffic control and weather forecasting.

The basic flying unit will continue to be the squadron, and will be commanded by a lieutenant colonel with an operations officer and a complement of pilots. However, each flying squadron will have its own maintenance officer to supervise flight line maintenance operations, as aircraft will be assigned at squadron level rather than to the wing.

The major reorganisation of the operational end of the Air Force is the idea of Chief of Staff General Merrill 'Tony' McPeak and has the backing of the Air Force Secretary. The transfer of responsibilities for air base operations to the lowest possible level, combined with the restructuring of the major commands, is designed to permit the new streamlined Air Force to be an effective deterrent with fewer flying wings. In addition, the constant need to operate efficiently within stringent budgetary limits has forced the Air Force to make these changes.

Wing changes at Mildenhall and Kadena

The 100th Air Refueling Wing was activated at Mildenhall on 31 January 1992 under USAFE control to replace the 513th ACCW as the major unit operating the base. Initially, the unit will not have any aircraft assigned as the EC-135s were withdrawn prior to the formation of the wing. However, the 100th ARW will eventually have approximately a dozen KC-135Rs when the SAC commitment of tankers on temporary duty is replaced by a permanent allocation. These will be joined by KC-135s visiting in connection with deployments, as well as those staging through to and from the Middle East. Once established, the wing will also replace the 306th Wing, which is the current SAC unit at Mildenhall. The RC-135 detachment will also be supported by the 100th ARW.

Mildenhall has become the home for the KC-10A commitment, involving a pair of stateside-based Extenders previously stationed on temporary duty at Zaragoza AB, Spain. The two aircraft relocated to Mildenhall during the first week of January 1992. The KC-135 detachment to Zaragoza, involving aircraft reassigned from Mildenhall, ended during mid-December 1991. The 4th Wing from Seymour Johnson AFB, North Carolina, was the first unit to provide the Extender detachment although it will be shared with the other two wings.

At Kadena AB, Okinawa, the 18th TFW gained composite wing status at the end of 1991 when it became the 18th Wing, with the assignment of the KC-135Rs of 909th ARefS from the 376th SW along with the E-3s of the 961st ACS. The realignment of flying squadrons under a single operator is the first such move to be carried out by an overseas-based unit and had been implemented ahead of similar moves planned for other USAF units.

Unit news

Several units have changed designation in recent months in order to conform with the requirement to delete prefix titles and to become the single manager at bases where there is more than one major flying wing under the same command. At Tinker AFB, Oklahoma, the E-3 Sentry operator has been redesignated 552nd Air Control Wing from Airborne Warning and Control Wing with effect from October 1991. The wing is gradually to reduce in size as squadrons and aircraft are assigned to other commands, with the 961st ACS already having transferred to PACAF and the 962nd ACS at Elmendorf AFB, Alaska, following soon after.

At Davis-Monthan AFB, Arizona, the 602nd Air Control Wing is in the process of inactivating, with the 355th FW becoming the primary unit. Two OA-10A squadrons at the base were designated the 22nd TASTS and 23rd TASS until 1 January 1992 when they were renumbered to the 333rd and 354th FS. These will join the A-10A-equipped 357th and 358th FS

which are already part of the 355th FW. However, the 354th FS will be in residence for only a short period, as it will inactivate later this year.

At Elmendorf AFB, Alaska, the resident 21st TFW was changed to fighter wing status in October 1991, although the title was short-lived; the 3rd Wing was reactivated as the major unit operating the F-15C/D/E on 19 December 1991. The latter wing was resident at Clark AB, Philippines, until mid-1991 when the eruption of the volcano from Mount Pinatubo forced USAF units to be relocated elsewhere. The 3rd TFW was on the verge of inactivating anyway, as its F-4s had all been withdrawn, but the disruption forced the 353rd SOW to relocate its Special Forces helicopters and aircraft to Kadena AB, Okinawa. The 3rd Wing has gained the 962nd ACS operating the E-3 as the second PACAF Sentry squadron. Remaining in Alaska, the 343rd TFW at Eielson AFB has also abbreviated its title to just 'Wing', with the OA-10As of the 11th TASS being joined by the F-16C/D of the 18th FS during the latter half of 1991. The build-up of composite units by PACAF appears to

Above: A T-45 lands aboard the USS John F. Kennedy. The possibility of a new engine for the new aircraft remains real. An Aéronavale order now seems unlikely, with French pilots more probably undergoing training on the type in the USA.

be far ahead of its European counterpart, where Spangdahlem AB, Germany, is the only base so far destined to operate mixed tactical operations, commencing later this year with OA-10As and brand-new F-16C/Ds of Block 50 construction.

A composite wing is being formed at Pope AFB, North Carolina, on 1 June 1992 under the 23rd Wing, replacing the 317th AW, which is the current unit at the base. The three squadrons of C-130Es will probably be reduced to two as some aircraft are reassigned elsewhere. The wing will gain 18 A-10As and six OA-10As initially, of the 75th FS (tailcode 'FT') with the F-16C/D added in 1993. The 23rd FW is currently stationed at England AFB, Louisiana, where it is in the process of retiring its three squadrons of A-10As prior to the transfer.

FIGHTERTOWN U.S.A.

Left: A recce-compatible F/A-18D of the newly-reformed VMFA(AW)-225 'Vikings'. The multi-sensor reconnaissance package intended for the aircraft continues to be dogged by problems, however. Replacement of the Marines' last A-6E Intruders is now well under way.

Right: With the disestablishment of Air Wing Six, VF-11 has switched from East to West Coasts, and picked up new F-14Ds in the process. Partner squadron VF-31 has made the same move.

Whiteman AFB, MO, is being prepared for a new composite wing to be formed by the middle of the decade and to include the B-2As of the 509th Wing. A statement issued during January 1992 quoted types and quantities as an unspecified number of 'Stealth Bombers' together with 24 OA-10As and 18 T-38As. The T-38s are likely to be employed as a cheap alternative for B-2 aircrew to maintain their monthly flight hours. The Air Force Reserve is due to move their A-10s of the 303rd TFS from Richards-Gebaur AFB, Missouri, to Whiteman AFB by 1994, although it is unlikely the composite wing will be made up of front-line and Reservist squadrons.

The Air Force Reserve is to assume control of Grissom AFB, Indiana, when the Air Force vacates the base in 1994, with plans to establish the first AFRes composite unit under the 434th Wing. The wing will be composed of KC-135Es from the 72nd ARefS and A-10As of the 930th TFG/45th TFS, which are both resident at Grissom AFB.

The Air National Guard implemented changes to the designation of its units on 15 March 1992 to bring the service in line with its front-line counterpart. This involved the removal of the prefix 'tactical', along with some other minor amendments. Squadrons whose designations were Tactical Air Support (TASS), Tactical Fighter/ Tactical Fighter Training (TFS/TFTS), and Fighter Interceptor (FIS) have all been retitled as Fighter Squadrons (FS), while Tactical Reconnaissance (TRS) and Tactical Airlift (TAS) have both had the 'tactical' identifier removed and are now RS and AS respectively. Air Refueling Squadrons have not changed title, although the abbreviation ARefS is now ARS. The latter was formerly the abbreviated title of Air Rescue Squadrons, which are now simply Rescue Squadrons (RQS). Titles which remain unchanged are Composite Squadrons (CS) and Special Operations Squadrons (SOS). These changes are also applicable to groups and wings which make up the chain of command of the Air National Guard.

Left: An increasing number of T-34Cs are finding their way onto FRSs as hacks and range safety aircraft. This one wears the colourful markings of VF-124 'Gunfighters', the West Coast Tomcat RAG.

Below: The US Marine Corps have lost two of their oldest and proudest units due to the latest round of defence cutbacks. VMFA-333 'Shamrocks' and VMFA-531 'Gray Ghosts' have both been disestablished. Two VMFA-333 aircraft are seen here, in happier times.

AAC Penetrator offered as hi-tech Huey replacement

As of mid-February 1992, American Aircraft Corporation's Penetrator – a prototype assault-life gunship created by mating the Vietnam-era UH-1 Huey with state-of-the-art composites – had completed 16 flights and logged 10 hours of flying time. The AAC Penetrator was unveiled at Rialto, California, on 17 December 1991 and has been undergoing flight testing since.

The tandem-seat Penetrator is designed to serve as both a troop transport and a gunship. Retaining the Huey's rotor system and the Lycoming T53 turboshaft power train, the Penetrator is an all-composite, compound helicopter with a needle nose and a set of stub wings. To enhance aerodynamics performance, the helicopter's fuselage has a multi-facetted, Nomex-reinforced Kevlar surface and is free of exposed landing gear, struts or other protuberances. To further reduce drag, all machine-guns, cannons and some rocket launchers will be carried internally.

The Penetrator is configured in a reversal of the two-seat tandem cockpit of the Bell AH-1 Cobra: pilot in front with weapons operator in the second seat. A further two weapons operators will be housed aft of the main cabin, which can carry up to 10 troops.

Plans call for the forward-facing weapons operator to control two machine-guns, a 20-mm cannon, two forward-firing 37-mm rocket pods and up to eight missiles. The aft-facing crew has 220° swivelling machine-guns. Although the prototype is equipped with skids, the production aircraft will have retractable landing gear. AAC's John Carney says that the Penetrator 'out-Hinds' the Soviet Mi-24D ('Hind') attack helicopter, with better 'co-operative' firepower and greater speed, range, agility and endurance.

Ideal customer for the Penetrator could be any of the nations now operating about 5,000 Hueys worldwide. No orders have been confirmed, but AAC reportedly has concluded an agreement with an Israeli firm for remanufacture of 50 Penetrators and also claims a 'Pacific Rim nation' as a pending customer.

15

BRIEFING

McDonnell Douglas/Singapore Aerospace A-4SU

Singapore's Super Skyhawk

Singapore declared its first A-4SU Super Skyhawk fighter fully operational on 24 February. At Tengah air base the island's Defence Minister, Dr Yeo Ning Hong, told VIPs and other guests at an inauguration ceremony that the multi-million dollar Skyhawk upgrade programme had established Singapore Aerospace as a major aerospace company in Asia.

The aircraft on parade belonged to No. 145 'Hornet' Squadron of the Republic of Singapore Air Force (RSAF). Not only had they been re-engined by Singapore Aerospace with the modern General Electric F404-GE-100D turbofan, they had also undergone a comprehensive avionics modernisation at the company's Paya Lebar facility. The avionics package, named DELPHI, was developed by Ferranti Defence Systems of the UK, now part of GEC-Marconi.

The result, according to RSAF commander Brigadier General Michael Teo, is "a fighter pilot's aircraft with a navigation and weapons delivery system comparable to a new fighter." Teo told the ceremony that the commissioning of the squadron was a major landmark for the RSAF. The service has two other Super Skyhawk squadrons, Nos 142 and 143, each with some 20 aircraft. These machines have already been re-engined, but have yet to be refitted with the avionics upgrade.

The DELPHI package comprises a GEC-Ferranti Type 4510 Head-up Display and MED 2067 head-down Multifunction Display; a Litton LN-93 ring-laser gyro INS; Bendix flight data recorder; and a mission computer complete with data transfer module for computerised mission planning. The aircraft have been re-wired with the standard MIL 1553B databus.

No. 145 Squadron has been working up on the Super Skyhawk with avionics upgrade since early last year. Dr Yeo revealed that the systems had been subjected to rigorous operational testing, including a demanding deployment to Australia last August for Exercise Pitch Black. "The Super Skyhawk perfomed impeccably," he continued, "and achieved a near-perfect serviceability rate throughout the exercise."

The A-4 Skyhawk first entered service with the RSAF in 1974, when 40 former US Navy aircraft were removed from desert storage in Arizona and refurbished to the original, basic A-4S standard. Singapore subsequently purchased some 100 additional aircraft from the same source, cannibalising some of them to provide serviceable airframes.

Some minor improvements were made to the aircraft in the early 1980s, resulting in the A-4S1 version. But, according to Dr Yeo, in 1984 the government was faced with a choice of replacing "these modestly-equipped, oldish aircraft with a new-generation fighter, or upgrading the Skyhawk into a state-of-the-art platform."

The former option was not affordable, he continued, and so the Super Skyhawk programme was born. "By upgrading the aircraft locally," he added, "we could further build our indigenous capability for future support of the RSAF's complex aircraft systems."

Phase One of this effort involved the replacement of the A-4's 8,400-lb (3810-kg) thrust J65 engine with the F404. No. 143 achieved initial operational capability with the re-engined aircraft in March 1989. Six of these aircraft were displayed as the 'Black Knights' aerobatic team during 1990.

The avionics upgrade has been conducted as a completely separate Phase Two development. One of the factors governing the choice of Ferranti's package was a refusal by the US government to allow American contractors to release computer system software codes to Singapore. A great deal of the Super Skyhawk's weapons delivery software has been developed by Singapore Aerospace and its local partners.

February's ceremony marked the first time that journalists have been allowed to visit Tengah air base since a massive redevelopment programme to provide hardened shelters and new squadron facilities got underway in the early 1980s.

Below: Seldom can a major aircraft update programme have caused so little external change as Singapore's A-4SU conversion.

Right: No. 145 'Hornet' Squadron is the first Skyhawk user with the new Delphi avionics package as well as the F404 engine.

Kaman MMIRA

MMIRA technology demonstrator

Kaman Corporation is investing heavily in the flight test programme for its MMIRA (Multi-Mission Intermeshing Rotor Aircraft), a lightweight helicopter intended as a demonstrator for future unmanned helicopters for military use.

The MMIRA aircraft, registered N3182T, was first flown on 23 December 1991 at Bloomfield, Connecticut, by long-time Kaman test pilot Al Ashley.

The MMIRA aircraft is powered by a 380-hp (284-kW) Lycoming 17A gas turbine engine and uses the twin intermeshing rotor blade concept employed since 1947 with every major Kaman helicopter except the H-2 Seasprite. The contra-rotating main rotors with servo-flaps near the tips make the aircraft extremely quiet for surveillance/reconnaissance missions, and avoid the power drain of a tail rotor. The aircraft has a high aspect ratio tail fin with a movable rudder surface tied directly to rudder pedals. The pilot's compartment is designed to be removed so that the aircraft can be flown, eventually, as a drone.

The Kaman aircraft now flying is the largest of three concepts the company explored before producing the testbed. MMIRA is aimed at simplicity, ease of maintenance and suitability on the battlefield. The manufacturer sees the prototype as a

Right and far right: Kaman's bizarre-looking MMIRA prototype is a demonstrator for a planned range of UAVs (Unmanned Aerial Vehicles).

Below: Kaman's MMIRA features side-by-side intermeshing rotors. The cockpit is designed to be replaced by a drone package.

proof-of-concept vehicle and would manufacture future UAVs (unmanned aerial vehicles) based on the general concept rather than the actual design. In a press briefing on 11 February 1992, company founder Charles H. Kaman called MMIRA "the start of a family of hardware designed to show off hi-tech."

Kaman described a variety of uses for robot helicopters which are simple, economical and avoid risk to a human crew. He noted that pilotless helicopters would have been useful at Chernobyl, where Soviet pilots were exposed to lethal radiation from a runaway nuclear reactor. The helicopter executive also pointed to fisheries law enforcement and anti-drug efforts as possible applications, although Kaman intends to focus on purely military uses for the MMIRA concept

before looking for a civilian market. Kaman claimed that the MMIRA can loiter at 10,000 ft (3048 m) for "close to half a day at a time" and that it has "near infinite life" on its transmission and rotor blades.

The manufacturer has considerable experience with unmanned helicopters. In 1950, Kaman tested a remotely-controlled HTK-1 and the company's founder was quoted at the time as saying it would be useful in a nuclear emergency. In the early 1960s, seeking to develop a system to communicate with US strategic missile submarines, Kaman tested the SVLF (Shipboard Very Low Frequency) System aboard two QH-43G Husky drones which were taken to sea on the cruiser USS *Wright* (CG-2). Though the Navy eventually chose a different system which uses an antenna trailing

behind a fixed-wing aircraft (currently, the E-6 Hermes), not a single mishap occurred during extended QH-43G sea trials, and the helicopter system proved to be operationally feasible.

The MMIRA vehicle has an empty weight of just 3,800 lb (1723 kg) yet can carry a 6,000-lb (2721-kg) payload with an endurance of up to 15 hours. Kaman envisions an operational version carrying a variety of sensors, radar, IR, TV and laser. The practicality of the aircraft is enhanced greatly, Kaman believes, by its ability to use GPS (global positioning system) for precision navigation in a combat theatre.

Kaman recognises that it must compete with other UAVs (unmanned aerial vehicles) which are farther advanced in development, such as the Canadair CL-227. The firm is not yet looking at overseas buyers, but would team up with a partner if it saw an opportunity to sell a MMIRA derivative in Europe.

BRIEFING

Cessna L-19E

Bird Dogs for Malta

Following a recent 'Briefing' on the Maltese Helicopter Flight, *World Air Power Journal* has received an update concerning the recent acquisition of fixed-wing aircraft. After 20 years of helicopter operations, the Helicopter Flight, Armed Forces of Malta (AFM), has finally received its first fixed-wing equipment – five Cessna L-19E Bird Dogs. These were flown to Malta by Italian personnel on 4 February 1992.

Although there are no Maltese pilots for these aircraft as yet, four AFM personnel are to be sent abroad for training. Under AFM command, the aircraft will be used for coastal patrol, SAR and pilot training. The acquisition of these aircraft can be considered a milestone, but is regarded as a stepping stone towards obtaining a larger twin-engined aircraft. It is believed that talks on obtaining such an aircraft have commenced.

Although American-owned, and purchased from the United States for what has been described as a nominal price, these aircraft were used by the Italian army, based at Viterbo, north of Rome. They are described as having low flying hours and being in good overall condition, something which is quite evident even to the untrained eye.

The arrival of these Bird Dogs does not spell the end of rotary wing operations, however. The Helicopter Flight, which will be renamed the Air Squadron after an AFM re-organisation, is to receive two Nardi Hughes helicopters from Italy, while talks are also underway on re-commissioning the three Alouette helicopters donated by Libya.

The exchange documents were signed by AFM commander Brigadier Maurice E. Calleja and Lieutenant Colonel Giorgio Cannarsi, who was also one of the ferry pilots. Upon their arrival, Brigadier Calleja attached the new roundel which will adorn all Helicopter Flight aircraft, a red and white roundel with the George Cross on the white centre. A fin flash, consisting of a miniature Maltese flag, can also be seen in the photographs.

The aircraft were delivered still wearing Italian military identifications and US manufacturer's numbers, although the former were all but obliterated. Like the AB 206 Jet Ranger, and four Bell 47G-2s, the Cessnas will be allocated civil registrations, the table below showing both the previous military markings and their new identity.

9H-ACA 61-2972/ E.I.-34
9H-ACB 61-2983/ E.I.-2
9H-ACC 61-2986/ E.I.-25
9H-ACD 61-2990/ E.I.-26
9H-ACE 61-12281/E.I.-12

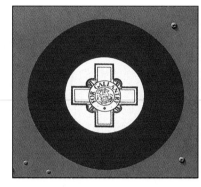

Above: The Cessnas have a new national roundel, complete with George Cross.

Below: Hardly marking a major shift in the balance of air power in the Mediterranean, Malta's Helicopter Flight has received five Cessna L-19E Bird Dogs.

Right: The Maltese Cessnas will initially be flown by Italian pilots, while Maltese pilots are trained overseas.

Minsk-Machulische
CIS aircraft competing for funding shown to VIPs

On 13 February 1992, at Machulische air base near Minsk, the aerospace organisations of the former Soviet Union, now operating under the umbrella of the Russian Aviation Trade House (part of the Ministry of Industry) displayed their latest aircraft to the visiting heads of state and defence ministers. Lined up on the apron, faced by the Su-27s of the 'Russian Knights' and the MiG-29s of the 'Swifts' aerobatic teams, were examples of all the major aircraft programmes.

Heading the line-up was the prototype Mil Mi-34 'Hermit', which was accompanied by three other Mil helicopters, the Mil Mi-24P 'Hind-F', the Mil Mi-17, and the Mil Mi-26. Next were five Sukhois, comprising a Sukhoi Su-24 'Fencer-D', an Su-25T, the Su-27IB, the Su-27M, and an Su-27K. Next to the carrier 'Flanker' was the FBW/glass cockpit

MiG-29M, which was displayed next to one of the MiG-29K prototypes, and a MiG-31M. Molniya/Myasischchev sent an example of the M-17 Geophysica 'Mystic-B', this wearing a new colour scheme with dark blue undersides. A joint CIS/Chilean operation involving these aircraft seems likely later this year. The familiar Beriev A-40 Albatross prototype, still wearing Paris codes, was next in the line-up, dwarfed by an An-124 which wore Soviet air force colours and the 'Antonov Airlines' legend. Next was an Il-78 'Midas' tanker (again in air force, not Aeroflot markings). The line was concluded by three strategic bombers, comprising a Tu-95MS-6 'Bear-H', a Tu-160 'Blackjack', and a Tu-22M-3 'Backfire-C'.

Of these, the Su-25T, MiG-29M, MiG-29K and MiG-31M were described as not being 'core programmes' by Vladimir Laptev, Presi-

dent of the Russian Aviation Industry Union. This is particularly surprising in the case of the Su-25T, which has been flying for some time, and for which several prototypes exist. At one time, the aircraft was quoted as having a 1992 in-service date, so the withdrawal of funding (if it has occurred) marks a very late cancellation. The demise of the MiG-29M may be less of a surprise, since it represents an interim aircraft which may be a luxury, and a threat to funding for more advanced projects. Development may be continuing for export, with the possibility that India might co-fund production. An example of the Tu-160 'Blackjack' bomber was also present, production of this aircraft having already been halted by President Yeltsin after some 22 airframes were completed.

The progress of the Soviet Union's latest fighter programmes was not re-

vealed, however, and Mikoyan's EFA-like 1-42 (I-42?) Mnogofunktsionalnii Istrebityel (Multi-function fighter) and their ATF-equivalent, known as the Type 701 or Mnogofunktsionalnii Dalnii Perekhvatchik (long-range multi-function interceptor) remain under wraps. The Su-37 (perhaps a competitor to the 1-42) has been shown in model form (most recently at Dubai) but its status also remains unclear, and speculation that it is regarded as a core programme seems unfounded. If anything, the hype surrounding this aircraft might suggest that it has failed to secure CIS funding, and that Sukhoi are seeking a production partner. Sukhoi's ATF-type, the S-32, also remains untalked about and unseen.

A final absentee from the line-up at Minsk was the surviving Yak-141 'Freestyle' prototype, which has also reportedly had funding withdrawn. Most of the above aircraft types will be described in briefings in this and future volumes of *World Air Power Journal*.

Above: The Mil Mi-34 'Hermit' was designed as a replacement for the Mil Mi-1 in the training, light observation and liaison roles. Its future is uncertain, with few orders.

Above left: The Tu-22M-3 'Backfire-C' is the latest and most capable version of the Tu-22M, with new box-section variable intakes. The aircraft carries missiles underwing and on a rotary launcher in the bomb bay.

Left: A single example of the newer Tu-160 'Blackjack' was also displayed. Production of this capable strategic bomber has reportedly been halted by President Yeltsin, and only two squadrons are operational.

Left: The future for Myasischchev's M-55 'Mystic-B' seems happier, with strong interest from Chile and some funding from the air forces of the former Soviet Union.

Below: Although it represents a major improvement over the standard Su-25, the Su-25T (or Su-34) seems unlikely to enter production.

MiG-29K (possibly 'Fulcrum-D')

Carrier 'Fulcrum'

Mikoyan claim to have been working on a naval MiG-29 derivative for some 10 years, in order to provide a multi-role fighter to serve aboard the *Kuznetsov* and her sister carriers, which are now under construction. It remains unclear as to whether the aircraft is in competition with the navalised Su-27K, or whether it is designed to augment the larger, longer-ranged interceptor.

At least two MiG-29K prototypes have been noted operating from the carrier *Kuznetsov* (formerly *Tbilisi*). While they may not be fully representative of any production carrier-borne MiG-29 variant, they do differ in many ways to standard 'Fulcrum-As'. Initially thought to have been based on early 'Fulcrum-A' airframes (one, coded '311', was thought to have been the last prototype, '9-11'), the MiG-29Ks lack the usual 'Fulcrum' overwing chaff/flare dispensers, although they also lack the ventral fins associated with the prototypes and with the earliest production MiG-29s. The spine is slightly larger, and recontoured in just the same way

as the spine of the MiG-29M, and like the MiG-29M the aircraft has a single large airbrake further forward on the spine than the upper and lower airbrakes on previous 'Fulcrum' variants. Whether the MiG-29K is based on the MiG-29M airframe or vice versa remains unknown.

The tailfin has also been slightly changed. Fitted with the extended-chord rudders of later 'Fulcrum-As', the MiG-29K's rudder trailing edge drops vertically down to line up with the trailing edge of the lower fin, which has been extended aft and has lost its slope. The lower corner of the rudder is still slightly cropped, but the fin trailing edge/rudder junction has been modified so that there is no cut-out.

The heavy intake door system has been removed (presumably to save weight) and has been replaced by lighter grilles. The overwing auxiliary intakes have also gone, allowing the space they used to occupy to be taken by a large fuel tank of aluminium lithium construction, and of about 2500-litre (550-Imp gal) capacity. (This was

shown in the Soviet Pavilion at Paris.) The MiG-29K prototypes have been 'navalised' by the substitution of an arrester hook for the braking parachute, and by the provision of folding wings and a strengthened undercarriage. The second MiG-29K, coded '312', exhibited all the above features when it was shown at Minsk-Machulische as part of a VIP display for CIS leaders in February 1992.

Equipment changes seem to include a new defensive ECM system (with bulged wingtips apparently housing passive receivers) and a new IRST (with the glazed ball replaced by a more solid-looking turret, perhaps indicating the installation of an imaging IR device). The radome is of more attractive profile, without the slightly concave conical leading edge

of the 'Fulcrum-A' radome. This is more aerodynamically efficient and is thought to indicate that the new Zhuk radar has been fitted.

Various intakes and antennas are changed, with the aircraft losing its small undernose sensor/equipment pod for the first time. Some kind of antenna (or MDC?) is embedded in the rearmost part of the canopy, consisting of eight parallel fore-and-aft strips, linked by their trailing edges. A retractable inflight-refuelling probe is fitted below the port side of the windscreen. The aircraft apparently incorporate various corrosion protection measures. The MiG-29K also seems to have flaps of increased area and droop. The aircraft has eight underwing hardpoints, and these can carry AA-11 or 'Amraamski' AAMs out-

Right: The first MiG-29K in flight. The aircraft features increased area trailing-edge flaps and dogtooth on the tailplane leading edge, and seems to have extended chord tailplanes, extending further aft.

Below: The second prototype of the MiG-29K is seen on the deck of the Admiral Kuznetsov (formerly Tbilisi). The folding wings, wingtip ECM bulges, reconfigured radome and dorsal airbrake of this variant are clearly visible.

Mikoyan MiG-29K

The first prototype MiG-29K as it appeared during recent trials aboard the *Kuznetsov*. Only two of the possible four hardpoints under each wing are fitted, and the aircraft has a fully-covered inflight-refuelling probe. It also wears camera calibration markings on nose and tail, and these have displaced the naval ensign from the fin to the engine intakes; otherwise the aircraft is similar in appearance to the second prototype.

Powerplant
The MiG-29K is reportedly powered by the improved, uprated Isotov (Sargisov) RD-33K engine, like the MiG-29M. Exactly how this differs from the standard RD-33 is unknown.

Wing
Wing folding is not the only innovation on the MiG-29K's wing. The aircraft also has increased area trailing-edge flaps, and bulged wingtips housing EW equipment.

Spine
The MiG-29K has a slightly bulged fuselage spine, though this is only really visible in plan view.

Radar
The radome of the MiG-29K differs in detail to that fitted to the standard MiG-29, with no concave curvature at the tip. This is believed to indicate the installation of the new Zhuk radar.

Arrester hook
The MiG-29K has a long, square-section, hydraulically-actuated arrester hook which folds up to lie along the underside of the beaver tail when not in use. A deeply grooved end lessens the chance of a wire 'skipping' out of the hook.

Left: The MiG-29K taxis on the deck of the Kuznetsov, unfolding its wings. It seems to share a common airframe with the FBW MiG-29M, although whether it has FBW flight controls and a glass cockpit remain unknown.

board and the AA-10 'Alamo' AAM or X-31 ARM or other ground attack weapons inboard.

For trials aboard the *Tbilisi* (as it then was) '311' initially made 20 launches (using the vessel's ski jump, running up against the unique deck re-strainers, since no catapults are fitted). The MiG-29K landed on *Tbilisi* after the first Su-27K, but did make the first fixed-wing launch from the new ship. Approaches are flown at some 130 kt (240 km/h; 149 mph) and about 14° α, some 25 kt (46 km/h; 29 mph) lower and 3° higher than a normal approach. The RD-33K engine provides useful extra thrust, making the missed approach/go-around case less critical.

What may have been a standard 'Fulcrum-A', coded '18', was also in-volved in these early trials, probably making a series of touch-and-go land-ings to familiarise test pilots with *Tbi-lisi*'s deck. At one stage '311' carried 50 small black anchors, each with a red star superimposed, and four of them with a white numeral '5' below the port canopy rail, indicating 66 suc-cessful arrested landings. By this time Mikoyan's Roman Taskaev (star of various Farnborough and Paris air show displays) had joined Chief Test Pilot Valery Menitsky and project pilot (and deputy Chief Test Pilot) Takhtar Aubakirov, who had made the first 20 launches.

Mikoyan MiG-29K

Since the view from the rear cockpit of the MiG-29UB is inadequate for aircraft-carrier operations (even without the increased angle of attack used on a carrier approach), Mikoyan have proposed a new two-seat trainer variant for naval training. Designated MiG-29KU, the aircraft will incorporate the same naval modifications as the MiG-29K (folding wings, removal of the intake doors, corrosion resistance, etc) with a new stepped cockpit, covered by a huge bubble canopy, which will give what Rostislav Belyakov, OKB head, calls "a hunchbacked appearance". Whether the MiG-29KU will retain radar is unknown. Some reports suggest that the MiG-29KU has been abandoned.

India is a possible export customer for both the MiG-29K and MiG-29KU, since it hopes to acquire a third (conventional) aircraft-carrier.

Above: The second MiG-29K is shown on display at Minsk, armed with X-31 anti-radar missiles inboard and AA-11 'Archers' outboard. The retractable inflight-refuelling probe is shown extended. The forward probe door has been removed.

Left: Anchors and red stars indicate the number of deck landings made by the No. 1 MiG-29K.

Far left: Mikoyan's Roman Taskaev sits in the cockpit of the first MiG-29K. A fitment for some kind of helmet sight is visible on the front of his flying helmet. Embedded antennas are visible in the canopy itself.

Below: The second prototype at Minsk. The square-section arrester hook and beaver tail are clearly visible, along with the revised fin trailing edge below the extended rudders.

MiG-29M (NATO ASCC reporting name unknown, unofficially dubbed 'Fulcrum Plus')

Second-generation Superfighter

Many Western analysts have wrongly attributed the MiG-29M designation to the big-spined MiG-29 fighter known to NATO as 'Fulcrum-C'. In fact, although the MiG-29M does incorporate a large fuselage spine (albeit that of the MiG-29K and thus of a totally different shape to the spine fitted to 'Fulcrum-C') it is the designation applied to a completely new variant, which incorporates a quadruplex Fly-By-Wire control system and a modern glass cockpit with two CRT displays. The aircraft has a new radar (possibly the Zhuk also fitted to the MiG-29K) and a refined and updated IRST, similar to that fitted to the naval 'Fulcrum'. This reportedly has better sensor cooling, giving increased detection range. Early reports suggested that the MiG-29M was a one-off technology demonstrator, but it now seems that it may be intended as a new production variant, with up to five prototypes flying.

Although described by the Bureau as being "based around the aerodynamically stable MiG-29 airframe, but different in every respect," the MiG-29M appears to be very much a minimum-change aircraft, probably based on the MiG-29K airframe. Possibly with a slight increase in wing area (with an extended leading edge, and possibly with new flaps and ailerons), the MiG-29M and MiG-29K both have a tailplane which seems to be about 12.5 per cent larger, with increased chord but no increase in span. The tailplane has a small dogtooth on the leading edge, but this is much less prominent than has been shown in Western artists' impressions, and may even merely be a slightly open slat. Other external changes include an extended and reconfigured rear fuselage (this allowing the centre of gravity to be moved aft), removal of the undernose sensor/equipment fairing and a recontoured (and possibly shortened) radome which lacks the distinctive double curvature on its leading edge. Some have suggested that the LERXes appear sharper than normal.

The (first?) MiG-29M prototype was converted from the pre-production aircraft '9-15', and first flew in its new guise during November 1989. It is reportedly powered by two RD-33K engines. Like the MiG-29K, the aircraft has eight underwing hardpoints, and these are used to carry a new long/medium-range AAM outboard and a variety of weapons inboard, including the X-29 (NATO AS-14 'Kedge') air-to-surface missile. The aircraft also seems to have the MiG-29K's unusual antennas embedded in the rear part of the cockpit canopy. The MiG-29M has no overwing auxiliary air intakes, though they have been painted on the first prototype at least to confuse onlookers or opponents. It may be that the overwing air intake/intake door system is not compatible with the new RD-33K engine. This does allow the fitting of the same extra internal fuel tank as is used by the MiG-29K. The first prototype wears the code '155' (one of the MiG Factory numbers, and often used for various projects, including the Ye-155, as a sort of 'lucky number') on its intakes. During 1990 the VPK commission reportedly refused certification because of radar problems, although earlier FBW control system problems have reportedly now been solved.

Central funding for the MiG-29M may not have been obtained, and Mikoyan are reportedly looking for an international partner to put the aircraft into production. India is the obvious candidate.

Below and bottom: The first public-domain photos of the MiG-29M, displayed at Minsk. Overwing auxiliary air intakes are painted on to the aircraft, which is similar to the MiG-29M, albeit without wing folding and arrester hook, and with a different tail fairing between the engine nacelles.

Sukhoi Su-27K 'Flanker-B2'

'Flankers' all at sea

The Su-27, with its unique combination of long range, high performance and unmatched agility, was a natural contender for inclusion in the air wing of the Soviet Union's new generation of conventional aircraft-carriers, which began with the *Tbilisi* (since renamed *Kuznetsov*). The Soviet navy required a multi-role fighter, capable of performing interception, tactical fighter and reconnaissance tasks, almost certainly designed as a competitor (and not a complement) to the MiG-29K.

Navalising the 'Flanker' was a major task, and resulted in an aircraft which looked distinctively different to the land-based Su-27 'Flanker-B'. Most obviously, the Su-27K has a pair of moveable canard foreplanes, which give extra lift at low speeds. The aircraft is also fitted with a ventral square cross-section arrester hook, which is mounted below a shortened inter-engine bullet fairing (shortened to reduce the chance of a tailscrape during a high α landing). Although the wing and tailplane planforms are unchanged, both incorporate powered folding mechanisms, to reduce the amount of space required on a crowded hangar deck. Tailplane folding is very unusual, and is necessitated by the broad span of the Su-27's tail unit.

Sukhoi have also taken the opportunity to redesign the 'Flanker's' control surfaces, with full-span, three-section trailing edge flaps replacing the simple half-span inboard flaps of the original Su-27. The inboard two sections operate symmetrically as flaps during approach and landing, with the outboard segments operating differentially as ailerons. In normal flight, the outboard and middle sections operate differentially as three quarter-span ailerons, augmented by differential tailplane movement.

The undercarriage was substantially 'beefed up' to meet the sink-rate requirements of the no-flare carrier landing, and the possibility of a pitching deck on impact. Undercarriage strengthening necessitated the adoption of twin nosewheels.

Other specifically naval modifications almost certainly include comprehensive corrosion protection/resistance and the provision of tie-down points. The Su-27K also incorporates some improvements first flown on experimental land-based 'Flankers', the most notable being a retractable inflight-refuelling probe.

It seems that several (at least five) Su-27K prototypes have been completed, and at least three of these have been photographed operating from the *Tbilisi/Kuznetsov*. These aircraft carry a variety of colour schemes, and have been seen carrying various (mainly air-to-air) weapon loads. One aircraft (coded '69') was fitted with a single underwing pylon (outboard of the wing fold) with a suspended twin carrier on each wing. The other aircraft have generally had the same pylons as the land-based 'Flanker-B'. One Su-27K has been photographed with what appears to be a small camera pod on the forward centreline pylon, but this may have been for test and not reconnaissance use.

A single Su-27K (coded '79') was displayed alongside an Su-27IB and Su-27M at Minsk-Machulische in February 1992, where it was announced that the Su-27K had been selected for production, apparently in preference to the smaller MiG-29K. The aircraft at Minsk appeared to

Above: The Su-27K prototype lands on the dummy deck at Saki.

*Below: Early carrier trials take place aboard **Kuznetsov** (then the **Tbilisi**).*

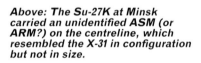

*Above: The Su-27K at Minsk carried an unidentified **ASM** (or **ARM**?) on the centreline, which resembled the X-31 in configuration but not in size.*

*Left: The same Su-27K sits side by side with the No. 2 MiG-29K on the deck of the Kuznetsov. The carrier's air wing will almost certainly contain both aircraft types, with the new Yak-44 as an **AWACS** platform.*

*Below: An anonymous-looking Su-27K is prepared for launch during early trials on the **Tbilisi**, as it then was. A huge jet-blast deflector is raised behind the aircraft.*

carry a fairly conventional air-to-air weapon load, with four AA-11 'Archers' under the wingtips and on the outboard pylons, and with four AA-10 'Alamos' on the other underwing pylons. The pylons on the underside of the engine intake trunks were fitted, but were empty – however, the centreline hardpoints carried something of a surprise.

Suspended from a deep pylon was a previously unknown air-to-surface missile, similar in configuration and shape to the X-31 anti-radiation missile, but very much larger. This new missile is estimated to be some 6-8 m (20-26 ft) long, extending as it does from the start of the jetpipes forward to the engine intakes. It may be an anti-ship missile in the same class as the British Sea Eagle. This might indicate that the aircraft has been ordered as a multi-role naval fighter, lending credence to reports that the multi-role MiG-29K has not been selected.

An unusual rear view of the Su-27K shows the square-section tailhook, folding wings and tailplanes, and unidentified missile on the centreline.

Sukhoi Su-27M 'Flanker Plus'

New FBW 'Flanker' revealed

Publicly revealed at Minsk on 13 February 1992, the Su-27M 'Improved Flanker' marks a possible Mid Life Upgrade configuration for the Su-27. Differing little from the standard 'Flanker-B' in appearance, the Su-27M is reportedly a very different machine under the skin. Reports indicate that the aircraft has both a new fire control radar and an improved cockpit with CRT displays. It may also have a new flight control system, perhaps with digital rather than analogue signalling.

The aircraft at Minsk was coded '706' and carried an unusual warload, with unidentified laser-guided bombs under the intake trunks, and a single X-29T air-to-surface missile under the port wing. All other pylons were left empty, except the wingtips, which each carried a dummy AA-10 'Alamo'. In an interesting departure from standard practice, and perhaps marking a move towards Western style 'toning-down' of markings, the Su-27M carried its star in outline form only, with its codes in dark blue outline numerals.

The prototype Su-27M was also displayed at Minsk. The aircraft carried a pair of unidentified laser-guided bombs under the intake trunks.

BRIEFING

Sukhoi Su-27IB 'Platypus'

Enigmatic Su-27 variant detailed

When Tass released a series of photographs taken on the *Admiral Kuznetsov* during August, one showed an unusual-looking Su-27 on approach. The photograph was of poor quality, but seemed to show a side-by-side two-seater with a broad, flat, chined nose. (These chines flow back to become the wing leading-edge root extensions). Inevitable speculation followed, most analysts agreeing that it was a dedicated carrier training variant, with side-by-side seats to give the instructor a better view forward over the nose. This supposition was based on the fact that the aircraft was photographed making a carrier approach, and that it shared certain features (most notably canard foreplanes) with the Su-27K, but ignored the fact that the aircraft seemed to have no arrester hook.

The new two-seater is very similar in overall configuration to the carrier-borne Su-27K, with the same canard foreplanes, but without (it later transpired) wing or tailplane folding, and without the ventral fins fitted to most 'Flankers'. The cockpit is moved forward, with the space behind being humped to accommodate extra fuel and possibly new avionics items. The Su-27IB does have the same strengthened undercarriage as the Su-27K, with twin nosewheels, allowing it to operate at higher all-up weights than the standard fighter 'Flanker'. The nosewheel has, however, been moved forward, and now retracts aft. It is covered by four separate undercarriage doors. The aircraft also features the slightly taller fins of the normal Su-27UB 'Flanker-C' trainer, to compensate for the increased side area of the re-profiled nose. Various pitots and aerials seem to have been moved, and the aircraft also seems to lack the enormous dorsal airbrake of earlier Su-27 variants.

Later speculation, from more reliable analysts, pointed to the aircraft being the long-promised fighter-bomber version of the Su-27, and this seemed to be borne out by the appearance of the aircraft at the major closed aircraft display at Minsk-Machulische on 13 February 1992, when most of the former USSR's new aircraft projects were lined up for inspection by the heads of state and defence chiefs of the Commonwealth of Independent States. Positioned alongside an Su-27K and the Su-27M was the same two-seater, coded '42'. Information boards announced this aircraft to be the Su-27IB, and averred that it was a 'fighter-bomber'. The nickname 'Platypus' was widely used. It has been suggested that the 'Platypus' is intended as a replacement for early 'Fencer-Cs' in the ground attack role.

To lend further support to the fighter-bomber theory, the aircraft at Minsk carried an array of air-to-air and air-to-ground ordnance, although many of the other aircraft

Above: Certainly the ugliest variant of the Su-27 'Flanker', the Su-27IB remains an enigmatic aircraft. Described as an all-weather attack aircraft, it lacks radar or electro-optical (EO) sensors, so may merely be an aerodynamic prototype. The aircraft at Minsk did, however, carry an array of air-to-ground weapons, and was equipped with a retractable inflight-refuelling probe.

Right: The first photo of the Su-27IB (actually blue 42, the same airframe displayed at Minsk) seen in the West showed it on approach to the Tbilisi, apparently about to land beside a MiG-29K and a pair of Kamov Helixes. This led to a great deal of speculation as to the aircraft's role. Even then, no arrester hook or folding wings were visible.

present carried similar (and often unlikely) loads. It was as if some conscript had been told to simply load weapons on to all the aircraft, and had sometimes done so in an inappropriate fashion.

The aircraft carried a pair of X-31 ARMs under the intake trunks, with a single previously unidentified weapon between the nacelles. This had a non-articulated laser head similar to that fitted to the X-29L, mated to a more bomb-like rear half, with a constant section tubular tail, possibly housing some kind of booster, or perhaps housing a retard mechanism. Under the wings the aircraft carried a pair of LGBs (inboard), with an X-29T to port and an X-29L to starboard on the central underwing pylons. No laser illuminator, spot tracker or designator was visible.

In the furthest outboard pylons the aircraft carried a pair of the new, unidentified AAMs jokingly referred to as 'Amraamski' – supposedly a fire and forget long-range air-to-air missile. The total lack of a radar could mean that these were hung on to the Su-27IB purely for show, or that they require no illumination. These substantial missiles featured long strakes along the body, with 'latticed' or gridded tailfins. The grids consist of a network of diagonal aerofoils or vanes set at right angles to the airflow, within a rectangular box. These generate considerable lift by giving a large amount of effective wing area within a small space. Similar wings have been used on the SS-23 'Spider' ICBM, and are most efficient at high angles of attack and very high speeds. Lift coefficient remains constant throughout a wide range of angles of attack, minimising trim problems as propellant is burned, and relatively small control movements (using relatively little power) have a great effect.

Like the Su-27K, the new two-seater is fitted with a neat retractable inflight-refuelling probe below the port windscreen. The latter is divided vertically, while the cockpit seems to be covered by a pair of separately hinging panels, which open upwards and outwards, like those on the 'Fencer'.

The 'fighter-bomber' description applied to the Su-27IB may, however, be rather misleading. For a fighter-bomber (particularly one touted as the Soviet equivalent to the F-15E) the lack of an attack/terrain-following radar would seem to be a major handicap, as would the total lack of electro-optical sensors. For the fighter role, the loss of the IRST would also be a problem. The nose is metal and its unusual shape would make the propagation of radar signals difficult. Unless aircraft '42' is a mere aerodynamic prototype (perhaps with an unrepresentative nose shape), it would seem more likely to be a straightforward trainer, though perhaps this could form the basis of a dedicated attack aircraft. *Jane's Defence Weekly* reported Mikhail Simonov, Designer General of the Sukhoi OKB, as stating that the Su-27IB was "better for instruction in carrier landing and air-to-surface weapons delivery" than as a dedicated operational strike aircraft.

Right: A head-on view of the Su-27IB shows the canard foreplanes (which may have slightly more dihedral than those fitted to the Su-27K) and the distinctive flattened nose shape. The strengthened and relocated nose undercarriage is also clearly visible. The aircraft carries a pair of X-29 (NATO AS-14 'Kedge') missiles underwing, with a pair of laser-guided bombs inboard of those. A pair of X-31 anti-radar missiles is carried below the intake trunks, with an almost impossibly small degree of ground clearance.

Below: The Su-27IB at Minsk did carry air-to-air armament, with the same GSh-301 cannon in the starboard wingroot and with AA-11 'Archers' on the wingtips. Most interesting were the new AAMs carried just inboard of the wingtips. Dubbed 'Amraamski' in the West, these large, sharply pointed missiles are fitted with square, grid-like tailfins set at right angles to the airflow. Inside the squares are tiny aerofoils, forming a diamond grid pattern, which are parallel to the airflow.

VC-5 'Checkertails'
& Mount Pinatubo

Above: One of VC-5's TA-4 Skyhawks, operating from Misawa, Japan, flies past the huge cloud of ash thrown up by the eruption of Mount Pinatubo. Ten of the squadron's Skyhawks were evacuated to Japan, the others already being on detachment to Osan, Korea.

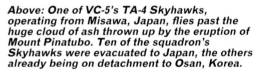

Left: An SH-3G of VC-5 the 'Checkertails' cavorts over typically lush Philippine scenery.

Based since 1975 at Cubi Point, Republic of the Philippines, and one of the farthest-flung US Navy squadrons, VC-5 had a ringside seat for the eruption of the Mount Pinatubo volcano in June 1991.

Fleet Composite Squadron Five (VC-5), based at Naval Air Station Cubi Point, provides an impressive list of services throughout the Western Pacific. Douglas A-4E Skyhawks serve as adversaries for Seventh Fleet and allied forces throughout Westpac. The 'Checkertails' provide dissimilar air combat training, and threat simulation for war-at-sea exercises.

The squadron's Sikorsky SH-3G Sea Kings provide the primary search and rescue (SAR) and medical evacuation (medevac) services for Subic Bay, and also transport VIPs, recover drones, and insert US Marine Corps fire teams. The SH-3G came into service in the early 1960s, and

the original service life was 10,000 hours. Two of VC-5's H-3s have exceeded the 10,000-hour mark and performed well in the adverse conditions.

Coup attempts, earthquakes, monsoons, strikes, typhoons, restrictions . . . VC-5 has seen them all. In June 1991, the 'Checkertails' faced a different challenge. What had started as small vents in Mount Pinatubo's peak eventually became one of the largest volcanic eruptions of this century. Mount Pinatubo is only 20 miles (32 km) north of the Subic-Cubi naval complex and 45 miles (72 km) north-west of Manila, the Philippine capital.

The steam vents appeared in early April, and as

seismic activity rapidly increased members of the US Geological Survey Teams knew a major eruption was imminent. On the morning of 12 June, Mount Pinatubo erupted after a 600-year slumber, sending a giant mushroom cloud more than 60,000 ft (18288 m) into the air. Luckily, Subic and Cubi had no ash fallout thanks to favourable winds which blew the ash over the South China Sea.

Because of the probability of continued volcanic activity, 10 of VC-5's 13 A-4s evacuated Cubi and a detachment was set up in Misawa and later Atsugi, Japan, to provide adversary training for Carrier Air Wing Five. This was in addition to a detachment already in Osan, Korea.

The volcano coughed up more ash on 13 and 14 June; this time the winds were not favourable, and the naval facility was sprinkled with 1 in (2.5 cm) of ash. On 15 June, dubbed 'Black Saturday' by those who lived through the dis-

Above: Those VC-5 SH-3G Sea Kings that do not wear toned-down markings carry a colourful yellow and black checkerboard band around the tailboom. Many of the unit's Sea Kings entered service during the early 1960s and two have exceeded 10,000 flying hours. The unit's tailcode is 'UE'.

Below: A toned-down VC-5 Sea King, up to its axles in ash, stands on the lower slopes of Mount Pinatubo. The volcano's dust cloud is visible in the background. Left: Ash and smoke billow from Pinatubo after the eruption. The mushroom cloud caused by the eruption rose 60,000 ft into the air.

aster, the sun never really shone. The day included a black blizzard of rain mixed with ash and quarter-sized rocks, volcanic thunder and brilliant lightning, as the earth shook for nearly six hours – non-stop! All of this coupled with a typhoon.

A blanket of ash

When the sun finally rose on 16 June, the naval complex looked like a nuclear wasteland. Mount Pinatubo had dumped 8-10 in (20-25 cm) of ash on the base. Two hundred and forty buildings had been severely damaged. The thick, green jungle was now a collection of grey sticks. The mixture of water and ash proved to be devastating, stripping the trees of their branches and leaves. The eruptions had thrown no less than 4 km^3 of ash and rock into the air and blown a 2-mile (3.2-km) crater out of Mount Pinatubo's peak.

On 13 June, VC-5 had been tasked with flying a passenger transfer from Baguio City, approximately 125 miles (201 km) north of Subic Bay, to the American Embassy in Manila. While Checker 42, an SH-3G, was en route to Manila the volcano erupted, spewing ash into Cubi's airspace. The ash fallout forced the helicopter to remain overnight at the Embassy and subsequently for 'Black Saturday'. Checker 42 was the first aircraft to fly after the disaster. Commander Jeff Stine, VC-5's commanding officer, and Lieute-

nant Millard Porter manned Checker 42 on the morning of 16 June, not aware of the extent of the disaster that had befallen Subic Bay.

"As we approached Corregidor Island, I realised the power of the eruption," said Lieutenant Porter. "It looked like it had actually snowed in the Philippines."

"Getting closer to Cubi, the ash cover increased, it looked like a moonscape," said Commander Stine. "It really didn't look that bad, but then I saw a DC-10 standing with its nose wheel (raised) off the ground, due to the amount of ash on the tail. I saw the rest of the base, then I realised the magnitude of the destruction."

The NAS Cubi tower had limited operation

and Checker 42 landed at the lower carrier pier, which is 1 mile (1.6 km) across the airport from the VC-5 hangar. The helicopter's wheels sank in the ash 1-2 in (2.5-5 cm).

On 17 June, Lieutenants Mark Watson and Cliff Keeney flew to Manila to pick up Ambassador Nicholas Platt, US Ambassador to the Philippines, and take him to view the damage at Subic-Cubi.

"Our biggest concern," said Lieutenant Watson, "was how to avoid the ash. We couldn't fly in the clouds because we didn't know where the ash was."

VC-5's H-3s soon became the primary platforms from which to view the volcano and keep

VC-5 'Checkertails'

base commanders informed of Mount Pinatubo's activity. Every day posed new problems for flight operations; there was no source of information on operating in such conditions. The Naval Air Training and Operating Procedures Standardization Program (NATOPS) does not address 'ash ops', nor had any squadron pilots ever encountered anything like Mount Pinatubo.

As the ground soaked up the rains brought by Typhoon Yunya, blowing ash storms were common, creating a challenging environment in which to land an aircraft. Lieutenant Junior Grade Brian Snell explained, "Landings were a challenge. There was a fine layer of ash everywhere. Normal hover landings could not be made."

Flights for science

No-hover approaches were flown to avoid the complete grey-out caused by the dust cloud generated by rotor downwash, creating instant Instrument Flight Rules (IFR) conditions. There was also the possibility of engines flaming out.

Only a few days after the eruptions, the 'Checkertails' were tasked with flying the US Geological Survey Teams to the volcano so they could lay new seismic sensing equipment, the old equipment being covered with ash or destroyed by the fierce eruptions.

VC-5 was once again blazing new trails. To fly the geologists and their equipment to the volcano required precision flying around an active crater that was capable of erupting at any time. The different drop zones where the scientists needed to place their equipment were not readily accessible, even by helicopter. The rock and ash covered the mountain, leaving few flat areas on which to land.

The aircrews often made precarious one-wheel landings to allow the scientists to set up their equipment. The high gross weight of the helicopter, coupled with the mushy, ash-covered terrain, caused the aircraft to tend to sink into the ground and required the pilot to hold power to prevent the helicopter from settling in the ash.

All of the volcano flights were in addition to the already high level of support in Subic and Cubi, and because of the shutdown of Clark Air Base the squadron was the only SAR/medevac asset in the Philippines. VC-5 also supported Operation Fiery Vigil (the evacuation of dependants from Subic and Cubi) and damage assessment flights over US bases.

Since Mount Pinatubo erupted in June, the 'Checkertails' have successfully flown multiple search and rescue missions, and 11 medevacs, transported over 500 personnel and moved over 20,000 lb (9072 kg) of cargo.

Below: Two McDonnell Douglas A-4E Skyhawks of VC-5. The squadron commander's aircraft, coded '00', retains high-visibility tail markings, although national insignia, 'Navy' and 'VC-5' legends remain firmly toned down. The toned-down aircraft (inset) is more typical of the squadron's A-4Es. The aircraft are used to provide a range of services to fleet units in the area.

Above: Heavy rain turned the ash produced by Pinatubo into thick grey mud, making operations difficult and unpleasant. VC-5's Sea Kings operated throughout, becoming the main vehicle by which geological survey teams visited the site, and by which on-site commanders obtained intelligence on the volcano's activity.

Above: VC-5's A-4E Skyhawks are used primarily for adversary training, and as such are unarmed. The various adversary units are the last US military operators of the single-seat Skyhawk, apart from a handful in the test community and a rapidly-dwindling number of Marine Reserve squadrons.

Right and below: The after-effects of the eruption of Mount Pinatubo. A thick layer of ash covered everything, burying plants, defoliating trees and damaging buildings. The build-up of ash on the tailplanes of this DC-10 (below) caused a huge shift in its centre of gravity, raising the nosewheel off the ground.

Bell/Boeing
V-22 Osprey
To be, or not to be?

Described by one leading Marine General as "Our most critical aviation requirement" and "Our number one aviation priority", the V-22 represents the ideal solution to many military requirements, offering fixed-wing standards of speed and payload with helicopter versatility. Yet production funding has not been forthcoming, and the aircraft's future looks uncertain.

Perhaps more than any other aircraft since the Wright brothers, the Bell/Boeing V-22 Osprey is the harbinger of new technology. In a nutshell, it can do everything a helicopter can do, while flying twice as far at twice the speed (for any given fuel burn). It thus promises utterly new capabilities to every military force in the world and to almost every commercial air carrier. How strange, then, that for years it should have been regarded as a prime candidate for cancellation.

As is so often the case, the basic trouble is money. Thirty years ago there was no problem in finding the money to pay perhaps 100 ground personnel to look after each aircraft. Today such profligate use of manpower is out of the question. Accordingly, for over 20 years air forces – including army, navy and marine air forces – have specified increasingly severe numerical requirements for reliability, maintainability and combat readiness for each new major type of combat aircraft. The first aircraft to enter service designed to meet these new requirements was the F/A-18 Hornet, and it proved that such demands could actually be met. Though considerably more complicated and advanced in concept than the F-4 and A-7 which it replaced, it needed only a fraction as many people to look after it.

The V-22 Osprey has been designed to meet even more stringent figures for reliability and maintainability, and this new technology does not come cheap. Where older aircraft incurred RDT&E (research, development, test and engineering) costs measured in millions, today's hi-tech aircraft have development costs running into billions. This in itself makes them stand out like sore thumbs in a defence budget that has to be severely pruned according to some arbitrary yardstick based on supposed shrinking foreign threats, reallocation of resources and the need to carry out dozens or even hundreds of programmes to modernise old equipment.

The picture is compounded by the fact that, throughout the whole expensive development period, the government – in the United States, in the person of the Defense Secretary – has to continue to find the huge sums needed to operate the older aircraft. Looking back, these cost the proverbial peanuts to buy, but in a new era of very expensive manpower they cost enormous sums to maintain. What makes the position more distressing is that the decisions are really taken by politicians, and there is hardly a politician anywhere who is prepared to take the long view. Even at the level of Secretaries – of the Navy, Air

Force or Commerce, for example – they are interested in 'here and now' costs. Back in 1990 US Defense Secretary Richard B. Cheney did his best to eliminate the V-22 from his budget (because at a stroke it would 'save' $1.3 billion) and replace it by additional purchases of traditional helicopters such as the CH-47 or CH-53. Such slick decisions overlook two giant factors: one is that the old-technology helicopters cost far more to operate; the other is that they cannot do anything remotely resembling the same job. The V-22 is one of the few aircraft that can truly be called unique.

Tilt-rotor history

The idea of a tilt-rotor aircraft goes back at least 80 years. Under such names as gyroplanes, heliplanes and convertiplanes, they have been the subject of countless patents, but not much flying hardware. A typical example from the past is the heliplane proposed in 1937 by L. E. Baynes in Britain. His idea was a two-seat ship-based warplane with two 15-ft (4.57-m) rotors driven by gas turbines pivoted to the end of a 21-ft (6.4-m) wing. Gross weight with two 20-mm cannon and much combat gear was calculated at 6,000 lb (2722 kg) and maximum speed at 365 mph (587 km/h). By chance, all this was very close to a 'convertaplane' specification published by the USAF Air Materiel Command in 1951.

This 1951 requirement led to Sikorsky, Bell and McDonnell all receiving US Air Force Phase I contracts. All used different techniques, and Bell picked the tilt-rotor concept. The resulting aircraft, the XV-3, or Bell Model 200, was a neat

Left: V-22 No. 3 hovers above the deck of the USS Wasp during initial shipboard compatibility trials. The aircraft met the weight and space limitations of the ship's elevators and (remarkably) hangar deck. Automatic blade-folding and wing-stowing was demonstrated, the process taking less than two minutes.

Top: The first V-22 transitions from helicopter to aeroplane mode. When the aircraft was rolled out it wore US Marine Corps camouflage, which was washed off prior to the start of flight testing. US Marine Corps support for the programme has been unwavering from the beginning.

Above: Bell's XV-15 of 1976 proved the tilt-rotor concept, and was used as a model by the V-22 team. In many respects the V-22 can be seen as a scaled-up, modernised XV-15, and the early aircraft has been of enormous value.

Left: The V-22 Ground Test Article basically consists of an Osprey wing and engines mated to a section of fuselage. It has been used to prove many of the V-22's unique features, including the blade-folding and wing-stowing mechanisms and, of course, the tilt-rotor mechanism itself.

blend of aeroplane and helicopter powered by a 450-hp Pratt & Whitney Wasp Junior piston engine mounted amidships. Ahead of it was the cabin, which could seat four. On each side were wings with a span of 30 ft (9.14 m), on the tips of which were the 25-ft (7.62-m) diameter three-bladed rotors. Electric motors at the wingtips could tilt these rotors down to the horizontal position, when they became propellers. The XV-3 was rolled out at Fort Worth on 10 February 1955, hovered on 11 August of the same year and completed the world's first conversion from helicopter to fixed-wing mode on 18 December 1958.

By sheer chance the other partner on the V-22, Boeing Helicopter Co., also pioneered this kind of technology, but in their case using the tilt-wing technique. In this arrangement the proprotors – now accepted as the term for a tilting rotor – were mounted on a wing which was hinged to the fuselage. Funded by the Navy, and then by the US Army, the VZ-2 or Model 76 was produced by Boeing's predecessor company, Vertol. Powered by a Lycoming T53 turbine limited to 800 shp, the Model 76 first flew in April 1957 and made its first full conversion from the hovering mode to the aeroplane mode in July 1958. Thus, both partners have getting on for 40 years of experience in the challenging tilt-rotor field.

New tilt-rotor aircraft

Even before the XV-3 programme was completed, Bell Helicopter received, in November 1965, an Army contract for a new tilt-rotor aircraft. This paid for a growing programme of studies and tests, one tunnel test model reaching a scale speed of 478 kt (550 mph; 885 km/h). The design was frozen on 26 September 1973, and on 22 October 1976 the first of two Bell XV-15 tilt-rotor aircraft was rolled out from the Fort Worth plant. The finely streamlined fuselage had two ejection seats in the side-by-side cockpit. The cabin at the rear, stripped of instrumentation, could have seated nine. On top was a slightly forward-swing wing carrying a 1,550-shp T53 engine on each tip, geared down to a three-bladed 25-ft (7.62-m) diameter proprotor. The XV-15 did everything it was supposed to do, reached 346 mph (557 km/h) in level flight, and drove home the tilt-rotor message all over the United States.

So impressive was the sleek XV-15 that demand grew for the obvious next generation: a bigger and much more powerful tilt-rotor to meet the needs of the US armed forces. This programme was launched by then-Defense Secretary Frank Carlucci in December 1981. Known as the JVX (code for joint-services advanced vertical-lift aircraft) programme, it was unique in that every branch of the armed forces expressed a need for it (and the civilian potential was obvious). There is no doubt that non-American forces and airlines viewed the launch of the JVX not only with intense interest but also with wistful envy.

There was no industrial competition; instead, Bell Helicopter Textron and Boeing Helicopter (then known as Boeing Vertol) announced a teaming agreement on 7 June 1982. Since then the work has been shared on an approximately 50/50 basis. A convenient work split was provided by the fact that the wing is pivoted to the fuselage; accordingly, Boeing is responsible for every

The cockpit of the V-22 is entirely modern, and is dominated by large multi-function CRT type displays. Each pilot has a control column, rudder pedals and a left-hand power lever.

Bell/Boeing V-22 Osprey

1 Starboard rotor, glass-fibre blades
2 Blade-folding hinge joint
3 Articulated rotor hub
4 Swashplate mechanism
5 Main rotor transfer gearbox
6 Rotor head hydraulic actuator (3)
7 Intake particle sensor
8 Allison T406-AD-400 turboshaft engine
9 Pylon actuating screw jack
10 Pylon support bearing
11 Outboard elevon
12 Inboard elevon
13 Elevon vane/sealing plate
14 Starboard wing auxiliary fuel tanks (4)
15 Fuel feed tank
16 Pneumatic leading-edge de-icing boot
17 Infra-red signature suppression exhaust duct
18 Rescue hoist/winch
19 Starboard side two-segment entry doorway
20 TACAN aerial
21 IFF aerial
22 ILS glideslope aerial
23 Starboard side avionics equipment racks
24 Pilot's seat
25 Instrument console (multifunction glass-panel displays)
26 Windscreen wipers
27 Pitot heads (3)
28 Control column and pedals (fully duplicated controls)
29 AN/APQ-174 multifunction radar
30 Fixed inflight-refuelling probe
31 AN/AAQ-16 Forward Looking Infra-Red (FLIR)
32 Twin nosewheels, aft retracting
33 Nosewheel hydraulic jack
34 Radar warning antenna
35 Downward vision window
36 Window hatch emergency release
37 Thrust/power control lever (collective)
38 Co-pilot's seat
39 Port avionics equipment racks
40 Avionics cooling air grille
41 Port main fuel tank
42 Underslung load hooks, fore and aft
43 Roller-conveyor track
44 Cabin escape hatch, fore and aft
45 Folding troop seats, 12 per side
46 Swivelling carousel wing mounting ring frame
47 Wing rotating screw jack
48 Electrical equipment stowage

Specification
Bell/Boeing V-22 Osprey

Engines: two 6,150-shp (4586-kW) Allison Gas Turbine Division T406-AD-400s; take-off, sea level, standard day (USMC) 4,200 shp (3132 kW), (USN, USAF) 4570 shp (3408 kW); one engine inoperative 5,920 shp (4415 kW)

Rotor system: rotor diameter 38 ft 0 in (11.58 m); total disc area 2,268 sq ft (210.7 m²); total blade area 261.52 sq ft (24.3 m²)

Dimensions, external: length overall 57 ft 4 in (17.48 m), stowed 62 ft 7 in (19.08 m); width, proprotors turning 84 ft 7 in (25.78 m); height overall 21 ft 9 in (6.63 m); blade/ground clearance, helo 20 ft 10 in (6.35 m); wheelbase 21 ft 10 in (6.65 m)

Dimensions, internal: maximum length 24 ft 2 in (7.37 m); maximum width 5 ft 11 in (1.8 m); maximum height 6 ft 0 in (1.83 m)

Accommodation: cockpit 2, cabin 5

Weights: empty 31,818 lb (14433 kg); operating 32,623 lb (14798 kg); maximum take-off, VTO 47,500 lb (21546 kg), STO 55,000 lb (24948 kg); cargo hook capacity, single 10,000 lb (4536 kg), dual 15,000 lb (6804 kg)

Fuel capacity: sponsons 1,228 US gal (4649 litres); wing 787 US gal (2979 litres); cabin, self deploy 2,436 US gal (9221 litres)

Range: maximum fuel 2,100 nm (2,417 miles/3889 km); combat SAR 1,020 nm (1174 miles/1889 km); amphibious assault 515 nm (593 miles/954 km)

Performance: USMC amphibious assault, standard day: maximum speed at sea level 300 kt (345 mph; 556 km/h); 283 kt (326 mph; 525 km/h) demonstrated at 17,500 ft (5334 m) and 350 kt (403 mph; 649 km/h) in dives; rate of climb, sea level, vertical 1,090 ft/min (332 m/min), maximum 2,320 ft/m (707 m/min); service ceiling 26,000 ft (7925 m), with one engine inoperative 11,300 ft (3444 m); hovering ceiling out of ground effect 14,200 ft (4328 m)

49 Hydraulic and electrical services rotary connector
50 Engine interconnection cross-shaft
51 Central combining and transfer gearbox
52 Generators (2)
53 Auxiliary power unit [APU]
54 Oil cooler
55 Port elevons
56 Cargo-loading ramp hydraulic jacks
57 VHF/UHF aerial
58 HF/SSB aerial
59 Rear cabin roof escape hatch
60 Troop commander's communications aerial

Left: The No. 1 V-22 in helicopter mode. In comparative studies, the V-22 proved itself three times as survivable and twice as productive as an all-helicopter force in the amphibious assault role.

Below: The No. 4 V-22 was the first to fly in Marine Corps camouflage. It was the first prototype intended to be used for operational evaluations, as well as for propulsion studies, climatic laboratory tests and performance evaluations.

thing below the wing, plus avionics integration, while Bell is responsible for the remainder. A major milestone was the publication on 14 December 1982 of the Joint Services Operational Requirement, following the DSARC (Defense Systems Acquisition Review Council) go-ahead. From the outset the biggest and most immediate need was that of the Marine Corps. The Corps specified a primary mission for three crew and 24 combat-equipped troops carried at 250 kt over a radius of 200 nm (230 miles/370 km), with hover out of ground effect at destination at 3,000 ft (914 m). The Air Force demand was even

61 Fin leading-edge de-icing boot
62 Rudder hydraulic actuator
63 Starboard rudder
64 One-piece elevator
65 Anti-collision light
66 Port rudder
67 Rear radar warning antenna
68 Elevator hydraulic actuators (3)
69 Port rotor
70 Articulated rotor hub
71 Constant velocity joint
72 Engine air intake
73 Rotor transfer gearbox
74 Cargo loading ramp
75 Gearbox oil tank and cooler
76 Tilt axis gearbox drive shaft
77 Tilt axis gearbox
78 Infra-red suppression exhaust mixer air fan
79 Mixing/cooling air intake
80 Internal air baffles
81 Variable geometry exhaust doors
82 Nacelle pylon in forward flight position
83 Port Allison T406-AD-400 engine
84 Pylon screw jack hydraulic motor
85 Port engine fuel feed tank
86 Sponson-mounted air conditioning pack
87 VOR aerial
88 Leading-edge de-icing boot
89 Main undercarriage hydraulic retraction jack
90 Tie-down shackle
91 Fuel filler cap
92 Twin mainwheels, aft retracting

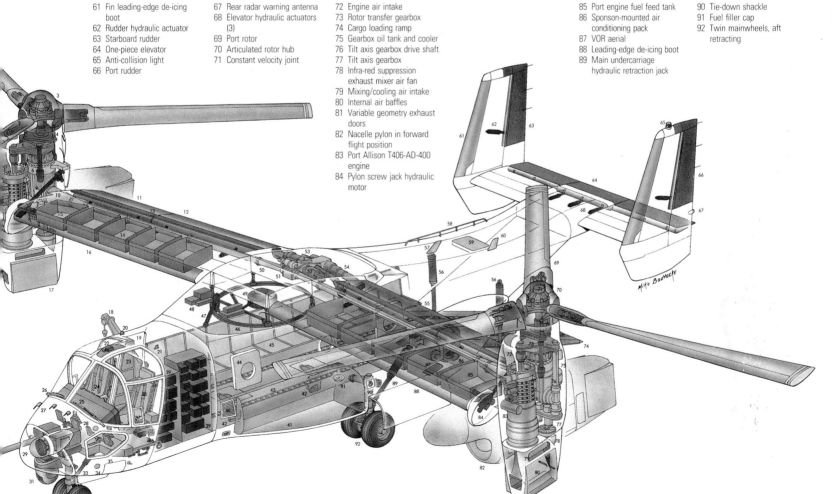

Sequence above: *A series of pictures showing the No. 3 Osprey operating from the USS Wasp, the Marine Corps' latest amphibious warfare ship, during December 1990. About the size of a World War II aircraft-carrier, the Wasp's primary role is to provide for the embarkation, deployment, landing and support of a Marine Corps landing force. As such it represents just the sort of ship that an operational V-22 would have to operate from. V-22s Nos 3 and 4 flew out to the ship from the NATC at Patuxent River for a series of comprehensive shipboard compatibility tests. Two USMC and one USN pilots flew the aircraft during these trials, supervised by Bell/Boeing test pilots. The trials showed that there was ample visibility to allow the pilot to approach the ship and take off and land with complete safety. The V-22 also demonstrated sufficient stability to safely hover over a pitching, rolling deck.*

Left: *Two V-22s and a single CH-53 helicopter can be seen on the deck of the USS Wasp (LHD-1). The tremendous width of the V-22, with its rotors turning, can clearly be seen.*

Below: *The No. 4 V-22 sits, rotors folded, behind a plane-guard US Navy SH-3 Sea King. Search and rescue will be one of any military V-22's many roles. With its wings folded, the V-22 is not much larger than a Sea King.*

tougher: though the load in this case was only 12 troops or 2,880 lb (1306 kg) of internal cargo, carried at the same speed, the radius demanded was 700 nm (805 miles/1296 km), with hover at destination at 4,000 ft (1219 m) at 95°F (35°C). The Army and Navy also listed their requirements, but the hardest one was the radius called for by the Air Force.

Clearly the demands made it mandatory to avoid compromises wherever possible, and this was especially the case with the engine. By early 1984 the engine choice had been narrowed to two finalists: the General Electric GE27 and the Pratt & Whitney PW3005. Both were completely new engines in the 5,000-shp class, with extremely challenging performance, especially in the matter of fuel economy and ratio of power to weight. In January 1983 programme management had been transferred to the Navy, so Navy Secretary John Lehman could call the shots. In December 1985 he announced the startling choice of Allison as supplier of the engine. In his view, even though it forced the USAF radius to be reduced to 550 nm (633 miles/1018 km), the T406 engine was preferable because it was derived from the T56, in worldwide use on the C-130 and P-3, and thus posed less technical risk. Such arguments have invariably proved to be fallacious. At the same time, the T406 is very much better than the T56, because it is a free-turbine engine (the power turbine being derived from that of the XCH-62 Heavy Lift Helo engine, the T701), with a vastly improved compressor with six rows of variable stators, single-crystal HP turbine blades, and a Fadec (full-authority digital electronic control). Moreover, it is rather more powerful than the rival engines, being rated at 6,150 shp and with the potential of 7,400 shp a little later with higher temperatures. It goes without saying that Allison have designed the T406 for maximum reliability and minimum maintenance. It could well be the basis for a future C-130 engine. A single-shaft engine, such as the T56, could not readily be used in the V-22 because both proprotors would then be rigidly geared to both engines; with the T406 they are connected to the power turbines only.

On 15 January 1985 Lehman announced that the JVX would be designated V-22 and named Osprey after the maritime bird of prey. By late 1985 virtually all the main subcontracts had been let, and construction went ahead on many large new facilities, especially for composite airframe structures. Colonel Harry M. Blot, USMC, a very experienced Harrier pilot, was appointed programme manager and on 21 May 1986 flew an XV-15 to experience tilt-rotor technology at first hand.

First roll-out

In the first week of May 1987 Bell and Boeing announced completion of the first wing and fuselage structures. Later that month they signed agreements to market the V-22 and derivatives to foreign customers, and over the ensuing two years signed memorandums of understanding covering assessments of requirements in overseas markets with (in chronological order): British Aerospace, Mitsui & Co./C. Itoh & Co (Japan), Dornier (Germany) and Aeritalia (now Alenia) in Italy. V-22 aircraft No. 1 was ceremonially rolled out – wearing Marine Corps camouflage – at Bell's flight research centre at Arlington, Texas, on 23 May 1988. Its first flight was made on 19

March 1989 and first full conversion from helicopter to aeroplane mode on 14 September of that year.

On the negative side, it had long been evident that the Department of Defense was not only anxious but also virtually forced to make very large cuts in its FY 1990 budget. The V-22 was an obvious target, yet another example from many large programmes in several countries where the top decision-takers said, in effect, "We can save a lot of money here, don't tell me how important/futuristic/indispensable it is." On 19 April 1989 new Defense Secretary Dick Cheney announced FY 1990 cuts totalling $10 billion, one of the biggest supposed savings (R&D cut by $221.2 million and all $1.3 billion production funding, for the first 12 V-22s for inventory) being the deletion of all V-22 funding. In such a crisis situation manufacturers have only limited power on Capitol Hill, but the armed forces – even the little Marine Corps – have plenty. Seriously concerned about the approaching obsolescence of the CH-46E force, and limitations and high costs of the CH-53D and E force, the Marines joined with Bell/Boeing in a spirit almost reminiscent of the Marine defence of Wake Island.

In November the National Authorization and Appropriation Acts authorised $255 million for V-22 R&D in FY 1990 funds and also authorised DoD to obligate all remaining FY 1989 advanced procurement funds. On 1 December Cheney's deputy ordered the Navy to terminate all V-22 funding with FY 1989 funds, but on 7 March 1990 the General Accounting Office said this was improper. After much argument it was clear Congress was gradually becoming better informed about the V-22 and more supportive, and on 5 November 1990 FY 1991 provided $238 million for R&D, $165 million for long-lead production items and $15 million for items unique to a Special Operations Force version, and restored $200 million of the previously withheld FY 1989 long-lead production funds.

Still determined to kill the programme, the DoD budgets for FY 1992 and FY 1993, announced on 4 February 1991, again contained no funding for the V-22. However, in April 1991 the Desert Storm Dire Emergency Supplemental Authorization Act directed the obligation of $200 million (from FY 1989 funds) to the V-22 programme. The House Armed Services Committee proposed that FY 1992-93 should fund six opeval (operational evaluation) 'production-representative' aircraft, and it began to look as if the DoD attempts at outright cancellation might be defeated. A minor hiccup was the loss of the No. 5 aircraft on 11 June 1991, but the cause was soon identified.

To a remarkable degree the V-22 is a scaled-up XV-15, and this obviously reduces the risk in such areas as aerodynamics, stability and flight control. On the other hand the V-22 is several times heavier and more powerful, has a totally different structure, is designed to fold for shipboard operation and also is intended to withstand strikes by 23-mm projectiles (with the hope eventually of surviving 30-mm fire). Not least, of course, the different versions carry different operational equipment.

Over 59 per cent of the airframe is made of composites, only 1,000 lb (454 kg) of the empty weight being metal. Ruling material in the wings is Hercules IM-6 graphite/epoxy, though each leading edge is three detachable segments of aluminium alloy with a Nomex honeycomb core. On each trailing edge are two-segment graphite single-slotted flaperons with titanium fittings. The fuselage is mainly of AS4 graphite/epoxy, as is the twin-finned tail which is made by Grumman. All three landing gears have twin wheels and retract rearwards hydraulically, the main units into large sponsons. The two Allison T406-AD-400 engines are installed on the wingtips in Bell-built nacelles mainly of GFRP (glass-fibre reinforced plastics). In an emergency landing on water the fuselage and sponsons provide inbuilt buoyancy, while the nacelles serve as pontoons giving lateral stability against capsizing.

Each engine drives a Bell three-bladed rotor with a diameter of 38 ft (11.58 m). A transverse cross-shaft drives both proprotors in the event of failure of either engine, the shaft having an OEI (one engine inoperative) rating of 5,920 shp. Normally the segmented steel shaft is unloaded, though it is used during the starting cycle to transmit drive torque from the centrally mounted APU (auxiliary power unit), a 350-shp unit which not only starts the main engines but also drives two electric generators and an air compressor, giving the V-22 total autonomy without the need for any assistance from ground services. The wing centre-section also contains a drive gearbox, rotor-phasing drive-system mechanical lock and a brake to bring both proprotors quickly to rest.

The fundamental feature of a tilt-rotor aircraft is that the proprotors can be tilted from vertical (the helicopter mode) to horizontal (the aeroplane mode). In the V-22 the angular range is 97° 30′. Each engine nacelle is mounted on a conversion spindle at its mid-point and is driven by an electric screwjack actuator. Should an actuator fail with the V-22 in forward flight (a very unlikely occurrence) special standby safety mechanisms can return the two nacelles to the helicopter mode, enabling the aircraft to make a safe vertical or run-on landing.

The proprotors themselves are in several respects unique. Their blades are made from advanced combinations of glassfibre and graphite composites, with abrasion-resistant metal leading edges, statically and dynamically balanced and of high-twist design with a tapered format and square tips. Each is mounted in elastomeric spherical bearings, and has a remarkable hinge near the root which enables it to be folded in the plane of rotation by inbuilt actuators. But the most remarkable aspect is probably the flight-control system. Not least of the unusual features is that completely different systems are needed for flight in the helicopter mode and in the aeroplane mode, though all are controlled by the same cockpit interfaces and changeover from one mode to the other is smooth and automatic.

As ships are normally approached from the port side the Navy and Marines V-22 versions, at least, are normally commanded from the right-hand seat in the side-by-side cockpit, which offers all-round vision through the windscreens, overhead, side and knee windows and an overhead rear-view mirror. Civil and USAF preference is for a left-seat captain. The crew are protected by a strong anti-plough bulkhead in front, the seats are boron carbide and polyethylene laminate stressed to 30g, and the whole cockpit is designed to be proof against bird-strikes and rifle-calibre ammunition. The pilot's primary flight-control inputs are two sticks, pedals and left-hand power levers. Unlike a helicopter collective these levers move in the aeroplane sense, forwards towards full power.

Helicopter to aeroplane

All flight controls are digital FBW (fly by wire) using a standard dual MIL-1553B bus system. The PFCS (primary flight-control system) processors and AFCS (automatic flight-control system) processors are triply redundant, for near-total reliability, while the hydraulic elements are duplicated. Full automatic-stabilisation, autopilot and formation-flying modes are provided. In the helicopter mode the V-22 is flown just like a helicopter, with a collective and a cyclic. The aerodynamic control surfaces are of course inoperative, and all manoeuvres are effected by the proprotors. In the aeroplane mode the reverse is true. All manoeuvres are effected by the flaperons, elevator and rudder, and the proprotors become propellers, though with beta (direct pilot) control of pitch.

Thus, in a vertical lift-off and all helicopter flight modes control is provided solely by governing swashplates giving cyclic control of pitch of the proprotors. In this mode lateral control is simple, being achieved by differential collective pitch. Translational flight is more difficult, being achieved by cyclic pitch variations governed by the three swashplate actuators – each triply redundant, like the avionics – in each proprotor spinner. A button on the control column controls the lateral swashplates to give sideways flight with wings level. Forward swashplates control forwards or rearwards flight, the cruising speed in this mode being 115 mph (185 km/h).

Conversion into aeroplane flight can be completely automatic. As the engine nacelles pivot round to the horizontal attitude, so do the flight-control signals increasingly switch to the aero-

Bell/Boeing V-22 Osprey

The No. 2 V-22 prototype wears an overall white colour scheme, with high visibility red panels on nose and tail. The first of three prototypes for which Boeing has responsibility, No. 2 was intended to test the primary and automatic flight control systems, perform icing tests, demonstrate flying qualities and conduct various development tests. The loss of aircraft No. 5 has increased the number of tasks.

Above left: US Marine Corps and US Navy V-22s will be captained from the right-hand seat, following normal helicopter practice, while the USAF will probably have a captain in the left-hand seat.

Fuselage
About 60 per cent of the airframe is of composite construction. The fuselage is formed from composite stringers, frames and preformed skin panels, with metal fasteners.

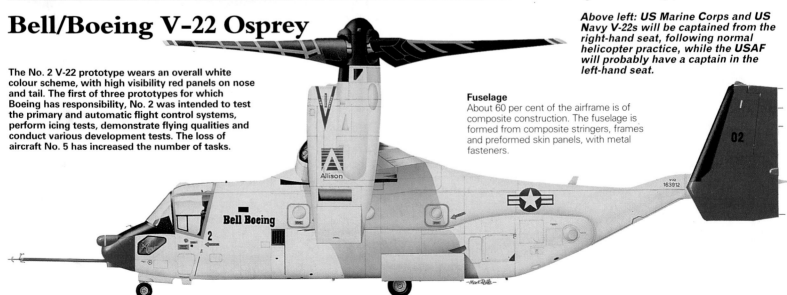

Powerplant
Allison won the competition to power the V-22, its 6,150-shp T406-AD-400 turboshaft based on the ubiquitous T56, beating the Pratt & Whitney PW3005 and the General Electric GE27, both of which had greater power-to-weight ratios and superior fuel economy and which had been developed under the US Army's Modern Technology Demonstrator Engine programme. The engines are housed in Bell-built wingtip tilting nacelles and feature Lucas Full Authority Digital Engine Control Systems, with analogue backup.

Accommodation
Pilot (right-hand seat), co-pilot (left-hand seat) and crew chief form the crew of the USMC V-22. They sit on crashworthy armoured seats built by Simula Inc. from a boron carbide/polyethylene laminate, which are capable of withstanding strikes by 0.30-in bullets or 14.5g or 30g forward decelerations. The main cabin can accommodate up to 24 fully-equipped troops or 12 litters and attendants. In cargo configuration, there are energy-absorbing tiedowns, a 2,000-lb capacity internal winch system, and removeable roller rails.

Composites
The extensive use of composites gives a 25 per cent weight saving over an equivalent all-metal aircraft, together with good corrosion resistance, ballistic tolerance, inherent buoyancy and the likelihood of a much longer life.

Proprotors
The 38-ft diameter three-bladed contra-rotating proprotors have special high-twist tapered blades with elastomeric bearings. The blades can be given 45° of twist (the optimum angle for high lift) because in forward flight, when the blades are moved through 90°, the extra twist does not produce significant drag as it would in a fixed-rotor helicopter. The rotor blades incorporate a powered-folding mechanism and separate swashplates.

Tail unit
Of Hercules AS-4 graphite/epoxy composite construction, the entire tail unit of the V-22 is built by Grumman, and incorporates rudders and elevators.

Prototypes
Six aircraft, on Navy account, with BuAer Numbers 163911-163916:
No. 1 (Bell): system checkout, tiedown tests, taxi tests, exploration of flight envelope, flight loads, vibration, aeroelasticity, maximum weight take-offs and landings, high-altitude flights
No. 2 (Boeing): primary and automatic flight-control systems, development tests, icing tests and demonstration of flying qualities
No. 3 (Bell): exploration of flight loads, vibrations and acoustics, examination of flight loads, demonstration of structural capability, sea trials
No. 4 (Boeing): initial propulsion studies, development and operational tests, climatic-laboratory studies, demonstration of proprotor performance and operational evaluations
No. 5 (Boeing): avionics development, Navy/Marines mission equipment, avionics/AFCS, terrain avoidance/terrain following, development and operational evaluations
No. 6 (Bell): aircraft equipment, electronic (shielded hangar) tests, development/operational tests, and operational evaluations

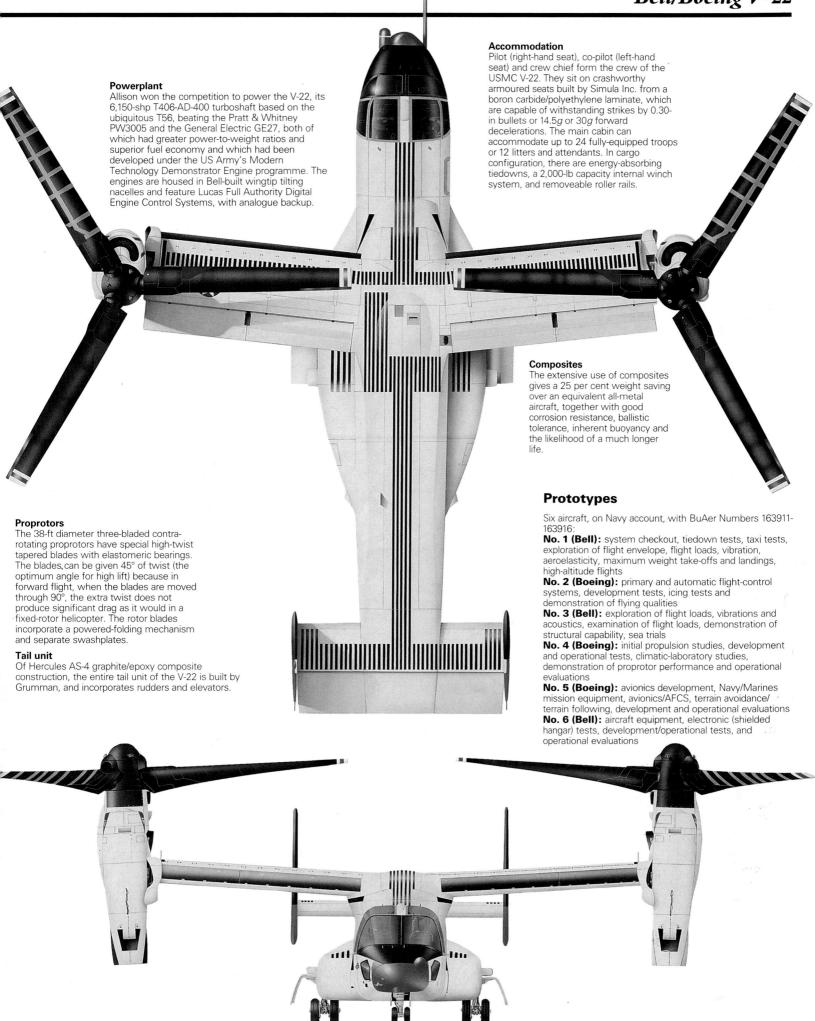

plane-type aerodynamic surfaces. During helicopter flight the wing's trailing-edge surfaces, comprising two flaperons on each wing, droop sharply to reduce the negative lift of the wing in the rotor downwash. During conversion to aeroplane flight the flaperons are progressively raised until they come into full use as flaps or ailerons driven by hydraulic power units linked to the FBW flight controls. The tail has two elevators and two rudders, similarly controlled by triple actuators on each elevator and a single power unit on each rudder. Handling of the V-22 in aeroplane flight is indistinguishable from that of other fixed-wing machines.

The cockpit has no dial instruments and no toggle switches. Instead, every panel space between the numerous large windows is devoted to six large (8×8 in/20×20 cm) colour CDUs (control/display units). Four of these multifunction displays present flight attitude, performance and navigation information, engine behaviour, systems monitoring and radio frequencies. The other two, at lower centre, access all on-board systems, via illuminated pushbutton interfaces.

One of the tasks controlled by a CDU pushbutton is to fold the aircraft for shipboard stowage. Shipboard operation was expected to give rise to unique problems, partly because of such things as pilot view in lateral approaches, control in turbulence downwind of the ship and the fact that as the V-22 came in over the side one proprotor would be in ground effect above the deck, giving enhanced lift, while the other was blowing down past the side of the ship. Tests in December 1990 by Nos 3 and 4 aircraft showed that there were no problems. The No. 4 aircraft

Below and right: The No. 1 V-22 in flight. The V-22's wing is of mainly composite construction, with a high-strength torsion box made from one-piece upper and lower skins with moulded ribs and bonded stringers. The trailing edge has two-segment single-slotted flaperons, which are of graphite construction with titanium fittings.

was put through the folding cycle on the deck of the USS *Wasp*. Under computer control the proprotors and linking shaft are first braked so that one blade is pointing directly inboard on each side. The other two blades on each proprotor are then folded inboard, and the nacelles rotated to the horizontal (aeroplane mode) position. Finally the wing is rotated through 90° to lie fore and aft, lugs and slide shoes travelling round a 7.6-ft (2.31-m) diameter stainless steel ring called a carousel in the top of the fuselage. When folded, the port engine is just beyond the nose and the starboard engine in front of the tail. Folding takes 120 seconds, but will be 90 seconds in production aircraft.

V-22 systems are designed for near-zero maintenance. JP-5 fuel is housed in three sponson tanks and two self-sealing feed tanks adjacent to the engines, while Navy and Air Force versions have eight extra tanks in the leading edges, a total of 2,015 US gal (7627 litres). For self-deployment ferry up to four quickly-fitted tanks (each 602 US gal/2279 litres) can be installed in the fuselage, and an inflight-refuelling extensible probe can be fitted in the nose. To reduce weight the

triple hydraulic systems operate at 5,000 psi (34475 kPa). Electric power is generated by two 40-kVA constant-frequency alternators and two 50/80-kVA variable-frequency generators (one driven by the APU). The ECS (environmental control system) in the aft section of the left sponson supplies filtered air to the cockpit and cabin, for avionics cooling and to maintain an internal overpressure for NBC protection. Each engine inlet, spinner, proprotor blade and cockpit windshield has electrothermal de-icing, while the leading edges of the wings and tail are fitted with pneumatic de-icer boots. Onboard systems generate oxygen for the people and nitrogen for inert-gas tank pressurisation.

Payloads and missions

Basically, today's V-22 is a transport, carrying passengers internally and cargo either internally or as one or two slung loads. The unobstructed cabin has a width of 5 ft 11 in (1.8 m), height at the centreline of 6 ft (1.83 m) and length of 25 ft 2 in (7.37 m). It has composite floor panels stressed for intense point loads, all bulky loads and vehicles being loaded/unloaded via the full-section

Right: Like a helicopter, the V-22 can carry underslung loads. It has two external cargo hooks and a rescue hoist, and its twin side-by-side rotors make it less sensitive to wind direction.

rear ramp door with hydraulic actuators. The main troop door is at the front on the right side, the top part hinging in and upwards and the main door section folding out and down to provide integral steps. The usual personnel fit is 24 crashworthy fold-away seats facing inwards. In the rescue or medevac mission 12 litters can quickly be fitted, plus seats for three attendants; a 600-lb (272-kg) hydraulic winch is added.

In cargo missions the maximum internal load is 20,000 lb (9072 kg), loaded and positioned by a hydraulic winch and pulley system of 2,000-lb (907-kg) capacity, together with removable floor roller rails. Slung loads can be carried on either a single external hook of 10,000-lb (4536-kg) capacity, or on two hooks disposed in front of and behind the centre of gravity, in which case the combined load can be 15,000 lb (6804 kg). Use of both front and rear hooks on a single slung load

enables cruising speed to be set at 200 kt (230 mph; 371 km/h). An important advantage in slung-load or rescue operations is that the contrarotating proprotors are insensitive to wind speed or direction.

All V-22s built for US military customers would have the same core avionics, comprising dual AYK-14 mission processors, a dual 1553B bus system, data acquisition and storage system, VHF and HF secure voice communications, an integrated navigation system (ring-laser inertial navigation system, TACAN, VOR, digital map displays, attitude/heading reference system, radar altimeter and ILS), and comprehensive tactical devices including IFF, radar/infra-red warn-

ing systems, an AAQ-16 undernose forward-looking infra-red, AAR-47 missile warning system and chaff/flare dispensers. All aircraft would have a pilot's night-vision system and Honeywell integrated helmet display system. Aircraft for the Navy and Air Force would in addition be equipped with a Texas Instruments APQ-174 terrain-following multifunction radar in a thimble on the left side of the nose, and USAF V-22s would also have UHF communications. Various weapon fits have also been studied, though none has been specified by existing customers.

Non-military uses

It is safe to say that virtually every military force, at least in the developed world, is watching the progress of the V-22 with much more than academic interest. As for paramilitary (such as disaster relief and coast guard) and commercial operators, there is no doubt that the future could be open-ended. The following quotes are selected from dozens. Admiral Paul A. Yost, Jr, Commandant, US Coast Guard, ". . . within 15 years the V-22 will largely replace the helicopter."

The No. 2 V-22 approaches a drogue towed by a KC-130 tanker. Access to the cabin is by a two-part main cabin door in the starboard forward fuselage, the upper half (outlined yellow) opening upwards and inwards, and the lower half opening downwards and outwards and incorporating integral steps.

Two V-22 prototypes fly past. The rear aircraft is in full 'aeroplane' mode, while the nearest aircraft is transitioning to the helicopter mode.

Left: The camouflaged No. 4 V-22 is seen operating aboard the USS Wasp. The similarly-painted No. 5 aircraft was lost in a fortunately non-fatal crash.

It is . . . the answer to a Coast Guard Commander's prayer." Fred Stewart, Chief, Office of Planning, California Department of Transportation, "In the next 20 years passenger emplanements (in California) will double, from 56.1 to 114.7 million. There are already too many aircraft for too few runways . . . We envision the tiltrotor as a possible means to alleviate . . ." Morris E. Flater, President, HubExpress, "There are 1,600 airline gates in the US, or about four aircraft per gate. By 2005 we will have doubled the aircraft; where will they go? Tiltrotor service could increase the capacity of our airports by 30 per cent without spending a dollar of our scarce tax revenues." Many other observers have commented on the long range and high cruising speed of the tiltrotor, enabling it to react to sudden emergencies far quicker than any other means of transport. They have also commented on the fact that a fully equipped 'vertiport' would cost only 'a few hundred thousand dollars', in contrast to the five runways of Denver's new airport which cost $81 million each.

On the whole the flight-test programme has gone equal to or better than predicted with no unexpected features. There was just one well-publicised setback when aircraft No. 5 crashed on 11 June 1991. The cause was quickly traced to an assembly fault in the lateral control system. The cockpit contains three FBW interface units, each connected by a 120-wire bundle plug con-

nector. The vyro unit (roll-rate sensor) uses wires 59 and 60. The six aircraft wire bundles and plugs were all assembled together in 1988. When Aircraft Nos 1 and 3 were complete an installation problem was identified, wires 59 and 60 being transposed (reverse-wired) in one of the roll-rate sensors. This still enabled the two good channels to vote the unique signal off-line. Amazingly, with aircraft No. 5 not only did the problem persist but in this case two of the three roll-rate sensors were reverse-wired. The pilots quickly recognised the problem but, after several unsuccessful attempts at a landing the aircraft went divergent in the lateral (roll) axis and impacted the ground. Somewhat belatedly the problem was made impossible to repeat, and V-22 flight clearance was renewed on 10 September. Since then the remaining five aircraft have returned to flight status, and at the time of writing (November 1991) No. 1 had logged 177 hours in 176 flights (one of which, on 9 October 1991, was 1,200 miles/1931 km in a little over five hours from Patuxent River to its home base at Arlington, TX, with a stop for fuel at Nashville); No. 2 had logged 216.1 hours in 149 flights; No. 3 128.5 hours in 110 flights; and No. 4 88.5 hours in 78 flights, a total of 610.1 hours in 513 flights.

In October all V-22 people were on tenterhooks. The House of Representatives had voted to provide the Navy $990 million to build three production-representative Ospreys, but the

Senate's two bills (authorisation and appropriation) provided merely $165 million to continue the flight-test programme. What would happen when Congress finally voted? On 13 November 1991 came the answer: both the Authorization and Appropriations Committees agreed to fund the V-22 programme in FY 1992 at $790 million. This comprised $625 million in new funds and $165 million transferred from unobligated FY 1991 Navy aircraft procurement funds. The $790 million was for three production-representative V-22s. The provision also made available $15 million from Defense Agencies funds for R&D and evaluation of the Special Operations CV-22A variant.

Positive report

The Report and Bill language was not only exceptionally positive with regard to the V-22 but unprecedentedly explicit in a reference to the Secretary of Defense. It included the following: "The conferees agree that the V-22 offers an answer to the Marine Corps medium-lift requirement and direct the Navy to promptly embark on a Phase II full-scale engineering development program to correct identified deficiencies and produce production-representative aircraft. The conferees expect the Navy to embark upon this program as soon as possible, and neither the Secretary of Defense nor any of his subordinates may take action which will un-

necessarily delay obligation of these funds.'' Congress expressed the view that the FY 1992 funds should enable the entire Joint Services Operational Requirement for the V-22 "to be demonstrated not later than 31 December 1996."

A price of $790 million for three V-22s bears little relation to the unit price in full production. The 'production-representative' aircraft will incorporate many (probably many hundreds) of engineering changes compared with the aircraft now flying. They will incorporate all the results of the exploration of the flight envelope, which was completed very soon after flight testing was resumed on 10 September 1991. In particular, the production aircraft will have more powerful engines, though it is not yet known whether these will be upgraded Allisons or one of the all-new alternatives from GE or Pratt & Whitney. No details have been given of the remaining changes.

One area where the programme has slipped slightly is in operational evaluation in the hands of users. One, and possibly two, V-22s were to have gone to the Marine Experimental Helicopter Squadron 1 (HMX-1) at Quantico, VA, in July 1991. Then, flown by HMX-1 pilots, it/they were to have gone to MCAS New River in August and to Yuma and Kirtland in September. This plan was killed by the loss of aircraft No. 5 and immediate cessation of flying until each aircraft had undergone detailed inspections and functional tests. There are hopes that this important evaluation in the hands of the principal user will take place in early 1992 and get the overall programme back on schedule.

One area where it is perhaps ahead of schedule is in planning for simultaneous military qualification and civil certification. The DoD and FAA (Federal Aviation Administration) reached an agreement in late 1988 for a complete exchange of flight test data. Not only does no commercial V-22 yet exist but neither do FAA criteria for certification. After all, it is unprecedented to have to lay down laws for a flying machine that is both a fast turboprop aeroplane and a helicopter. Ron Reber, Bell's civil tiltrotor programme manager, is sanguine that an airline V-22 will encounter few problems. "The FAA is advanced in detailed review of the hardware and the flight envelope. We hope to get a certification that will allow us to show what it can really do."

In recent months the interest of potential customers, military and civil, has sharpened perceptibly. With the FY 1992 vote by Congress the V-22 has turned the corner.

Above: *An unconcerned Bell technician films the No. 1 V-22 Osprey prototype being put through its paces at low level. With the engine pods swept forward like this, the V-22 can make short instead of vertical take-offs.*

Below: *Development funding for the V-22 continues to trickle through, but crucial production funding for the aircraft so desperately wanted and needed by the US Marines continues to be witheld.*

Variants

MV-22A: basic US Marine Corps aircraft, 552 required to replace CH-46 and CH-53. Multirole assault transport normally equipped for 24 troops and equipment, mission radius 200 nm

HV-22A: US Navy CSAR (combat search and rescue) vehicle, also for special warfare and fleet logistics to replace HH-3. Original requirement 50

SV-22A: tentative US Navy ASW (anti-submarine warfare) version to replace S-3 fixed wing. Required to operate large recoverable ASW sensors from high altitude. Original requirement up to 300

CV-22A: US Air Force long-range special-missions aircraft, carrying 12 personnel over radius of 520 nm. Requirement for 55

US Army requirement for 231 transports broadly similar to MV-22A withdrawn, but documented requirement remains for many missions and Army maintains presence in programme.

Cannon AFB
Home of the 'Aardvark'

Above: Official (top) and unofficial (below) 27th Tactical Fighter Wing badges. The wing has recently been redesignated, losing the word 'Tactical'.

Main picture: Distinctive dark grey camouflage marks these aircraft as recently refurbished F-111Gs. The F-111G is a relative newcomer, being the designation applied to former FB-111A strategic bombers converted for the tactical role with provision for using conventional bombs. Only 30 were produced (instead of the 60 originally intended), and these will soon be retired.

Cannon Air Force Base in New Mexico was named after General John Cannon, a former commander of Tactical Air Command. It is thus appropriate that Cannon is home to what was for many years TAC's most powerful bomber. Although Cannon's long-serving F-111Ds are now bowing out, the F-111 era has not ended.

The 27th Fighter Wing based at Cannon AFB, NM, will soon be home to all F-111 aircraft in the US Air Force inventory. Already based at Cannon are the 428th, 522nd, 523rd and 524th Fighter Squadrons. The 428th flies the F-111G (formerly SAC FB-111s). The remaining three squadrons currently fly the F-111D.

In the course of 1992, EF-111As from Mountain Home AFB and those based in the UK will be transferred to Cannon AFB as well. F-111Es from RAF Upper Heyford and F-111Fs from RAF Lakenheath are also transitioning to Cannon AFB, with some aircraft already on station, and these will replace all earlier models. It is estimated that over 90 F-111Es and Fs will eventually call Cannon AFB 'home'.

As the aircraft from other squadrons (flying the D, E and F models) go through regular maintenance, they too will be converted to the all-grey paint scheme currently sported by the F-111Gs of the 428th Fighter Squadron. In flight, the F-111G has noticeably longer wings than the other variants of the F-111. The wing tips of the D, E and F models reach about 2-3 ft less than the tips of the horizontal stabilisers when the wings are folded back. When the G model has its wings in the straight-back position, the wing tips line up with the tips of the horizontal stabilisers.

428th Fighter Squadron 'Buccaneers' (blue tails)

The 428th FS 'Buccaneers' aircraft are painted all grey with black radome and black markings. The fin flash is a light blue.

The 428th FS is primarily responsible for the training of F-111 aircrews for the 27th FW. New students fresh from undergraduate pilot and navigator training receive the longest and most intensive course, which lasts six months and consists of 35 flights. Students with previous flight experience or with a background other than the F-111 receive a modified course of instruction. The 428th FS also teaches intructor courses to replenish the instructor corps.

Once a student has achieved the required skill levels in the simulator, he progresses to the flying mission. Missions are divided into four phases of development. The initial transition phases covers basic aircraft handling. This is followed by the strike day and strike night phases covering low-level, terrain-following radar (TFR) and level and diving weapons delivery procedures and techniques. Ground attack, the final phase, expands these procedures and introduces the student to tactical formation, terrain masking and diversified tactical weapons deliveries required by operational squadrons. Upon graduation, the

students are assigned to either the 522nd, 523rd or 524th Fighter Squadrons.

The 428th has a proud heritage. It was formed on 28 May 1943 and later activated as a component of the 474th Fighter Group flying P-38s. The unit eventually served in the skies over Europe, beginning combat operations on 25 April 1944 with a fighter sweep over Normandy. Most of the missions flown by the unit were in support of ground forces, although some escort missions were flown.

The 428th was again activated for the Korean War as the 428th Fighter-Bomber Squadron. It was assigned to Tactical Air Command at Misawa Air Base, Japan, in July 1952. During the war, the unit flew F-84s from Kunsan and Taegu Air Bases and received the Distinguished Unit Citation and a Republic of Korea Presidential Unit Citation for its contributions during the conflict.

After Korea, in November 1954, the unit re-ported to Clovis AFB, NM, still assigned to the Tactical Air Command. The 'Buccaneers' flew F-86s and F-100s. From Cannon AFB (Clovis was renamed in June 1957), the 428th TFS deployed to Homestead AFB, FL, in support of the Cuban Missile Crisis.

In 1964, the unit made its first trip to Vietnam. As the 1960s drew to a close, the 474th TFW and the 428th TFS moved to Nellis AFB, NV. There they received the Air Force's newest aircraft – the F-111A. After only three months with the air-craft, the 428th deployed six F-111As to Vietnam. The squadron's stay in Vietnam was short-lived, as three aircraft were lost within four weeks. In order to correct suspected equipment problems, the unit returned to Nellis in November 1968. The 428th flew F-111As until 1975, when it changed to F-4Ds. The unit made another air-craft change in 1980 when it started training in the F-16A/B, continuing with the F-16 until the unit's inactivation in the summer of 1989.

In April 1991, the unit was reactivated once again and designated the 428th Tactical Fighter Training Squadron. The unit returned to Cannon AFB to operate the F-111G, an aircrew training model. The unit received its first G models in June 1990 and will be getting the F-111E during 1992. The unit was renamed the 428th Fighter Squadron on 1 October 1991.

Left: An F-111G approaches the tanker. The F-111G is something of a hybrid, combining the long-span wings of the F-111B and F-111C with the fuselage and engine intakes of the F-111D, a strengthened undercarriage and a different variant of the TF30 engine.

Above: Last chance check. Groundcrew check this F-111G for anything untoward before it taxis out for a training mission. Cannon's F-111Gs are operated by the 428th Fighter Squadron.

Left: The cockpit of the F-111 is covered by a pair of upward-hinging canopies. The whole cockpit section can be explosively severed from the rest of the airframe to become a rocket-powered escape capsule, fitted with parachutes and inflatable devices to cushion landing impact.

General Dynamics
F-111G

This F-111G serves with the 428th Fighter Squadron 'Buccaneers' at Cannon AFB, New Mexico, whose ownership is indicated by the blue band on the tailfin, and squadron badge on the forward fuselage.

Powerplant
The F-111G is powered by a pair of Pratt & Whitney TF30-P-7 turbofans, which featured higher turbine entry temperatures and rotational speeds by comparison with the TF30-P-3 of the F-111A. It did, however, feature Triple Plow 2 intakes, as fitted to the F-111C, F-111D and F-111F, which has no splitter plate but which stands well proud of the fuselage. Intake redesign produced three types of inlet (culminating in Triple Plow 2) but failed to cure the TF30's disastrous compressor stall and reliability problems. The engines (derived from the engines developed for the stillborn four-engined DC-9) are removed backwards. All accessories are grouped below the engines.

Wings
The heavyweight FB-111A adopted the longer-span wings of the intended carrierborne F-111B, which are also used by the Australian F-111C. The variable geometry wing is swept back for high-speed flight, or forward for better low-speed handling characteristics. Full-span flaps and slats are fitted to the leading and trailing edges.

Armament
The FB-111A, as a strategic bomber, normally carried six SRAMs (two in the bomb bay, four underwing) or free-fall nuclear bombs, though it could carry a theoretical load of 50 conventional Mk 117 750-lb bombs. As F-111Gs, smaller loads of conventional weapons are carried to conserve fatigue life.

Radar
The F-111G is equipped with the AN/APQ-114 attack radar, and AN/APQ-134 terrain-following radar, both of which were core elements in the third (IIB) avionics fit, and formed the basis of the F-111G avionics suite.

Undercarriage
Like the Australian F-111C, the FB-111A and F-111G have a strengthened undercarriage, capable of supporting higher take-off and landing weights.

522nd Fighter Squadron 'Fireballs' (red tails)

The 522nd FS's speciality is high-speed, low-level weapons employment during all weather conditions. The squadron was activated 1 February 1940 at Barksdale Field, LA, flying the B-18 and A-24 aircraft. Later designated as the 522nd Fighter Bomber Squadron, the unit saw action in the south-west Pacific, Mediterranean and European theatres. The 522nd flew A-24, A-20, A-36, P-40 and P-47 aircraft, and was eventually deactivated in November 1945.

The unit was reactivated on 20 August 1946, at Fritzlar, Germany. Though fitted with the P-47 it was soon re-outfitted with P-51s in 1947. The squadron returned to the United States, operat-

ing from bases in Maryland, Nebraska and Texas and, after a year with the P-51s, received the F-82.

In 1950, the unit's name was changed to the 522nd Fighter Escort Squadron and they later re-ceived F-84s. In December the unit moved to Taegu, Korea. Following several months of combat in the Korean War, the 522nd returned to the United States. For the next eight years Berg-strom AFB, Texas, was the unit's home. During that time it was redesignated the 522nd Strategic Fighter Squadron (1953), the 522nd Fighter Bomber Squadron (1957), and the 522nd Tactical Fighter Squadron (1958). The F-84s were re-placed by F-101s in 1957. The 522nd moved to Cannon AFB in 1959 where it was re-equipped with F-100s. Along with several other 27th Tacti-cal Fighter Wing squadrons, the 522nd saw several combat deployments to South East Asia.

Below and left: The badge of the 522nd Fighter Squadron is worn with pride on the noses of a third of Cannon's F-111Ds, and the shoulders of their lucky aircrew.

Above: Shorter wings identify this aircraft as an F-111D, the most common type at Cannon, used by three of the 27th Fighter Wing's four squadrons.

The F-100 was the squadron's aircraft until 1969, when the new F-111E arrived. In 1971 the F-111Es were sent to Royal Air Force Upper Heyford, England, and the unit temporarily operated F-111A.s The first F-111D came to the 522nd in May 1972. By November of that year, the 522nd became the first fully-equipped, combat-ready F-111D squadron.

In May 1977, the 522nd accomplished the first unit deployment of the F-111D, operating from Warner Robins AFB, GA, for three weeks. In September 1978, the 522nd accomplished the first overseas deployment of the F-111D, operating from Gardermoen Air Base, Norway, for three weeks. A joint US Air Force/US Navy exercise, Computex 3-79, was held in August of 1979 using the F-111D and crews from the 522nd for pathfinding and sea lane interdiction. In May and June of 1980, the 522nd deployed to Boscombe Down, England, for exercise Coronet Hammer, the first overseas squadron-sized deployment of the F-111D. In January 1983, the squadron deployed to Elmendorf AFB, Alaska, to participate in Brim Frost, an arctic exercise, and that summer went to Bright Star, a USCENTAF joint exercise in Egypt. The following month, the squadron again deployed eight aircraft to Boscombe Down, England, for Coronet Archer.

From August to September 1986 the 522nd Tactical Fighter Squadron accomplished several 'firsts' for the F-111D during a 12-aircraft deployment, Coronet Comanche, to Boscombe Down, England. It was the first deployment and re-deployment with no ground or air aborts and the first use of KC-10s for a European deployment. In June 1991, the 522nd accomplished another 'first' by being the first operational squadron to employ the GBU-24 low-level guided bomb at night during Combat Hammer 88-10. During 1992, the 522nd will retire the F-111Ds, replacing them with F-111Fs.

Cannon AFB: Home of the 'Aardvark'

523rd Fighter Squadron 'Crusaders' (blue tails)

The 523rd Fighter Squadron's history dates back to 1 February 1940 when it was activated at Barksdale Field, LA, as the 17th Bombardment Squadron (Light). Its first aircraft was the B-18. During World War II, the squadron saw action in the south-west Pacific, Mediterranean, and European theatres. It was redesignated the 523rd Fighter Squadron on 30 May 1944. By the end of the war, the unit had been re-equipped successively with the A-24, A-20, A-36, P-40 and P-47 aircraft. The unit was deactivated at Camp Shanks, NY, on 7 November 1945.

The 523rd was reactivated 20 August 1946, at Fritzlar, Germany, flying the P-47. P-51s eventually replaced the P-47s. The unit returned to the United States and was re-equipped with the F-82.

In 1950, the unit became the 523rd Fighter Escort Squadron and received the F-84. In December, the unit moved to Taegu Air Base, Korea. In 1951, after several months of combat in the Korean War, the 523rd was reassigned to Bergstrom AFB, Texas. During its eight years in Texas, the squadron went through several designations: 523rd Strategic Fighter Squadron (1952), 523rd Fighter Bomber Squadron (1957) and 523rd Tactical Fighter Squadron (1958). In 1957 the unit acquired the F-101. Two years later the 523rd moved to Cannon AFB where it was equipped with the F-100.

Along with other 27th Tactical Fighter Wing units, the 523rd saw deployments to South East Asia. From November 1965 to August 1973, the squadron was assigned to the 405th Tactical Fighter Wing stationed at Clark AFB, Philippines, with a detachment at Tainan AB, Taiwan. The unit deployed to Udorn Royal Thai AFB, Thailand, from April to October 1972, flying combat missions in support of the South Vietnam Army.

The 523rd returned to Cannon AFB on 31 August 1973 and began transitioning to the F-111D. In March 1981, the 523rd deployed to Sachon AB, Korea, to participate in the joint-service Team Spirit exercise. This month-long deployment was the first overseas deployment of

a Tactical Air Command replacement training unit. The unit has since returned to Korea for Team Spirit in 1983, 1985, 1987 and 1990. In August 1988 the 'Crusaders' became the first F-111 unit to deploy to Panama, as they participated in DFT 825/827 at Howard AFB, NV, in support of Red Flag, Copper Flag and WSEP exercises. The 523rd completed its RTU role on 1 October 1983. In 1992, the unit will retire its F-111Ds, replacing them with the F-111F.

Right: A pair of Cannon's F-111Ds on the prowl. The aircraft carry combined practice bomb carriers inboard, with empty multiple ejector racks outboard. Many of Cannon's F-111Ds retain the brown and two-tone green Vietnam-style camouflage first used by the F-111 in the 1960s, albeit with toned-down insignia.

Below: The long, shallow black radome covering the attack and terrain-following radars resulted in the F-111's 'Aardvark' nickname. This is now widely accepted, though there was a time when the aircraft's early problems earned it a variety of less flattering sobriquets. Here a 'Crusaders' F-111D awaits its crew on the Cannon ramp.

Above: The F-111Ds of the 523rd Fighter Squadron have a blue fintip, with the unit's 'Crusaders' nickname superimposed in white. The Cannon tailcode is 'CC'.

Left: A technician makes a close inspection of a Triple Plow 2 intake on an F-111D. The huge size of the mainwheel tyre is evident!

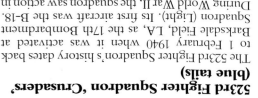

Above: An F-111D taxis out for a night mission. The aircraft's night/all-weather capability remains unmatched.

Right: A Cannon crew preflight their F-111D. The F-111D's expensive Mk II avionics limited procurement to 96, which were followed by cheaper F-111Fs.

Cannon AFB: Home of the 'Aardvark'

524th Fighter Squadron 'Hounds' (yellow tails)

The 524th was activated on 15 January 1941 at Hunter Field, GA, as the 11th Reconnaissance Squadron flying B-18 aircraft. It was redesignated the 91st Bombardment Squadron in 1941, the 524th Fighter-Bomber Squadron in 1943, and the 524th Fighter Squadron in 1944. In World War II, the unit fought in the Pacific, Mediterranean and European theatres, flying A-20, A-24, A-36, P-40 and P-47 aircraft.

Following deactivation at Camp Shank, NY, in 1945, the unit was reactivated on 20 August 1946 at Fritzlar, Germany, flying the P-47 and later the P-51. Prior to the Korean War, the 524th was stationed in Maryland, Nebraska and Texas, with conversion to the F-82 in 1948.

In 1950, the 524th became a fighter escort squadron flying the F-84. Late in 1950, the squadron went to Taegu Air Base, Korea, where it served in combat until moving to Bergstrom AFB, Texas, in mid-1951. In 1953, the unit was redesignated as the 524th Strategic Fighter Squadron and then the 524th Fighter-Bomber Squadron in 1957. That same year the unit transitioned to the F-101s and later that year was designated the 524th Tactical Fighter Squadron.

The squadron moved to Cannon in 1959 and converted to F-100s. During 1962 the unit deployed to MacDill AFB, FL, in support of the Cuban Missile Crisis. Late in the year the 524th TFTS deployed to Takhli Royal Thai AFB, Thailand. From 1969 to 1972, the 524th converted to the F-111 aircraft flying the F-111A, F-111E and F-111D models.

In October 1978, the 524th TFTS was the primary squadron deployed for Bold Eagle-Surge Delta 78. This deployment to Homestead

AFB, FL, was the first time a full-strength squadron of 24 F-111D aircraft was deployed. The 524th TFTS participated in Coronet Beacon in October 1979. Six deployed aircraft flew 18,000 miles (28967 km), crossing two continents. The deployment consisted of four weeks in Australia and three weeks in Korea.

The squadron was redesignated the 524th Tactical Fighter Training Squadron on 8 July 1980. The squadron was renamed the 524th Fighter Squadron on 1 October 1991 and will convert to the F-111F during 1992.

Above left: The Aardvark's F series designation belies its huge size and uncompromised optimisation for a single role – tactical bombing. A degree of self-defence capability can be achieved by fitting an AIM-9 Sidewinder or two, but a fighter? Never!

Above: Boomer's eye view of a Cannon-based F-111D crew enjoying a top-up. Cannon's F-111Ds are being replaced by older F-111Es (once regarded as an interim variant) and cheaper F-111Fs (originally built as a budget version of the F-111D). The weapons system of the F-111F is of far greater capability and easier to maintain, but harder to use.

Below: F-111Ds waddle along the taxiway at Cannon. The aircraft's low-slung undercarriage gives it an ungainly and clumsy appearance on the ground. F-111Es and F-111Fs from bases in the United Kingdom will replace Cannon's F-111Ds and F-111Gs during 1992, having themselves been supplanted by F-15Es and a reducing requirement for Europe-based strike aircraft.

Above: Although an escape capsule theoretically allows the crew to operate in shirtsleeves, they always wear the full fast-jet flying suit and associated equipment. The badge of Cannon's fourth F-111 unit, the 524th Fighter Squadron, is carried below the wingroot of this F-111D.

Below: Night falls, but the working day is just beginning for this F-111D. The aircraft has seen active service in Vietnam, in the attack on Libya and in the Gulf War, usually attacking vital targets at night. The introduction of newer types like the F-117 and F-15E has reduced the USAF's dependence on the F-111, but Cannon is set to echo to the howl and roar of TF30s for years to come.

DASSAULT
MIRAGE 2000

Latest in a long line of distinguished warplanes to bear the Mirage label, the 2000 began life as a fighter to re-equip France's interceptor squadrons, but has emerged as a true multi-role performer. Representative of France's resolve to provide its forces with high-technology weapons indigenously, the delta-winged fighter forms the cornerstone of the Armée de l'Air, and will partner the new-generation Rafale when it enters service.

The latest embodiment of Mirage versatility is the 2000D, a 2000N optimised for conventional attack missions. This is the first true D-model, seen carrying MATRA laser-guided bombs and an ATLIS laser designator, with Magic 2 self-defence missiles. The 2000D will enter service first with the Armée de l'Air's 3 Escadre de Chasse.

Dassault hoped the 2000 would repeat the sales success of previous Mirage fighters, but it has faced stiff opposition from the F-16 and F/A-18, and comes at a comparatively high price. Nevertheless, some foreign interest has been generated, notably from India.

Dassault Mirage 2000

Far right: The first opportunity for the Mirage 2000 to see action came with the 1991 war against Iraq. 2000Cs from 5 Escadre de Chasse were despatched to Al Ahsa to join the coalition fighter effort. Flying long combat air patrols in concert with RAF Tornado F.Mk 3s, Saudi Tornados and F-15s and USAF F-15s, the Mirages were used to protect Saudi airspace and coalition aircraft, but did not get into action.

In both Hollywood and the French aerospace industry there is a preference towards re-use of titles which have proved successful. After the Mirage III had boldly imprinted the name of Générale Aéronautique Marcel Dassault on the map of world military aviation during the 1960s, its differently-shaped successor became the Mirage F1. Throughout most of the last decade and all of the 1990s, the currently-titled Dassault Aviation will be building a third-generation of Mirage, once again changed radically – in sophistication, if not in shape – from its predecessors. Whatever the commercial merits of retaining well-known names for new products, the practice performs a disservice to members of the design teams whose innovative work has kept Dassault's products competitive in a tough market.

That said, it must be confessed that the Mirage 2000 began life as a 'back burner' project which few would have considered likely to see the light of day. Dassault's design office at St Cloud, on the outskirts of Paris, began work on its Delta 1000 project in 1972, while a far greater proportion of effort was being expended on the proposed next-generation combat aircraft. This, the Mirage G8A – or Avion de Combat Futur (ACF) – was a fixed-geometry version of the Mirage G8, two prototypes of which were flown in 1971-72 as a belated French rival to the Panavia Tornado. The Armeé de l'Air (AA) wanted a Mach 3 fighter, not a Tornado-type interdictor lacking in air combat capability, so the G8 was re-designed as a 14-tonne Super Mirage G8A (or F8) with either one or two seats. To provide power, SNECMA began development work on a new turbofan designated M53, two of which would be installed in each Super Mirage.

Truth gradually dawned that the ACF was too ambitious for France. Even on estimated costs – which are invariably exceeded as a programme progresses – an ACF was two-and-a-half times the price of a Mirage F1. Accordingly, the number to be bought was reduced from 200 to 100, and in September 1975 the recently-ordered second prototype was cancelled in conjunction with a reduction in the rate of expenditure. The decision followed only a week after production authorisation had been granted to the M53, but assembly of the first aircraft continued in order that it should fly in July 1976. That was not to be, for a meeting of the National Defence Council on 18 December 1975 decided to concede the inevitable and cancel the ACF.

The decision was not unexpected, so the real news story centred on the unknown aircraft which had been metaphorically rolled out at the same Council meeting and authorised on the spot to replace the ill-starred Mirage F8. By this time, the design was known as Delta 2000, although that was quickly to become Mirage 2000. In March 1976 – and not for the first time – the AA wrote an official requirement around a set of Dassault performance estimates and put its full weight

Below: The first impression released of the Mirage 2000 showed the type's generic similarity to the Mirage III, notably in the general layout, cockpit and intake design. Unlike many of today's familiar warplanes, the first impression bore a surprising resemblance to the real thing.

behind getting the aircraft into service as soon as possible, with the first 10 to be delivered before the end of 1982.

Return to the delta

Any similarity between Mirage III and Mirage 2000 merely serves to confuse the uninitiated. The first-generation Mirage was designed as a tailless delta to combine low wave drag and high internal volume and, co-incidentally, to simplify construction and thus reduce cost. Compared with an aircraft of more common configuration, it has a lower radar signature from many aspects and the increased reliability stemming from fewer control surfaces. Disadvantages of the wing shape are a seriously impaired sustained-turning rate and a requirement for long runways. When taking off, raising the elevons to rotate the aircraft simultaneously generates a downward component of drag which resists the machine leaving the runway. Such a force has to be large (i.e. a significant movement of the control surface is made) because the aircraft's centre of gravity is ahead of its aerodynamic centre and the elevon is to the rear.

The turn rate suffers from a delta's low aspect ratio, causing high induced drag so that, in short, while the delta can carry more fuel and fly faster in a straight line, it is at a disadvantage in close combat. Landing can be a disconcerting experience for, despite a low wing loading, the Mirage III must land fast and with a high nose-up angle. In such a regime, a huge increase in power is required to produce a small boost in lift – and if the pilot attempts to raise velocity by dropping the nose, he is liable to produce sink instead of speed. Trailing edge flaps, which are the normal slow-speed flying device, cannot be fitted to a delta as the back of the wing is actually performing the task of horizontal tail surfaces as well as that of the ailerons.

Dassault left these troubles behind in the Mirage F1. With its thin wing generously provisioned with high-lift flaps fore and aft, the second-generation Mirage was a more agile and tractable performer at all but high level, where acceleration and supersonic ceiling were reduced in comparison to the Mirage III. Greater thrust, compact avionics and better use of internal space gave the F1 improvements in range and combat load, but there was a practical limit to exploitation of these areas. For 'grandson of Mirage', Dassault would have to pull something else out of the hat.

Left: Externally, the Mirage 2000 second prototype appeared little different from the EC 2/10 Mirage IIIC it is escorting here, but underneath the skin was a fighter from two generations down the line. Fly-by-wire controls alleviated many of the minuses of the delta wing, while retaining the excellent high altitude performance, internal volume and other pluses of the configuration.

Below: In the shape of the 2000N, the latest Mirage has been adopted for nuclear strike and low-level attack roles.

With considerable experience of both pure delta and conventional swept-wing fighter design, St Cloud elected to combine the best of both while eliminating many of their negative aspects. For the Mirage 2000, high usable volume and low wave drag were assured by returning to the delta configuration. Less immediately obvious is the adoption of negative longitudinal stability in conjunction with an automatic flight control system (AFCS) and 'fly-by-wire' control surface movement. In this, the Control-Configured Vehicle (CCV) approach, the aircraft is made longitudinally unstable by having the centre of gravity behind the aerodynamic centre, instead of in front of it. The AFCS computer maintains stability and translates the pilot's commands into manoeuvres. Compared with the case of a Mirage III forcing itself back onto the runway when raising the elevons to lift the nose, the Mirage 2000 slightly lowers elevons to pivot the aircraft – and increases lift in the process. Similarly, landing is simpler, with the Mirage 2000 approaching at 140 kt (260 km/h; 162 mph), compared to 184 kt (340 km/h; 211 mph) for a Mirage III. Any observer of a Mirage 2000 air display cannot help being impressed by the low-speed, high

Above: The Mirage 2000-01 first flew on 10 March 1978, flown from Istres by Jean Coureau. During its first flight the aircraft was pushed to Mach 1.3 in afterburner, validating the basic handling and performance of the new fighter.

Right: The first two Mirage 2000s seen together, along with 03, these being the only aircraft completed with the original tall fin. 02 joined the flight test programme on 18 September, its first hop being accomplished by Guy Mitaux-Maurouard.

nose-up passes formerly attempted only by conventionally-shaped aircraft. To improve control at such attitudes, the air intakes have strakes to control shedding of fuselage vortices.

By recourse to computer-aided design, Dassault was able to maximise the size of wingroot fairings with minimal drag penalty. The extra space in these 'Karman fairings' accommodated fuel and equipment which would otherwise have had to go further outboard, demanding stronger and heavier wing construction. The Mirage 2000 'added more lightness' by recourse to new constructional materials, benefitting from such projects as trials of a boron-fibre rudder tested on a Mirage III in 1976 and a complete stabilator fitted to a Mirage F1 soon afterwards. Titanium and carbon-fibre similarly combine strength and lightness, bringing the aircraft close to its goal of a thrust:weight ratio of unity.

New engine

The basics of design thus satisfied, the Mirage 2000 had a long way to go before entering service. Some items from the ACF were salvaged, one of the most vital being the M53 engine. That the Mirage 2000 would need only one of these powerplants instead of the ACF's two served merely to cut SNECMA's potential profits while doing nothing to reduce the development effort. A single-shaft reheated turbofan (or, perhaps more accurately, a continuous-bleed turbojet with a low bypass ratio of 0.32), the M53 was first bench-tested in February 1970 and taken aloft in the starboard pod of a Caravelle testbed on 18 July 1973. French jet engines tend to be less sophisticated than those built in the UK and USA, but that is not to deny that the M53 is a comparatively light and simple powerplant.

Of modular construction, it has a straightforward design featuring only three low-pressure turbine stages, five high-pressure stages and two turbine stages, all on a single spool. Its afterburner can be used without restriction throughout the flight envelope, which extends to Mach 2.5 at high altitude. Development orders totalled 20, comprising three for bench trials, 10 for air- and ground-testing, three for supersonic trials and four for the ATF programme. M53 met Dassault for the first time at Istres on 22 December 1974 when one of the three supersonic engines was flown in the prototype Mirage F1E – a contender for the European fighter competition won by the General Dynamics F-16 Fighting Falcon.

The F1E's career ended as a testbed for the Mirage 2000 programme, initially with the M53-2, following completion of its 150-hour bench test at Saclay in April 1976. In this form

Left: Following cancellation of the ACF, Dassault privately developed a scaled-up Mirage 2000 known as the Super Mirage 4000, intended primarily for long-range interception and low-level attacks. First flying on 9 March 1979, the 4000 remained in prototype form only, and was later used for tests in connection with the Rafale programme.

the M53 was rated at 8500 kg (18,739 lb) with reheat, improved to 9000 kg (19,842 lb) in the M53-5 version with which series manufacture was launched. For this variant, the successful 150-hour trial was accomplished in May 1979.

Three prototype Mirage 2000s ordered in December 1975 had increased to four and to a Dassault-funded two-seat aircraft within a year. A commendable 27 months after the ACF had been cancelled, Mirage 2000 No. 01 was airborne. Hand-built at St Cloud, the prototype was taken by road to Istres for assembly, flying from there on 10 March 1978 in the hands of Jean Coureau. In the 65-minute sortie, No. 01 accelerated to Mach 1.02 on the 5500 kg (12,125 lb) of thrust of its M53-2, then climbed to 12192 m (40,000 ft) for an afterburner run at Mach 1.3. At the time, the Mirage F1E had flown 189 hours and the M53 Caravelle a further 500 or so. By the end of May, No. 01 had demonstrated Mach 2 and an indicated air-speed of 650 kt (1205 km/h; 749 mph) during a total of 13 sorties. The slow-speed characteristics were convincingly demonstrated in public at Farnborough during September 1978 when Dassault's Guy Mitaux-Maurouard provided a

Left: The first Mirage 2000s were hand-built at the company's St Cloud facility, but production machines are assembled at Mérignac. Here 11 of the order from Abu Dhabi are seen in various stages of final assembly.

show-stopping performance, including a 25° nose-up fly-by at only 100 kt (185 km/h; 115 mph), despite the machine having accumulated only some 60 hours.

In a similar but more closely monitored vein, Maurouard and Jean-Marie Saget flew 22 sorties from Istres between November 1980 and March 1981, following which the Mirage 2000 was cleared for all manoeuvres between zero airspeed and 800 kt (1480 km/h; 920 mph). For these trials, various combinations of external fuel tanks and weapons were fitted to No. 01, which was flown at angles of attack exceeding 30°. Fitted with four air-to-air missiles (AAM), the aircraft demonstrated a roll rate of 270° per second throughout the flight envelope. At the same time, the first of two static airframes (No. 06) in the Toulouse fatigue rig was used to clear the Mirage 2000 for load factors up to 9g.

It was with an M53-5 installed that 2000-02 first flew at Istres on 18 September 1978, Maurouard being in command for the 50-minute mission. Early trials work concerned the SFENA digital autopilot and weapons carriage and separation. A dummy MATRA R.550 Magic was dropped on 9 March 1981, followed by a MATRA Super 530F on 27 July, while several missions were flown with 1700-litre (374-Imp gal) underwing tanks. After contributing over 500 sorties to the trials programme, No. 02 met an untimely end – and Saget very nearly so – when contaminated fuel caused it to flame out at 76 m (250 ft) while on approach

Right: From the outset the Mirage 2000 displayed excellent control at low speed and high angles of attack, and this became a regular and spectacular feature of air show routines. Full-span leading edge flaps greatly enhanced low-speed lift, while the fly-by-wire system easily maintained stability. The small intake strakes controlled fuselage vortices across the wing roots.

Below: With its grey scheme and little in the way of markings, the 2000-01 looked every inch a prototype. For its appearance at Farnborough in 1978, the nose was adorned with the red devil badge of SPA160, later to be carried on the fins of EC 2/4 Mirage 2000Ns.

to Istres on 9 May 1984.

Earmarked for weapons trials, No. 03 first flew at Istres on 16 April 1979, fitted with nine hardpoints – although not until 13 November 1980 did it become the first Mirage 2000 to fly with radar (an RDM, as described below). In the course of official trials by all three aircraft at the Centre d'Essais en Vol section at Istres during May 1980, Mirage 2000 hours topped 500, including six sorties flown by pilots of the military trials unit, CEAM. The short programme enabled the AA to see in detail what was happening to 43 per cent of its equipment budget. Afterwards, No. 01 was fitted with an M53-5 powerplant and then progressed to the definitive M53-P2. The prototype ended its career with retirement to the Museé de l'Air at Le Bourget in 1988. No. 03 flew firing trials of the Super 530F and Magic missiles in 1982, then received an RDI radar for the first launch of a Super 530D from a Mirage 2000 on 26 October 1984.

No. 04 joined its companions in the air on 12 May 1980, fitted from the outset with the full weapons system and being to proposed production standards in other respects. Few changes had to be made to the Mirage 2000 as a result of early flight-testing, but of those which were the most noticeable was a reduction in fin height, in conjunction with an increase in fin sweep. This was brought in with No. 04 and retrospectively applied to earlier aircraft (starting with No. 01 early in 1979), as were extensions to the Karman wingroot fairings to well beyond the trailing edge line. More searching examination would reveal re-designed air intake boundary layer diverters, while an internal modification concerned the FBW system. Mechanical back-up had been available to the triplicated system first installed, but the Mirage 2000 progressed subsequently to quadruplex FBW on roll and pitch axes and triplex FBW for rudder deflection. Nos 03 and 04 flew proving trials with an AA Boeing C-135F tanker in the autumn of 1980 and remained at Istres for more weapons and ECM development work. Like the two before them, the third and fourth aircraft initially flew unpainted. No. 02 received a smart colour scheme of white overall, with patriotic red and blue trim, for the 1979 Paris air show and was later joined in this guise by No. 01 – although without the tricolour fin. No. 03 adopted a purposeful light grey and blue disruptive camouflage scheme.

Left: The Mirage 2000-02 emerged little different externally from the first machine, but did feature the M53-5 powerplant in place of the M53-2. The Dash 5 engine was marginally more powerful, and was the initial version used for production aircraft.

Above: An indication of further developments was provided by 02 at the 1980 Farnborough show, when it was displayed carrying a heavy load of air-to-ground stores. From the outset the standard Mirage 2000 was intended for multi-role operations, but in practice most users have employed the type for fighter duties. By this time 02 had received the shorter fin of production aircraft.

Left: Still sporting the tall fin, 2000-02 appeared at the 1979 Le Bourget show in a strikingly patriotic colour scheme. The first two aircraft were not fitted with radars during the flight test programme.

Mirage 2000 cockpit

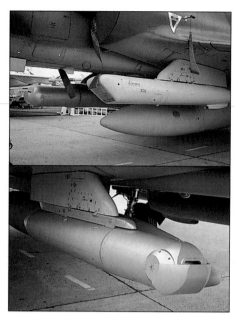

Two systems associated with the Mirage 2000N/D are a forward-looking infra-red sensor (top) and an ATLIS laser-designation pod (above). The ATLIS has TV sensors for daylight operation with a bore-sighted laser. A visor protects the sensor window when not in use.

Below: The Mirage 2000C has an integrated warning/countermeasures system, for which this is a wingtip RWR antenna array.

Above: The cockpit of an export Mirage 2000E shows the steeply raked dashboard that gives the pilot an exceptional view to either side of the nose. The cockpit is dominated by one large CRT for the radar and the HUD, which conveys most combat information, although most other instruments are dials. In the upper right position is a circular display for threat warning.

Right: This is the APSI (Advanced Pilot System Interface) cockpit for the Mirage 2000-5, featuring four CRT displays covering most aircraft and avionics functions, including radar (centre). The cockpit also has a Thomson-CSF VEH 3020 holographic HUD. The only conventional dialled instrument remaining in the cockpit is the clock at left!

Inside the Mirage 2000

Left: The Antilope V radar of the 2000N/D works in J-Band. It is used for mapping and terrain following in addition to an air-to-air function.

Dassault Mirage 2000

1 Pitot head
2 Glass-fibre radome
3 IFF aerial array
4 Cassegrain monopulse radar antenna
5 Scanner tracking mechanism
6 Thomson-CSF RDI pulse-Doppler radar module
7 Radar altimeter aerial
8 Angle-of-attack transmitter
9 VHF aerial
10 Formation
11 Rudder pedals
12 Static port
13 Dynamic pressure heads
14 Flight-refuelling probe
15 Frameless windscreen panel
16 Head-up display
17 Instrument panel shroud
18 Engine throttle lever
19 Nosewheel hydraulic jack
20 Twin nosewheels, aft retracting
21 Landing taxiing lamps

22 Nosewheel steering jack
23 Electric equipment bay
24 Intake half-cone centre-body
25 SEMB licence-built Martin-Baker F10Q ejection seat
26 Upwards-hinging canopy
27 Canopy actuator
28 Canopy hinge point

29 Emergency release handle
30 Boundary layer spill duct
31 Air conditioning pack
32 Intake suction relief door
33 Moveable intake centre-body screw jack
34 Fixed intake strake
35 Pressure refuelling connection

36 DEFA 544 30-mm cannon
37 Ammunition magazine
38 Forward fuselage integral fuel tanks
39 Avionics equipment bay
40 Dual IFF aerials
41 Fuel system equipment
42 Centre fuselage integral fuel tanks
43 Mainwheel bay
44 Airframe mounted accessory equipment gearbox
45 Generator cooling air exhaust
46 Engine intake compressor face

47 Bleed air pre-cooler
48 Anti-collision light
49 Starboard leading edge slats
50 Radar warning antenna
51 Starboard navigation light
52 Outboard elevon
53 Wing attachment fuselage main frames
54 Hydraulic equipment bay
55 Engine igniter unit
56 Digital engine control unit
57 SNECMA M53-5 afterburning turbofan engine
58 Afterburner ducting
59 Rudder hydraulic actuator
60 Boron/epoxy/carbon fin skin panels
61 Formation lighting strip
62 Forward ECM antenna

63 VOR aerial
64 VHF aerial
65 Tail navigation light
66 Tail radar warning antenna
67 Composite rudder panel
68 ECM equipment housing
69 ECM auxiliary power unit
70 Afterburner nozzle control jacks

71 Rear ECM transmitting aerial
72 Variable area afterburning nozzle
73 Formation lighting strip
74 Chaff dispenser
75 Ventral brake parachute housing
76 Engine bay thermal lining
77 Flare launcher

78 Radar warning system dual mode processor
79 Port wing panel integral fuel tank
80 Inboard elevon hydraulic actuator
81 Port inboard elevon
82 Composite elevon panel construction
83 Outboard elevon hydraulic actuator

Radar
According to some unconfirmed reports, some of India's Mirage fleet may be fitted with the Antilope V dedicated strike/attack radar, but it is believed that most have the standard Thomson-CSF RDM export multi-role unit. The radar is a low pulse repetition frequency Doppler system, employing a travelling-wave tube coherent transmitter with an inverse cassegrain antenna. Included in the radar are options for continuous wave target illumination for use with Doppler homing missiles (i.e. the Super 530D), IFF interrogator and beam sharpening for improved ground mapping. Four basic modes are offered: air-to-air search and interception; low-level strike with terrain avoidance, mapping and blind let down; air-to-ground attack; and a maritime surface search/attack function.

In the primary air-to-air mode, the radar offers a 60° cone of coverage, antenna drive rates being either 50° or 100° per second, and cone coverage options of +/– 15°, 30° or 60° of scan being available. Detection capabilities range down to a target exhibiting a 5 m² radar cross-section, with ranges between 111 km (69 miles) for a high-altitude target to 46 km (29 miles) for a low-level target.

Gun engagements are aided by a 3.5° beamwidth radar which can be locked on at 18.5 km (11.5 miles) to provide automatic tracking within the field of view of the head-up display. Alternatively, a 'super-search' or vertical search mode can be employed for gun attacks.

Data is displayed on a large three-colour CRT in the centre of the cockpit console and on the HUD. BITE (built-in test equipment) is incorporated.

Guns
Single-seat variants of the Mirage 2000 feature a 30-mm cannon in each side of the lower fuselage alongside the intake trunks, each armed with 125 rounds. GIAT Industries is the prime contractor for the DEFA 554 weapon, which is a further development of the DEFA 552 and 553 fitted to earlier generations of French combat aircraft. The gun is a single-barrel, revolving-chamber weapon operated by gas. It fires a mix of rounds, including armour-piercing and HE incendiary. Improvements made to the DEFA 554 over earlier versions include two electronically-selected rates of fire – 1,800 rpm for air-to-air work and 1,100 for air-to-surface attack, and an automatic multi-shot cartridge-operated recocking system which fires if stoppages occur.

The weapon on its own weighs 80 kg (176 lb) and is 2.01 m (6 ft 7 in) long. The electronic fire control has four functions: firing completely inhibited, ½-second burst, 1-second burst and continuous fire, although the latter is not normally used in action. A temperature range of –54°C to 100°C can be handled.

Dassault Aviation Mirage 2000H (Vajra)
No. 1 'The Tigers' Squadron
Indian Air Force
Maharajpura AFB, Gwalior

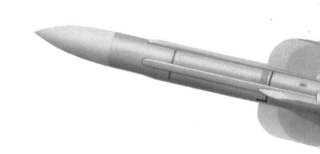

The high purchase price and considerable capability of the Mirage 2000 make it a prestige item for export customers, and consequently the type has not achieved the large overseas sales of its predecessors. India was the first customer, buying 40 aircraft comprising 36 2000Hs and four 2000TH two-seaters. Plans were laid to undertake production of the aircraft in India, the first batch being the assembly of Dassault-supplied kits followed by a larger batch of Indian-manufactured aircraft, the total amounting to 110 additional aircraft for another three squadrons. However, the Indian government ruled out this plan in 1984 when it announced it would opt for buying the MiG-29 'Fulcrum' (local name *Baaz*), of which 50 were initially ordered.

This aircraft is seen wearing the markings of No. 1 Squadron, which was actually the second to form, being preceded by No. 7, both formerly operating the Mikoyan MiG-21. Original plans had called for Nos 51 and 52 Squadrons to have been the Mirage operators. In Indian service the Mirages are principally employed on air defence duties, but also have secondary air-to-ground roles, including defence suppression with ARMAT missiles, counter-air sorties with Durandal runway-cratering bombs and general attack with conventional bombs and Belouga cluster weapons.

Super 530 missile
For the air interception role, the Indian Mirage 2000s carry the MATRA Super 530D missile. This is the latest in a development line stretching back to the original R530 which entered French service in 1963, with interchangeable IR or semi-active radar homing (SARH) seeker. The next development was the Super 530F, as used by the early Mirage 2000s with the unimproved RDM radar, which was chiefly introduced to provide better capability against high-altitude bomber targets.

Today's Super 530D shifts the target emphasis to low-flying aircraft, and incorporates a monopulse continuous-wave Doppler semi-active radar seeker. This still requires continuous illumination of the target by the launch aircraft throughout the engagement, whereas the forthcoming MICA has active terminal guidance. The 530D's AD-26 seeker also employs digital microprocessing, and with the monopulse characteristics provides excellent ECCM (electronic counter-countermeasures) compared to the earlier versions.

Vital statistics of the missile are a length of 3.80 m (12 ft 6 in), body diameter 263 mm (10.35 in), wing span 0.62 m (2 ft ½ in), warhead of 30 kg (66 lb) high explosive and active radar fuse. The missile is longer than the Super 530F, allowing it to accommodate more solid propellant, giving it a greater range of 40 km (25 miles). Engagement parameters include a maximum intercept altitude of 24400 m (80,000 ft), snap-up capability of 12200 m (40,000 ft) and snap-down down to targets flying at 60 m (200 ft). The fin arrangement consists of four long-chord rectangular wings, aft of which are four clipped rectangular control fins.

Magic missile
MATRA began development of the R550 Magic 1 missile in the mid-1960s, and it entered service in 1975 as a tail-chase infra-red homing missile. Entering service 10 years later, the Magic 2 is a significantly upgraded model with longer range, reduced launch preparation time and a much improved seeker head offering all-aspect engagement capability.

The new seeker head is made by SAT, and features gaseous nitrogen cooling (carried in the launcher). Improved sensitivity allows head-on engagements, and it has good IRCCM (infra-red counter-countermeasures), including the rejection of flares that may be fired by the target. The seeker can operate in two modes: in one it is slaved to the aircraft radar, which points it in the direction of the target, so designating the target, or it can be used in an autonomous mode which scans for a heat source upon which it locks without help from the radar system.

Both Magic 1 and 2 are externally similar, and have four fixed clipped delta wings at the front, immediately behind which are clipped rectangular control fins. At the rear of the missile body are four larger free-rotating fins. The missile has excellent manoeuvrability, and can be launched from aircraft making high-*g* manoeuvres. The solid propellant motor has been improved to give about 10 per cent greater thrust than the Magic 1, and the maximum effective range is increased from 3 km (1.86 miles) to 5 km (3.1 miles). Other figures are length 2.75 m (9 ft ¼ in), body diameter 157 mm (6.18 in), wing span 0.66 m (2 ft 2 in) and launch weight of 90 kg (198 lb). The 13-kg (28.6-lb) high explosive warhead is the same as that of the earlier version, but the Magic 1's proximity IR fuze has been changed to an RF sensor.

Left: A graphic illustration of what constitutes a modern fighter was provided by this superb Dassault-produced full-scale glass model of a 2000C showing much of its innards.

Right: All Mirage 2000s have been powered by the SNECMA M53, shown here in the interim 88.29-kN (19,842-lb) thrust M53-5 version which powered the early machines – bar the first prototype, which had the M53-2.

Specification
Dassault Aviation Mirage 2000C

Wingspan: 9.13 m (29 ft 11½ in)
Length overall: 14.36 m (47 ft 1¼ in)
Height: 5.20 m (17 ft 0¾ in)
Wheel track: 3.40 m (11 ft 1¾ in)
Wheel base: 5.00 m (16 ft 4¾ in)
Wing area: 41.0 m² (441.3 sq ft)
Empty weight: 7500 kg (16,534 lb)
Maximim take-off weight: 17000 kg (37,480 lb)
Maximum fuel/weapon load: 6300 kg (13,890 lb)
Maximum Mach no. at high level: Mach 2.2
Maximum level speed at low level: over 600 kt (1110 km/h; 690 mph) carrying 2000 kg (4,409 lb) of bombs
Minimum speed in stable flight: 100 kt (185 km/h; 115 mph)
Range: over 850 nm (1575 km; 979 miles) with 2000 kg (4,409 lb) of bombs, plus external tanks
Reaction time: under 5 minutes, from brakes-off to interception of Mach 3 target at 24400 m (80,000 ft)

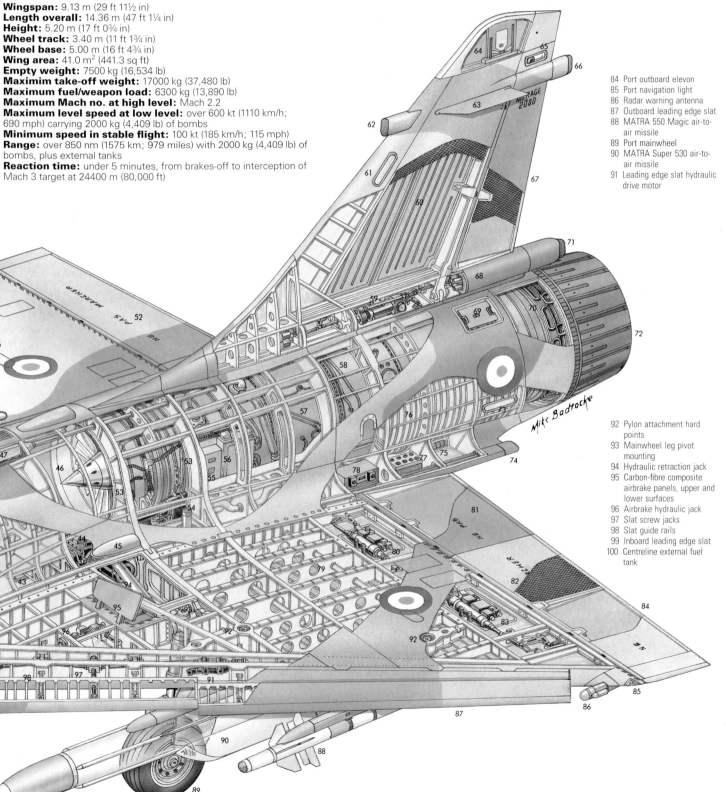

84 Port outboard elevon
85 Port navigation light
86 Radar warning antenna
87 Outboard leading edge slat
88 MATRA 550 Magic air-to-air missile
89 Port mainwheel
90 MATRA Super 530 air-to-air missile
91 Leading edge slat hydraulic drive motor

92 Pylon attachment hard points
93 Mainwheel leg pivot mounting
94 Hydraulic retraction jack
95 Carbon-fibre composite airbrake panels, upper and lower surfaces
96 Airbrake hydraulic jack
97 Slat screw jacks
98 Slat guide rails
99 Inboard leading edge slat
100 Centreline external fuel tank

Mirage 2000N

In its element, a Mirage 2000N flies through mountainous terrain. The Antilope 5 radar has terrain-following capability at much lower altitudes than this, although the large delta wing does not give the smoothest ride.

Service
Armée de l'Air plans call for 75 2000Ns and 105 2000Ds to be procured. EC 1/4 was the first operational unit, receiving its first machine on 30 March 1988, the unit declaring itself operational on 1 July.

Fuel
The internal fuel capacity is 3920 litres (862 Imp gal), usually augmented by two 2000-litre (440-Imp gal) drop-tanks. Inflight refuelling extends range for deep penetration missions.

Missile
The ASMP missile has a nuclear warhead with a yield of approximately 300 kT. Low-level launch range is about 100 km (62 miles), but when launched from high altitude can achieve 300 km (186 miles). It follows a pre-programmed flight using an inertial reference system.

Colour scheme
For its 2000N/D force the Armée de l'Air has chosen this two-tone dark grey/dark green disruptive pattern with light grey undersides. The markings are for EC 1/4 'Dauphiné'.

Powerplant
The 2000N features the standard definitive powerplant in the form of the SNECMA M53-P2, rated at 95.1 kN (21,385 lb) thrust with afterburner.

Radar
The Antilope V provides mapping functions and terrain-following flight down to 90 m (300 ft). Radar information is displayed on the head-up display and on a three-colour CRT head-down display.

Avionics and systems

In addition to the RDM radar, the Mirage 2000 is extensively equipped with defensive avionics and nav/comms equipment. The defences include a Thomson-CSF/Dassault Electronique ECM system with VCM-65 display and jammers housed in the leading edge of the fin and in the extended bullet fairing at the base of the rudder, MATRA Spirale passive countermeasures system and Thomson-CSF Serval radar warning receivers with antennas at the wingtips and the front of the fin fairing.

The weapon system has a Sagem Uliss 52 inertial platform, Dassault Electronique Type 2084 central computer, which is digital, and a Digibus databus. The data display system is the Thomson-CSF TMV-980, consisting of a VE-130 head-up and VMC-180 head-down displays.

Nav/comms equipment includes a Sfena 605 autopilot, LMT Deltac Tacan, LMT NRAI-7A IFF transponder, Socrat 8900 solid-state VOR/ILS, Sfena IO-300-A marker beacon receiver, TRT AHV-9 radio altimeter, TRT ERA 7000 V/UHF, TRT ERA 7200 UHF comms and Sextant Avionique Type 90 air data computer.

Aircraft systems include SEMB licence-built Martin-Baker F10Q zero/zero ejection seat, ABG-Semca air conditioning and pressurisation system, Eros oxygen system and two independent hydraulic systems pressurised to 280 bars each. Electric power is provided by two Auxilec 20110 air-cooled 20-kVA (400-Hz) constant frequency alternators, two Bronzavia DC transformers, one SAFT 40-Ah battery and an ATEI static inverter. The undercarriage is made by Messier-Bugatti with twin 360x135-6 nosewheels pressurised to 8 bars and steerable through +/− 45°, although the steering can be disconnected on the ground so that they are fully-castoring. Single 750×230-15 mainwheels on each strut are pressurised to 15 bars, and provided with Messier-Bugatti polycrystalline graphite disc brakes.

Wings

The multi-spar low-set wings feature a leading edge sweepback of 58° and a trailing edge sweepforward of 3° 30'. The tips are rounded off to a point. Most of the leading edge consists of two sections of manoeuvring slats, the inboard of which depresses 17° 30' and the outboard 30°. These are only employed during manoeuvring flight, being retracted during acceleration and cruise to reduce drag. On the trailing edge of each wing are two sections of elevons, which can travel through -16° to +25° and are constructed from carbon-fibre skin with honeycomb core. Both slats and elevons are operated by the fly-by-wire control system, and actuated by hydraulic servo units. There are no tabs incorporated, all trimming functions being performed by the central computer. Further control surfaces comprise a small airbrake above each wing.

Air-to-air missiles

MATRA supplies the main AAMs used by Mirage operators (although Abu Dhabi's aircraft are wired for Sidewinders). The Magic 2 is used for short-range engagements, while the Super 530D is used out to 40 km (25 miles). MICA is due to replace both missiles.

Above: Magic 2 has an effective range of up to 5 km (3.1 miles). The launch weight of 90 kg (198 lb) includes a 13-kg (28.6-lb) HE warhead, which is detonated by an RF fuse.

Above: Active radar MICAs are carried beneath a Mirage 2000-5. The radar version is identified by a pointed nose cone. All versions have a blast fragmentation warhead and a launch weight of 110 kg (242.5 lb).

Left: Mirage 2000-04 is seen carrying an example of each MICA variant, the EM active-radar version being carried under the port wing and the IR version under the starboard. Both versions employ inertial guidance, with mid-course update from the launch aircraft, before switching to either radar or IR terminal guidance.

Above and right: The MATRA Super 530D is the current principal missile of the Mirage 2000, seen above on a 2000C and right during a test launch from an Indian 2000H. The missile uses semi-active radar guidance with an active radar fuse.

Air-to-surface weapons

Primarily employed by the Mirage 2000D and 2000N, a variety of ASMs are in regular use, including the ASMP nuclear stand-off missile and the AS.30L for precision attacks. Other air-to-ground stores cover the range of bombs, cluster munitions, runway penetrators and a new modular stand-off weapon under development.

Right: A single ASMP is carried on the 2000N's centreline, usually in conjunction with a pair of Magic 2s for self-defence.

Far left: Designated using the ATLIS pod, the AS.30L is a laser-guided missile capable of exceptional accuracy. It has a 250-kg (551-lb) high-explosive warhead.

Left: ARMAT is a development of the Martel with a seeker which homes on radar emissions. The warhead is 150 kg (330 lb) of high explosive, launch weight is 550 kg (1,212 lb) and effective maximum range is 90 km (56 miles).

Above: Seen under the wing of a CEAM Mirage 2000 is the APACHE stand-off weapon. Jet-powered, the APACHE has pop-out wings to extend its range to up to 150 km (93 miles).

Right: The 305-kg (672-lb) Belouga cluster bomb dispenses 151 bomblets of three varieties (frag, anti-armour or area interdiction). The bomb is para-retarded to allow the aircraft to escape the blast pattern.

Reconnaissance

A lesser role for the Mirage 2000 is reconnaissance, for which a variety of centreline pods are available. The standard unit is the COR2 with a fan of standard cameras, the Harold LOROP (long-range oblique photography) system and SLAR (side-looking airborne radar). These are not carried in French service, as the Mirage F1CR performs the reconnaissance role.

Right: Various reconnaissance pod options for the Mirage 2000 are illustrated, including the COR2 camera pod and (centre) the TMV018 Syrel Elint pod.

Last of the five prototypes to fly, the Mirage 2000B two-seat No. B01, was airborne at Istres on 11 October 1980 with Michel Porta as pilot. The sortie increased Mirage 2000 flying hours to 660 and was followed by a further 19 flights and 17 hours by B01 during the next four weeks. An RDM radar was installed early in 1981 and a dummy Aérospatiale ASMP nuclear stand-off missile was fitted on the centreline for aerodynamic work associated with the 2000N programme. A useful demonstration vehicle for an increasing number of interested foreign pilots, B01 also participated in refuelling trials, and was painted white overall.

Mirage anatomy

Further reflecting the Mirage III and F1 programmes, the first production version of the new fighter was designated Mirage 2000C, there having been no 2000A. Dassault's plant at Argenteuil, on the western outskirts of Paris, was made re-

sponsible for fuselage production, and it was from here on 7 June 1982 that the first recognisable element of Mirage 2000C No. 1 was taken by road to Bordeaux-Mérignac. Here, it was joined with wings from nearby Martignas and a fin built by Aérospatiale at Nantes. Thomson-CSF provided the RDM radar and SNECMA the M53-5 turbofan, and with these and thousands of other sub-contracted items in place the aircraft conducted its maiden flight on 20 November 1982, with Guy Mitaux-Maurouard in command.

Representative in all essential constructional respects of the aircraft being built 10 years later, No. 1 was seen to have a low-mounted delta wing of variable cambered profile with 58° leading edge sweepback and a modest 3½° forward sweep to the trailing edge. Wing area is 41.0 m² (441.3 sq ft) to give a comparatively low wing loading – and thus good manoeuvrability – in the air combat configuration. Compared to 414.6 kg/m² (85.0 lb/sq ft) for the Mirage 2000's wing, that for the F-15C Eagle is 546.1 kg/m² (111.8 lb/sq ft). Heading the high-lift devices are full-span, two-segment, leading edge slats which are automatically deployed for combat manoeuvring but restricted in operation at other times to reduce drag. The entire trailing edge of each wing is occupied by two-piece elevons of composites materials with a deflection range of -16° to +25°. The Mirage III is again evoked by the carbon-fibre composite airbrakes mounted above and below the wings at about one-third chord. Construction includes integral tanks which hold some of the aircraft's 3980 litres (876 Imp gal) of internal fuel. 'Tank 1' actually comprises one tank in the centre of each wing and a smaller tank in the forward wing root. Wingtips have bullet-shaped mountings for radar warning receivers and direction-finding sensors.

Fin construction is based on two spars with a light alloy structure and makes use of boron and carbon composites for skinning. A sweepback of 53° is employed for the leading edge, with 17° at the rear, most of which is occupied by the inset composites rudder. The top of the fin accommodates horizontal VOR/ILS aerials and a dielectric cap covering VHF antennas, plus various active and passive ECM antennas. At the base of the fin, protruding rearwards above the afterburner nozzle, is a fairing which can be fitted with a rear transmitting aerial for electronic countermeasures. Messier-Bugatti (formerly Messier-Hispano) supplies the tricycle undercarriage – a commendably light unit representing only 2.2 per cent of the aircraft's AUW (all-up weight). The twin nosewheel leg retracts rearwards and can be steered electro-hydraulically 45° either side of centre while taxiing. Main-wheels, with anti-skid brakes and a tyre pressure of 15.0 bars (217 lb/sq in), retract inwards.

Left: Completing the five Mirage 2000 prototypes was B-01, the first two-seater. Here it is seen later in its career, wearing a standard two-tone camouflage and adorned with flags of the customer nations. The legend on the fuselage attests to its re-engining with the definitive M53-P2.

Left: B-01 seen in a more appropriate colour scheme for a French prototype, surrounded by many of the weapons intended for use with the aircraft. The aircraft itself was used later for 2000N trials, including carriage of dummy ASMP missiles.

Below: During weapons trials using 2000-03 and 2000-04 (illustrated), the Mirage was cleared for use of many air-to-ground stores. Here the Belouga cluster bomb is carried. The picture gives an excellent illustration of the pylons available for stores carriage.

Dassault Mirage 2000

Above: 2 Escadre de Chasse at Dijon-Longvic was chosen as the first Mirage 2000C operator. The initial aircraft had black radomes covering the RDM radar, and despite the carriage of Super 530 were restricted to launch of the Magic only.

Below: Rarely seen on the 2000C is the MATRA ARMAT, a long-range anti-radiation version of the Martel. The aircraft is from the initial S1 batch.

Fuselage structure is of traditional semi-monocoque, almost entirely of metal, with the obvious exception of a glassfibre radome in the nose. Composites are used to construct the nosewheel and mainwheel doors and avionics access panel immediately behind the cockpit canopy. Radar and a starboard-inclined inflight-refuelling probe are installed ahead of the fixed, single-piece windscreen. Probes are detachable and usually fixed to Mirage 2000B/Cs for specific missions; only the 2000N squadrons normally carry them at all times. The pressurised and air-conditioned cockpit contains a Martin-Baker F10Q ejection 'zero-zero' seat built under licence by SEMB and is covered by a one-piece canopy hinged at the rear. Radio and other avionics are housed in the fuselage spine which, on two-seat aircraft (2000B and 2000N/D/S), extends beneath the fin to replace lost space. A fairing under the fuselage contains a braking

Left: Troubles with the RDM radar spoiled the Mirage 2000C's entry into service, but the type introduced much better performance compared to the Mirage IIICs it replaced. Dijon has remained a major air defence base, with an additional type conversion commitment.

Above: This view of a 2000B leading a 2000C shows graphically the Karman wing root fairings that allow the internal carriage of much equipment, leaving the wing to be free from heavy structures. Also of note are the 'souris' air intakes which stand proud of the fuselage, and the bolt-on inflight-refuelling probe.

parachute or an optional arrester hook, but the hydraulically-lowering rear half of this (and the parachute) can be replaced by semi-recessed chaff/flare dispensers. Air intake trunks have a movable, half-cone centrebody of the kind pioneered by Dassault for the Mirage III. Dubbed *souris* (mouse) by analogy with the small rodent poking its nose out of a semi-circular hole in the skirting-boards, these are moved forward as speed increases to focus the shock-wave at the optimum point on the intake lip for pressure recovery and exclude unstable flow ('buzz') from the duct. Fuel storage comprises 'Tank 2' (four tanks surrounding the engine and its air duct); 'Tank 3', which is a single, small collector in the lower rear fuselage; and 'Tank 4' (three tanks behind the cockpit, which are reduced in capacity for two-seat aircraft).

Intake ducts act as mountings for a rectangular strake with curved leading edge, and below them in the fuselage are the ports of two DEFA 554 cannon of 30-mm calibre. Each of these weapons is provided with 125 rounds which can be fired at rates of 1,100 or 1,800 per minute. Two-seat Mirage 2000s lack cannon, but all variants have generous accommodation for external weapons carried on nine hardpoints. Five are under the fuselage in 'playing card' formation and two beneath each wing. Loads of up to 1800 kg (3,968 lb) are accommodated by the centreline and inboard wing positions, while the other four fuselage points will take stores up to 400 kg (882 lb) on each. Outboard wing positions are stressed for a 300-kg (661-lb) load, which usually is a MATRA Magic 2 AAM for offensive or defensive purposes. Attack versions of the aircraft are limited to a maximum of 6300 kg (13,890 lb) attached externally, including additional fuel. Three 'wet' pylons comprise the centreline, with a maximum capacity of 1300 litres (286 Imp gal), and the in-

Left: Aircraft c/n 15 was the last of the initial S1 batch with below-capacity RDM radar. Here it is seen after being brought to S3 standard, with improved RDM with full target illumination capability. The radomes were changed from black to grey in the interests of maintaining camouflage.

73

as a result of development delays with the definitive Thomson-CSF/Dassault Electronique RDI. Early production Mirage 2000s carried a Thomson-CSF RDM, its initials variously indicating Radar Doppler Multifonction (Multi-Role Doppler Radar) or Radar Doppler à Modulations (Modulated Doppler Radar). Initially intended only for exported Mirage 2000s, the RDM is a coherent, digital, frequency-agile radar operating in I-Band and equipped with modes for air-to-air (with or without Doppler), land attack and air/sea operations. In the first-mentioned case, RDM can look up or down, range while searching and track while scanning, illuminate targets for semi-active radar homing AAMs and generate aiming signals for air combat. Overland capabilities are contour mapping, real-beam ground mapping (60° each side of flight-path), terrain avoidance, ground moving target indication and navigation updating. At sea, RDM will designate targets for active homing anti-ship missiles, track while scan or continuously track, and undertake long-range searches. Options include IFF, Doppler beam sharpening, continuous wave illumination and raid assessment – the CW illumination being essential for firing the Mirage 2000C's standard armament of MATRA Super 530D AAMs.

When scanning 120° in azimuth, RDM is estimated to be capable of locating 90 per cent of fighter-size targets within a range of 45 nm (85 km/53 miles) on the assumption that they are presenting a 5 m^2 (54 sq ft) reflecting surface. (Head-on, however, a typical fighter displays only 2 m^2/22 sq ft.) With a 30° scan, range is boosted to 54 nm (100 km/62 miles) – the same range as for a patrol boat in sea-search mode. Selection of Doppler in air-to-air mode reduces the radar's range from 60 nm (111 km/69 miles) to 20 nm (37 km/23 miles). The flat-plate antenna is 65.5 cm (25¾ in) in diameter and produces a beam of 3.6°. Initially known as Cyrano 500, RDM was first airborne inside a Vautour IIN testbed (No. 337) in January 1980. A Falcon 20 (No. 131) joined the programme the following June, while Mirage 2000 No. 03 returned to the air on 13 November 1980 after retrofit and 2000B No. 01 followed early the next year. The trials included five prototype and

Radar testbeds

Much of the development work for the Mirage 2000 radar was accomplished at the Centre d'Essais en Vol. In addition to using Mirage 2000 airframes, notably 2000-03 and 2000-04, the organisation employed several radar testbeds, especially the Mystère 20. These, and a single Vautour, carry the radar

Refuelling of French tactical aircraft is routinely carried out by the Boeing C-135FR tankers of ERV 93. These Stratotankers fly with a short hose and drogue unit attached to the boom. Unlike the normal flying boom method, the receiver pilot is largely responsible for effecting the coupling, pushing the drogue a short way to force contact, after which the boomer can start fuel flow. Here the receiver is a Mirage 2000B of EC 2/2.

board wing positions, each of which will hold a 1700-litre (374-Imp gal) tank on the 2000B and 2000C. The centreline tank is stressed for supersonic flight, but with two of the larger tanks the Mirage 2000 is restricted to high subsonic speeds.

Flight control and avionics

Internally, the Mirage 2000C has a fly-by-wire flight control system with flying control servo units powered by two independent hydraulic systems, each operating at 280 bars (4,000 lb/sq in). Electrical power is supplied by two air-cooled 20-kVA 400-Hz constant frequency alternators. Standard avionics include a digital databus, SAGEM ULISS 52 inertial platform, Dassault Electronique 2084 central digital computer, Sextant AP605 autopilot, Thomson-CSF TMV-980 data display system (VE-130 head-up and VMC-180 head-down, both including radar and IFF data), LMT Deltac TACAN, SOCRAT 8900 VOR/ILS, TRT AHV-6 radar altimeter (AHV-9 on export aircraft) and Sextant 90 air data computer. Operational avionics comprise a Thomson-CSF Serval radar warning receiver with antennas at the wingtips and rear of fin.

Two types of radar have been flown in the Mirage 2000C

Left: *On entering service, the training role was initially undertaken by EC 1/2, but this was transferred to EC 2/2 when the escadron was established as the main OCU. It received the bulk of Mirage 2000Bs, although single examples are also assigned to operational units to maintain proficiency.*

three pre-production radars before series deliveries began in January 1983.

As first in service, RDM lacked its full potential. The initial 15 Mirage 2000Cs – known as S1 standard – had Batch 1 radar which lacked a target illuminator and restricted missile operations to the infra-red Magic. The next few machines were designated S2s and possessed improved Doppler look-down capability, but only when the S3 was introduced did RDM gain a target illuminator, allowing it to direct Super 530Fs of the kind used by the Mirage F1C. In all, 37 2000Cs and 15 2000Bs had RDMs, all of which were brought up to S3 configuration. All the initial 15 trainers and first 19 single-seat aircraft originally had black radomes, later machines (and some for export) having mid-grey for improved camouflage at medium altitudes.

Left: *5 Escadre de Chasse was the second wing to form on the Mirage 2000C, establishing at Orange/ Caritat. Notable on this EC 1/5 aircraft is the chaff/flare dispenser scabbed onto the underside aft of the fuel tank.*

scabbed onto the nose in an elongated radome. The use of such testbeds began in 1980, and continues today as successive modifications are introduced to the Mirage 2000 radar systems. The Mystères provide a cheaper alternative to flying an actual Mirage, and also have the onboard capacity for much equipment to test the performance of the radar. Other avionics systems have also been tested on the Mystère 20 and Vautour.

Left: *'CG' was one of the Mystère 20s used for Mirage 2000 trials, fitted with a modified Cyrano IV radar (service forerunner of RDM). Note the wing bullet fairing for associated equipment.*

Above: *145 is one of the Mystère 20s on current Centre d'Essais en Vol charge, with a radar testbed role. Here it is seen at the CEV's main base at Brétigny.*

Below: *307 was one of six Sud Vautour IINs used for radar trials. It was used for the RDI radar and firing trials of the Super 530D missile. This was the last airworthy example of the Vautour.*

Dassault's electronics company had a 30 per cent share in developing RDI, the intercept-optimised look-down/shoot-down pulse-Doppler radar. RDI is compatible with the Super 530D missile and reportedly has a range of 48 nm (90 km/56 miles) in look-down mode. It has a slotted flat-plate antenna and operates in I/J-Band with considerable protection against jamming. There are ground-mapping, contour-mapping and air-to-ground ranging modes, but the main tasks of the equipment are air-to-air search, long-range tracking and missile guidance, and automatic short-range tracking and identification. Main testbed for RDI development has been the first production Mirage 2000B, No. 501, which first flew on 7 October 1983. The 38th production Mirage 2000C was first with RDI, and 11 were built to the basic S4 standard, followed by 15 S4-1s and 11 S4-2s. From

No. 75 onwards, the build standard is S5, although S4s have been upgraded to S4-1s.

It would be inappropriate to conclude a review of RDM/RDI development without mention of the large fleet of aircraft which paved the way for installation of these radars in the Mirage 2000. No fewer than seven Falcon 20s and six Vautour IINs of the CEV were involved in radar/missile trials as detailed under the heading of Centre d'Essais en Vol in the review of Mirage 2000 operators. CEV also pioneered the aircraft's fly-by-wire system in a Mirage IIIB specially modified for unstable flight under the designation IIIB-SV (Stabilité Variable).

It will have been noted that missile capability of the Mirage 2000C is dependent upon the type of radar installed. Prime air-to-air armament is the MATRA Super 530, a weapon

which should not be confused with the first-generation R.530 carried by Mirage IIIs and early Mirage F1Cs. Fitted with a Dassault Electronique Super AD26 seeker head, the Mach 4.6 Super 530 has a 9000-m (29,530-ft) 'snap-up' capability, making it one of the most versatile of its kind in the world. It can turn at 20*g* at 17000 m (55,780 ft) and 6*g* at 25000 m (82,020 ft) – its ceiling – and has a range of up to 21.6 nm (40 km/25 miles) when delivering its 30-kg (66-lb) fragmentation warhead. First into service, in December 1979, was the Super 530F – 'F' for Mirage F1 – optimised for the Cyrano IV radar installed in Mirage F1s. Minor modification to the Mirage 2000C's RDM radar allowed 530F to be guided to its target by following a reflected illumination signal.

530D and Magic

In 1985, production began of the 530D – 'D' for Doppler – compatible with RDI radar installed in Mirage 2000Cs of the second AA wing to convert from earlier generations of Mirage, beginning in mid-1988. Also from MATRA, the infrared-guided R.550 Magic is a short-range weapon effective between 320 m (1,050 ft) and 5.4 nm (10 km/6 miles). In its Mk 2 form, available since 1984, it has a new proximity fuse for the 12.5-kg (27.6-lb) warhead and an improved seeker head which can be slaved to the Mirage 2000's radar, so that it looks where the radar is looking. Mirage 2000C No. 1 – the first production aircraft – undertook proving launches of Magic 1 with the CEV late in 1983, including one firing in stable flight at 29° angle of attack. Trials of the Super 530 proceeded in parallel, at first with dummy drops and then with live, but unguided, launches from the radar-less prototype No. 02. The first full-scale test took place on 26 October 1984 from No. 03. In combination with the definitive RDI radar, Super 530D and Magic 2 make the Mirage 2000C a potent interceptor at any height.

Product improvements

The Mirage 2000B has already been mentioned as a companion trainer to the 2000C and, rather confusingly, the pair are jointly referred to in France as the Mirage 2000DA, for Défense Aérienne (Air Defence). Addition of a second seat reduces internal fuel by 110 litres (24 Imp gal) to a new figure of 3870 litres (851 Imp gal), increases length by 19 cm (7½ in) to 14.55 m (47 ft 9 in) and adds 100 kg (220 lb) to the empty weight, making it 7600 kg (16,755 lb). The weight increase is

Dassault Mirage 2000

despite removal of DEFA cannon, in compensation for which a twin 30-mm cannon pod can be fitted externally. The installation was proved by trials with B01 but has not been generally adopted. French Mirage 2000Bs changed to RDI radar at the same time as the 2000C, but did not upgrade to –P2 turbofan engines.

Improvements to the Mirage 2000C since it entered service have included powerplant, as well as radar. As well as introducing RDI radar, the S4 version (beginning with 2000C No. 38) simultaneously marked a change to –P2 versions of the SNECMA M53. Weighing 1515 kg (3,340 lb) and with a 0.4 bypass ratio, new fan and low-pressure compressor, the M53 was persuaded to generate 6560 kg (14,462 lb) dry and 9700 kg (21,385 lb) with reheat in its current form, this having at first (and more sensibly) been designated M53-7. First flight was in re-engined Mirage 2000 No. 01 on 1 July 1983, the programme later being augmented by 2000C No. 2 after it had also been re-engined. As will become apparent later in this account, the –P2 joined the interceptor arm of the AA long after it had become available in export and other versions of the Mirage 2000.

Enhancement of the interceptor version, principally with exports in mind, was studied in 1984, launched in June 1986 and revealed the following year in the form of 2000-3 and 2000-5. The former modifies the Mirage cockpit with five multi-function display screens from the Dassault Rafale programme and first flew on 10 March 1988 serialled 'BX1'. Addition to the –3 of Thomson-CSF RDY radar, a new central processing unit and T-CSF VEH 3020 holographic HUD produces the 2000-5 and its so-called APSI (Advanced Pilot-System Interface). RDY first flew in a Falcon 20 in June 1987, followed by Mirage 2000B prototype B01 (re-numbered as 'BY1') in May 1988, and also single-seat prototype No. 03, but not until 24 October 1990 was a fully modified –5 flown in the form of an unserialled two-seat aircraft. (Meanwhile, BY1 had been renumbered BY2 and was shown at Farnborough in September 1990, prematurely marked as a 2000-5.) A single-place equivalent, almost equally anonymous as merely '01', followed it into the air at Istres on 27 April 1991, probably converted from one of three (CY1, CY2 or CY3) assigned to RDY testing. Project pilot for the –5 is Patrick Experton. The two full –5 aircraft have the enhanced ICMS Mk 2 self-protection suite, as evidenced by the extra pair of smaller sensors (front and rear) close to the fin-top. In the two-seat –5, there is a third small antenna on the fin leading edge. To meet additional power requirements for the added equipment, two 25-kVA generators are installed in

place of the 20-kVA pair.

The versatile RDY uses a high pulse-repetition frequency for long-range detection of low-flying targets; low PRF for high targets; and calls upon medium PRF to obviate any range/velocity ambiguities. With Doppler beam sharpening and synthetic aperture techniques, its ground-mapping resolution is of a high order, while signal processing is three times faster than the Hughes AN/APG-70 installed in upgraded USAF F-15 Eagles. Other new technologies employed include a travelling wave tube transmitter and analogue-to-digital converters. One reason for adoption of the APSI 'glass cockpit' is for ease of assimilation by the pilot of the wealth of data produced by modern sensors, of which radar is but one. RDY can track eight targets at any altitude while still scanning, and supplies the pilot with a situational analysis of the air battle and gives the option of multi-target tracking and IFF interrogation – the latter via four HF dipoles mounted in the 60-cm (23½-in) flat-plate, phased array antenna. Land, sea and air modes are similar to those offered by the multi-mode RDM.

With RDY are offered the forthcoming MATRA MICA (Missile d'Interception, de Combat et d'Autodéfense) and a further increase in powerplant thrust in the form of the M53-P20, rated at 10000 kg (22,046 lb). Fitted to a Mirage under the trials designation 2000-4, MICA seeks to standardise missile inventories by being available both with an IR seeker head and radar guidance. Unlike Super 530D, however, the latter mode is entirely fire-and-forget by reason of an active radar transmitter/receiver, although inertial guidance is expected to take the missile most of the way to its target. Despite the sophistication, MICA is to be only slightly larger and heavier than Magic and, following the launching of its development programme in May 1987, will be available in 1994, at the same time as Mirage 2000-5s. The first launch of MICA from a Mirage 2000C was undertaken on 9 January 1992 against a CT20 drone.

Optimised for long-range interception, but with a strengthened airframe for the rigours of low-level operation, the Mirage 2000-5 can ripple-fire Super 530D or BAe Sky

Flash, both of which are semi-active homing weapons. Full MICA capability will be six missiles, but for early trials the 2000-5s have been flying with four MICAs under the fuselage and two Magics on the outer wing pylons. The -5 has air-to-surface capability with new weapons such as the Aérospatiale AS.30L laser-guided missile and MATRA APACHE (Arme Propulsée A CHarges Ejectables) stand-off weapons dispenser. Over sea, the Aérospatiale AM 39 Exocet anti-ship missile can be employed, the RDY radar varying its waveforms to maximise range in different sea states. The versatility offered by the Mirage 2000-5 is a key marketing point in Dassault's attempts to sell more Mirages abroad, having failed to do so for three years – or seven years, allowing for cancellation of the Jordanian contract. The AA has no requirement for the aircraft, being committed to Rafale, but in order to enhance export prospects there are political moves to have it order a retrofit of existing aircraft, effectively making them 2000-5s.

Mirage 2000N

One of the primary roles envisaged for the ACF before its cancellation in 1975 was delivery of a new tactical stand-off nuclear weapon designed by Aérospatiale and known as

Above: Complete with dummy Magic 2 and MICA missiles, 'BX1' launches for a demonstration routine. This aircraft has been used for trials of the new cockpit, new engine and RDY radar.

Left: On display at Le Bourget, 'BY1' has a demonstration radome cut away to reveal the RDY radar. The new sensor is a state-of-the-art synthetic aperture radar, with the latest technologies incorporated to maximise its potential in the interception role, while providing high-resolution ground mapping for precision bombing. Such capability raises the radar into the class of the F-15's APG-70, although processing is said to be much faster.

ASMP (Air-Sol Moyenne Portée – Air-to-Ground Medium Range). This would also be issued to Mirage IVs of the AA's Strategic Air Forces and to the navy's Super Etendards, while ACF would use it to replace the 700-kg (1,543-lb) AN 52 22-kilotonne free-fall bomb carried since 1973 by some Jaguars and Mirage IIIEs of the Tactical Air Force (Force Aérienne Tactique – FATac). Similar to the AGM-69 SRAM issued to USAF B-52 and FB-111 units, ASMP is a 900-kg (1,984-lb) weapon with a yield of either 150 kilotonnes with the TN80 warhead or double that with a TN81. Dimensions include a length of 5.38 m (17 ft 8 in), mean diameter of 38 cm (15 in) and a 'wing' span of 96 cm (3 ft 1¾ in), the supporting surfaces actually being the air intakes on each side which provide dynamic lift. Power is generated by a two-stage rocket/

ramjet, the former (a powder propellant by SNPE packed in the ramjet's rear chamber) accelerating the missile to Mach 2 in about five seconds. In an automatic sequence lasting just one-tenth of a second, the missile's tail cone and air intake blanks are then jettisoned and kerosene fuel fed under pressure to the ONERA ramjet sustainer. Power may be modulated for manoeuvring.

ASMP is programmed before flight with directions, altitudes and speed requirements. Target data is loaded via a cassette into equipment in the launch pylon. Airborne, but before release, the SAGEM E 65 inertial system is aligned with the aircraft's equipment and the Dassault Electronique-Sextant CM84 computer fed with any last-minute changes to the flight plan – for example, to avoid any recently-deployed defences. Launch is undertaken between Mach 0.6 and 0.95 and, if released at high altitude, ASMP has a range of 135 nm (250 km/155 miles) at Mach 3. The more probable low launch reduces parameters to 43 nm (80 km/50 miles) and Mach 2. There is no 'intelligent' terrain-following capability, but pre-programming allows the ASMP to make a circuitous approach and employ terrain masking to good effect – assuming the launch point and the natural obstructions are where the computer has been told they will be.

In 1979, Dassault received the expected contract for two interdictor versions of the new Mirage, to be designated 2000P, for Pénétration. This was soon changed to 2000N (Nucléaire) to avoid confusion with the Mirage IVP. Because the interdiction workload would require a WSO to undertake radar navigation, control the ECM and manage armament, the 2000N was based on the 2000B trainer, but with local airframe strengthening to withstand the stresses of high-subsonic, low-level flight. Internal equipment differs considerably from the interceptor Mirage, stemming particularly from the need for greater positional accuracy.

Replacing RDM/RDI in the nose is a Dassault Electro-

nique/Thomson-CSF Antilope 5 radar, featuring a J-Band travelling wave tube transmitter and flat slotted-plate antenna with terrain-following, air-to-air, -sea and -ground, ground-mapping and navigation-updating modes. Antilope displays radar information in the HUD and the Sextant Avionique VMC 180 three-colour head-down display with moving map overlay (the ICARE – Indicateur CArtographie et Radar Electronique), and provides terrain-following capability down to 91 m (300 ft) and 600 kt (1112 km/h; 691 mph), automatically conforming to pre-set obstacle clearance heights and 'hardness' of ride. The WSO is also assisted by twin SAGEM ULISS 52 inertial navigation systems, two TRT AHV-12 altimeters and his own VMC 180 display

Left: The second development Mirage 2000N is seen in the configuration developed for the N' (N prime), later redesignated 2000D. This is a basic attack version of the nuclear striker.

Below: 4 Escadre de Chasse formed as the first Mirage 2000N wing, assigned to nuclear duties with the ASMP missile. Aircraft c/n 306 was an early K1 variant, lacking any conventional ordnance capability and originally delivered without the Spirale mechanical countermeasures system.

Dassault Mirage 2000

Far right: The full standard K2 variant of the 2000N is in service with EC 2/3 'Champagne' in a conventional attack role.

Top right: The Mirage 2000N-01 first prototype flew initially on 3 February 1983, and is depicted here with ASMP missile and the original small wing tanks.

Bottom right: Developed for the 2000N were 2000-litre (440-Imp gal) drop tanks, which feature an unusual bulbous front end. These offset the loss of the centreline pylon for fuel carriage.

Below: An EC 2/3 Mirage 2000N launches for a training mission under the power of its M53-P2 engine. In addition to the Antilope 5 radar, the 2000N introduces an extensive defence suite.

screen. There is a vertically-mounted Thomson-TRT camera.

For self-defence, the 2000N has Magics on the outboard wing pylons and Dassault Electronique Sabre jammers; it retains the 2000C's Serval RWR (wingtip and fin trailing edge antennas, plus VCM 65 cockpit display screen) and can be fitted with the MATRA Spirale integrated decoy system. Sabre consists of a rear-facing jammer at the base of the fin and a forward element protruding from the fin leading edge. MATRA Spirale comprises chaff dispensers (112 bundles in each) at the rear of the Karman fairings; twin Alkan LL5062 flare dispensers beneath the rear fuselage (in line with the wing trailing edge, each with 16 parachute-retarded flares) and, eventually, missile plume detectors in the rear of the Magic launch rails. Early 2000Ns lacked Spirale, but this has been retrofitted since 1989, the whole defensive system being known as ICMS (Integrated CounterMeasures Suite).

Advanced defensive systems

A more advanced system known as ICMS Mk 2 is under development for the Mirage 2000-5 and will feature all its components linked to a central interface and management unit for automatic operation. ICMS2 retains Spirale, Serval (modified) and Sabre, but adds a receiver/processor in the nose to detect missile command links. There are two detector-jammers, each of which has its own receiver for independence from the Serval system, resulting in an extra pair of small antennas above the principal installations on the fin, plus additions to the sides of the wingtip Serval antennas.

Jammers comprise a Thomson-CSF unit for use against SAMs, as well as the Dassault Electronique HF jammer effective with either airborne threats or SAMs. Carrying ASMP on its central pylon, the Mirage 2000N has only the inboard wing pylons available for additional fuel. This and the slight loss of internal storage resulting from the second seat is partly offset by fitment of large, 2000-litre (440-Imp gal) drop-tanks.

First flight of prototype N01 was at Istres on 3 February 1983, with Michel Porta as pilot. Wearing grey and green upper surface camouflage to indicate its low-level role, N01 was shown at that year's Paris air show, and was joined in the test programme by N02 on 21 September. Both had M53-5 turbofans. N02 has been retained at Istres for development work, including the Spirale system, while its companion has become the prototype 2000D.

The initial requirement was for 110 Mirage 2000Ns, which would be allocated 75 ASMP missiles, including 18 transferred from the Mirage IVP force when it disbands in 1996. However, plans changed as a result of delays with the Dassault Rafale programme and the consequent need for an interim replacement for Mirage IIIEs. A further 70 Mirages were added to FATac's re-equipment plans in the conventional attack role, for which the ASMP interface was deleted. Generally regarded as 'non-nuclear' aircraft (although they could have carried the free-fall AN 52) these were designated Mirage 2000N' (N Prime – N Apostrophe). A re-assessment of nuclear requirements resulted in later adjustments in the numbers of Ns and N's and, to simplify distinctions between

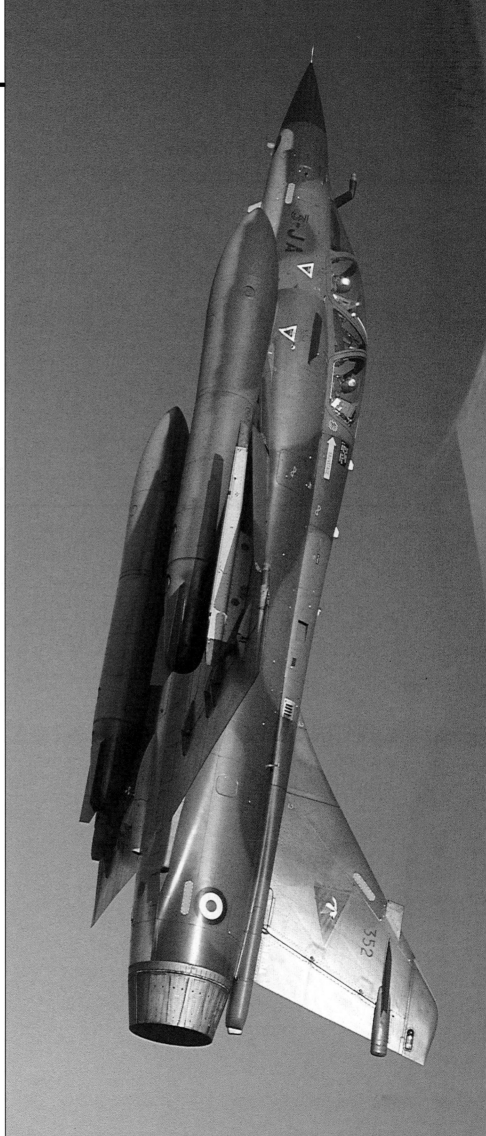

the two, the latter was redesignated Mirage 2000D in 1990. In the event, some 2000Ns were assigned to purely conventional attack prior to deliveries of the 2000D, although it is envisaged that about 20 of these aircraft will take up ASMP when the Mirage IVP retires. The first 31 2000Ns were K1 sub-types with only ASMP capability and which were retrofitted with Spirale self-defence after entering service, but production then switched to the K2, which will take either ASMP or up to 6300 kg (13,890 lb) of alternative ordnance and had Spirale from the outset.

This same weapon load is available for the 2000D – the 'D' claimed to indicate Diversifié (Diversified) – the prototype of which (D01, ex N01) flew on 19 February 1991. Deliveries to the AA are due to begin in 1993, allowing the initial squadron to form on 1 January 1994. Weapons which may be carried include the Aérospatiale AS.30L and MATRA BGL (Bombe Guidée Laser – laser-guided bomb), both of which are guided by a Thomson-CSF ATLIS laser pod on the starboard front underfuselage pylon. AS.30 weighs 520 kg (1,146 lb) and projects a 240-kg (529-lb) warhead at up to Mach 1.6 over a distance of 9.7 nm (18 km/11 miles), while BGL comes in 250, 400 and 1000 kg (551, 882 and 2,204 lb) sizes. The MATRA APACHE stand-off dispenser will be available in three sub-variants: Samanta against runways; Arcadie optimised for use against tank concentrations; and Mimosa with submunitions for general use. Development of APACHE was authorised on 11 September 1989 and the weapon, with a range of up to 81 nm (150 km/93 miles), will be available in 1994.

Up to two BGLs or APACHEs can be carried as alternatives to a similar number of MATRA ARMAT anti-radar missiles or Aérospatiale AM 39 anti-ship missiles. Less 'smart' are alternative loads of 18 Brandt BAP100 or 12

Dassault Mirage 2000

MATRA Durandal anti-runway weapons; up to 18 250-kg
(551-lb) bombs; 18 Brandt BAT120 anti-armour sub-muni-
tions; six MATRA Belouga cluster-bombs; six Brandt BM
250 or BM 400 modular bombs; Dassault CC630 gun pods
with two 30-mm cannon each; up to four MATRA F4 pods
of 18 68-mm rockets each and cannon pods to replace the internal DEFA weapons omitted from two-seat Mirage 2000s.
Other fitments can include an Intertechnique 231-300
'buddy' centreline refuelling pod; Dassault COR2 multi-
camera pod; Dassault AA-3-38 HAROLD long-range opti-
cal reconnaissance pod; Dassault NOR (Nacelle Optronique
de Reconnaissance) real-time recce pod; Dassault/TRT/
Intertechnique Rubis FLIR pod (port forward fuselage
station); a Thomson-CSF TMV 002 Remora jammer
(DB-3141 low-band or DB-3163 high-band); T-CSF TMV
018 Syrel Elint pod; and a large (550-kg/1,212-lb) Thomson-
CSF TMV 004 (CT51J) Caiman offensive ECM pod.

Export variants

By 1991, trials at Istres and Cazaux had validated 650 stores
permutations on Mirage 2000s – many of them for the 2000E
export version. At that time, all 157 export orders had been of
the 2000E series, although various suffixes have been used to
distinguish individual customers and 2000ED is assigned to
two-seat trainers. Mirage 2000E is a single-seat multi-role
aircraft with RDM radar (modified to illuminate targets for
Super 530D AAMs) and M53-P2 engine, a temporary exception to this rule having concerned early Indian aircraft,
which were delivered with -5s and retrofitted. Customers
have requested air defence or low-level camouflage together
with minor changes of equipment, such as installation of
Spirale chaff/flare systems for Greece and Abu Dhabi.

The 2000E, like other variants, has an external stores limit
of 6300 kg (13,890 lb). Added to aircraft's empty weight of
7500 kg (16,534 lb) and 3136 kg (6,967 lb) of internal fuel,
plus pilot, the resultant AUW is 17000 kg (37,480 lb). Full
weapon load will obviously reduce range considerably, but a
representative mission could involve dropping four 250-kg
(551-lb) bombs over 400 nm (740 km/460 miles) from base
or flying more than 1,800 nm (3335 km/2,072 miles) with the
full external load of three drop-tanks. Further details of variations between customers' aircraft are detailed later in this
article. The first export Mirage 2000 was an Indian aircraft
flown on 21 September 1984.

Above: The basic export version is the 2000E, although the suffix changes with the different customers. India was the first to order the aircraft, as the 2000H, with a further order cancelled in favour of the MiG-29.

Right: Having failed to secure the sort of export success for the fighter version gained with the Mirage III and F1, Dassault is hoping the 2000S will bring sales from air arms looking for a high-technology strike aircraft, but which cannot gain access to US technology.

Export sales have at least brought some new camouflage schemes to the Mirage 2000. Abu Dhabi introduced this two-tone sand scheme, while Peru has a similar but darker scheme. Egypt's aircraft wear a strange sea-blue upper surface colour.

Air-to-ground weapons
Peru's aircraft are equipped for a true multi-role tasking, for in addition to AAMs they regularly carry the ATLIS laser designation pod in conjunction with either AS.30L missiles or laser-guided bombs. Alternative loads include various 'dumb' bombs or reconnaissance pods.

Air-to-air missiles
Peruvian Mirages have the standard export RDM radar, and are equipped to launch the Super 530F missile (carried here). These are backed up by Magic 2 IR missiles, and the 30-mm DEFA 554 cannon.

A No. 7 'Battle Axe' Squadron Mirage leads a pair from No. 1 'Tigers' Squadron, representing the two front-line Indian Air Force units. In Indian service the aircraft is known as the Vajra, which translates as 'divine thunder'.

Subsequently, Egypt, Greece, Abu Dhabi and Peru have bought the Mirage 2000, while Jordan cancelled an order for 12 due to financial problems. Expanding the range available to potential customers, Dassault began in April 1989 by announcing an export version of the 2000D which would be available from 1993 – since revised to 1994 – as the Mirage 2000S (for 'Strike'). With Antilope radar and all features except ASMP capability, the 2000S surrenders the 2000E's interceptor capability in favour of the potential for all-weather interdiction. For the 1989 Paris and 1990 Farnborough air shows, Mirage 2000Ns have masqueraded in the static park as 2000S versions. By 1991, the Mirage 2000D was the latest variant and, despite a genuine prototype having then flown, another disguised 2000N appeared in its stead at that year's Le Bourget show.

The alternative designation, Mirage 2000R, is quoted by Dassault for eight aircraft supplied to Abu Dhabi for reconnaissance. However, these are essentially 2000Es employing some of the reconnaissance pod options described above. No Mirage 2000s have their radar replaced by a camera-filled nose, nor are there any known plans for such a conversion. Abu Dhabi's Mirage 2000s flew defence missions during the Gulf War of 1991, and French 2000Cs, deployed to Saudi Arabia, were also involved in hostilities, although none sighted an Iraqi aircraft.

For a variety of reasons, the Middle East arms market in which France has previously been successful has been less lucrative in recent years. During the mid-1980s, Saudi Arabia was a prospect for purchase of 46 Mirage 2000Es, although it appears that Riyadh may have been playing off France, the UK and US against each other to get the best deal on F-15 Eagles and Tornados. Libya was expressing an interest in up

Dassault Mirage 2000P

The only South American purchaser of the Mirage 2000, Peru originally ordered 24 2000P single-seaters and two 2000DP two-seaters, but subsequently cut the single-seat buy to 10. These aircraft equip Escuadrón 412 of the Grupo Aéreo de Caza 4 at La Joya.

Powerplant
The standard SNECMA M53-P2 engine was supplied with all export aircraft, this powerplant producing 64.3 kN (14,462 lb) thrust dry and 95.1 kN (21,385 lb) with afterburning.

Service
Peru received its first aircraft on 7 June 1985, but it remained in France for training. Deliveries to the South American nation began in December 1986, and Escuadrón 412 was established the following August.

Radar
Export aircraft usually feature the original RDM radar, compatible with Super 530Fs. The RDI fitted to most later Armée de l'Air 2000Cs is not approved for export.

Greece signed for 36 2000EG single-seaters and four 2000BG two-seaters to equip two squadrons assigned to the defence of the capital from their base at Tanagra.

to 100 Mirages in 1984, but prospects of a sale evaporated after Libya and France came to blows when Colonel Khadaffi failed to withdraw his forces from Chad. Interestingly, in 1990, Iraq was considering purchase of up to 50 Mirage 2000-5s for delivery in the mid-1990s, while Kuwait had been offered a part-exchange deal by Dassault involving trade-back of its Mirage F1s for over 20 Mirage 2000s. Both countries' plans were changed by events of the same year.

Marketing efforts have temporarily switched to Europe, where two nations have recently been assessing the merits of fighter candidates. Switzerland initially rejected the Mirage 2000, then re-opened its competition in 1989 to consider the 2000-5 and MiG-29 'Fulcrum' before reconfirming in June 1991 its original preference for the F/A-18 Hornet. At the same time, Finland was test flying the F-16 Fighting Falcon, F/A-18 Hornet, JAS 39 Gripen and Mirage 2000-5, prior to making a decision on 67 aircraft to be delivered from 1996 onwards. If unsuccessful in Finland, Dassault can look towards several more years of Mirage 2000 production from French orders but, even here, threatened financial constraints could result in cuts to planned procurement. All that can be said with certainty is that the last 2000 will roll from the Bordeaux assembly shops in about 1998, closing a remarkable chapter in French aviation history which, though dominated by the name of Mirage, has been characterised by success that is far from illusory.

Mirage 2000 Operators

France

Procurement of the Mirage 2000 by l'Armée de l'Air was planned until recently to reach 372 aircraft, comprising 169 2000C interceptors, 23 2000B two-seat trainers, 75 2000N nuclear strike aircraft and 105 2000D tactical attack versions. In 1991, however, the changed strategic situation in Europe resulted in a reduction of French defence spending. In order to maintain the Dassault Rafale's priority, cuts were made in the Mirage 2000 programme, comprising cancellation of all six 2000Cs to be funded in that year, and abandonment of 17 more 2000Cs to have been funded in 1992-94. Additionally, it was announced that no further Mirage 2000D orders were to be placed. The procurement record has been:

Year	Ordered	2000B	2000C	2000N	2000D	Delivered
1979	4	4				3
1980	22		22			2
1981	22	7	15			0
1982	nil					1
1983	30	6	9	15		9
1984	28	2	10	16		24
1985	28	2	10	16		45
1986	35	1	18	16		50
1987	35		23	12		47
1988	35		17		18	13
1989	33		12		21	61
1990	28	10			18	55
1991	18				18	
1992	nil					
TOTALS	**318**	**32**	**136**	**75**	**75**	

Delivery totals include export aircraft and prototypes.
Notes: France planned to order 25 Mirage 2000B/Cs in 1982 and 18 Mirage 2000C/Ds in 1992. The 1988 and 1989 budgets included eight and six Mirage 2000Ns respectively. These were retrospectively transferred to the Mirage 2000D contract to give the totals shown. A Mirage 2000B ordered in 1988 was later cancelled.

By December 1991, France had received some 192 production Mirage 2000s. Deliveries in 1992 are 16 2000Cs and six 2000Ns, following which the AA will receive 15 2000Ds and six 2000Cs per year until 1998, when all will have been received. Losses up to the end of 1991 comprised eight 2000Cs and two 2000Ns.

Mirage 2000Cs and 2000Bs – collectively known as 2000DAs – were delivered to the French air force's Air Defence Command (Commandement 'Air' des Forces de Défense Aérienne – CAFDA), for the re-equipment of three of its four wings. However, before the process could be completed, CAFDA's manned interceptors were transferred on 1 September 1991 to the Tactical Air Force (Force Aérienne Tactique – FATac). Each Fighter Wing, or Escadre de Chasse, has three Fighter Squadrons (Escadrons de Chasse) normally comprising two Flights (Escadrilles) each. The last-mentioned often maintain the traditions of a World War I unit, usually one equipped with SPAD fighters and hence having 'SPA' as a prefix to its number. Normally, No. 1 Flight applies its insignia to the left of the Mirage's fin, with No. 2 Flight appearing on the right, but there are exceptions. Additionally, squadron aircraft are identified by a number/letter code comprising the wing number followed by a letter to indicate the squadron and another for the individual aircraft. For example, the first squadron within No. 2 Wing is identified by the letter 'E', so its aircraft are marked 2-EA, 2-EB, etc. Usual complement is 15 aircraft and 18 pilots. Prototype and pre-series aircraft are numbered from '01' for each variant; production serial numbers begin at 1 for the Mirage 2000C; 301 for Mirage 2000N and 501 for Mirage 2000B.

Experimental aircraft are assembled and flown at Istres; production aircraft at Bordeaux. No. 1, the first Mirage 2000C, first flew at Bordeaux on 20 November 1982 and subsequently served with the CEAM military test unit and CEV trials establishment. Production Mirage 2000Bs made their first flights from 7 October 1983 onwards, but No. 501 was allocated to CEV, so No. 502

(flown 11 January 1984) became the first AA trainer delivery when assigned to CEAM. The same unit received the first Mirage 2000N, No. 301, on 19 February 1987.

Mirage 2000Cs and 2000Bs have been delivered in an upper surface disruptive camouflage scheme of light grey and light blue, with undersides entirely light grey. Black radomes on the first 19 Mirage 2000Cs and 15 2000Bs were replaced by medium grey. Camouflage contours vary minutely between aircraft. Two aircraft of EC 5 have received trial camouflage schemes, one of sand, the other of grey. Mirage 2000Cs have been built to seven production standards: Nos 1-15 were S1 version with RDM batch 1 radar; Nos 16-37 were S2 and S3 aircraft with improved RDM radars. All aircraft were later brought up to S3 configuration and currently serve with No. 2 Wing. Beginning with No. 38 the M53-5 powerplant was replaced by the higher-powered M53-P2 and radar was changed to RDI. Nos 38-48 were S4, but converted in service to S4-1, to which standard Nos 49-63 were built. Nos 64-74 are S4-2 aircraft, while the change to S5 was made with No. 75 in mid-1990. EC 5 uses mainly S4-1/2, whilst EC 12 is to standardise on the S5. All Mirage 2000Bs have -5 turbofans, but No. 515 and subsequent aircraft were fitted with RDI radar.

Initial armament comprised Super 530F and Magic 1 AAMs, now supplanted by Super 530D (S4/S5 only) and Magic 2. Usual configuration is Super 530 on inboard wing pylons and Magic outboard, the centreline carrying a 1300-litre (286-Imp gal) RPL-522 tank weighing 96 kg (212 lb) empty. Centreline pylon is an Alkan type 910 with a Dassault CRP-401 adaptor; inner wing pylons are Alkan 9005 and 9006; outer fitments, Alkan 6045 and 6046. MATRA LM2255 launch rails for Magic are attached to the last-mentioned, the Super 530 being mounted on an LM2153A rail inboard. For deployment in Saudi Arabia during 1990-91 an Alkan LL5062 chaff/flare system was scabbed to the lower rear fuselage, comprising three modules, each with either eight 74-mm flares or 18 40-mm chaff bundles. (Alkan is offering a chaff/flare pod designated LL5027 for the Mirage 2000, but none has been ordered.)

Mirage 2000N tactical low-level camouflage is green and mid-grey disruptive with light-grey beneath. There are points of commonality in pattern with the interceptor, but where these exist the 2000N is green where the 2000C is grey. Radomes of the 2000N are black, the dielectric portion being smaller than that of the 2000C and 2000B. One machine, No. 328, was used to test a desert camouflage scheme in 1989. Aircraft Nos 301-331 are to K1 standard with capability only to launch the ASMP stand-off nuclear missile. From No. 332 upwards, the 2000N-K2 adds tactical attack capability and, additionally, has the Spirale chaff/flare system, as evidenced by squared-off rear ends (containing chaff dispensers) to the wing/fuselage fairing. K1 aircraft are being retrofitted.

Details of Mirage 2000N (and 2000D) weaponry are given in the main text. Pylons (generally applicable to export Mirage 2000Es) comprise an Alkan 9005/9006 on the inboard wing – with Alkan 1405 stores adaptors, plus type 6045/6046 pylons and a 1216 adaptor outboard. The centreline ASMP pylon is specific to France, but an Alkan 910 is otherwise normal. For the four other underfuselage stores positions, Dassault CLB-501/502s go on the front and CLB-511/512s at the rear. In order to carry small bombs, a Dassault CLB-8 (four 250-kg/551-lb bombs or four Durandal) adaptor may be fitted to the inboard pylons or a Dassault ADP-III (same capacity) on the centreline. The Alkan 4036 adaptor carries two larger bombs. Outboard wing Magic attachments are as the Mirage 2000C.

France planned to acquire 110 Mirage 2000Ns in order to guarantee a ready force of 75 ASMP-armed aircraft in five squadrons. However, following a review of nuclear weapon requirements in 1989, this was reduced to three squadrons. Delays with the Rafale programme had meanwhile prompted procurement of 70 conventionally-armed attack Mirages which became the 2000D, and the 1989 forces re-alignment resulted in this target being increased to 105. In the original plans, Mirage 2000N/ASMP would replace aircraft carrying AN 52 nuclear bombs: two Mirage III squadrons in EC 4 (1/4 and 2/4) and three Jaguar squadrons in EC 7 (1/7, 3/7 and 4/7). Instead, three squadrons of EC 4 have ASMP and the second Mirage 2000N/D wing is EC 3, in the conventional role. Disbandment of one Mirage III/5 attack wing and forthcoming conversion of 51 Mirage F1C interceptors to F1CT attack configuration appears to have weakened the case for Mirage 2000D purchases much beyond the 75 on firm order. Some 20 Mirage 2000Ns may be used to re-equip the 91e Escadre de Bombardement (Mont-de-Marsan and Cazaux), which will retire its two squadrons of ASMP-armed Mirage IVPs in 1996.

__The Mirage 2000B/C (collectively known as Mirage 2000DAs) forms the backbone of the French air defence force, serving with three wings. Here early EC 2 aircraft put on a show for the camera.__

2e Escadre de Chasse

Aircraft: Mirage 2000C/B

First of the wings to operate Mirage 2000Cs, EC 2 was formerly attached to the FATac with two squadrons of Mirage IIIEs in the battlefield air superiority role and one squadron (EC 2/2) of Mirage IIIBEs, IIIBs and a few IIIRs as the type OCU. The wing transferred to CAFDA on 1 July 1983, although the OCU remained with FATac until 30 June 1986. Located at Base Aérienne 102, Dijon/Longvic, EC 2 is sole operator of the Mirage 2000C-S3 (i.e. aircraft Nos 1-37) with RDM radar and M53-5 powerplants. The wing did not participate in the 1991 Gulf War, but made the first long-range deployment in 1986 when a 2000B and a 2000C were flown to Indonesia for a trade display and amassed 83 hours each, including demonstrations in Malaysia, Singapore and Turkey. Again, between 30 June and 12 July 1989, four aircraft (including one 2000B) visited the French possessions of the Antilles and Guyana accompanied by a Hercules and C-135FR tanker, routeing via Istres and Dakar (Senegambia).

Individual squadrons are detailed below.

In addition to its air defence role, EC 2 has a training commitment, one of its squadrons acting as the Mirage 2000 conversion unit. Consequently, two-seat 2000Bs are a more common sight at Dijon than at other bases.

Escadron de Chasse 1/2 'Cigognes'

1e Escadrille: SPA3 insignia – *Cigogne de Guynemer* (stork badge of air ace Georges Guynemer's squadron – port)
2e Escadrille: SPA103 insignia – *Cigogne de Fonck* (stork badge of air ace René Fonck's squadron – starboard)
Codes: 2-EA to 2-EZ (radio call FUGEA/FUGEZ)

The 'Storks Squadron' stood down as a Mirage III unit on 23 December 1983, and on 8 April 1984 18 pilots and 91 technical personnel arrived at Mont-de-Marsan for conversion courses to the Mirage 2000C administered by CEAM. For pilots, the nine-week course began with three weeks of ground study at the Ensemble Mobile d'Instruction Mirage 2000, a travelling technical instruction unit established by the Ecole Technique de l'Armée de l'Air (GI 317) at Rochefort in February 1978. In the remaining six weeks, 30 hours were flown on Mirage 2000Bs and 2000Cs, including circuit work, low-altitude navigation,

instrument flying, aerobatics, combat, use of radar, air-to-air firing and night flying.

On 2 July 1984 – the 50th anniversary of the AA's foundation as a separate service – 12 Mirage 2000Cs transferred from Mont-de-Marsan to Dijon to be welcomed by Defence Minister Charles Hernu and AA Chief of Staff General Bernard Capillon. Because of a shortage of Mirages, four of the eight 2000Cs and three of four 2000Bs were CEAM or CEV aircraft with EC 2 markings temporarily applied for media effect. They returned to Marsan immediately, and it was not until early in 1985 that EC 1/2 had its initial complement of 12 single-seat aircraft (Nos 7 to 18), plus three trainers (Nos 504-506). Several of the former remain with the unit. Mirage 2000Bs were passed to EC 2/2 in 1986, but a solitary two-seat aircraft has been attached since mid-1990. The squadron's 20,000th Mirage 2000 hour was flown on 11 September 1990, when No. 4 2-EJ had a large squadron badge applied beneath the fuselage to mark the occasion.

Left: This EC 1/2 machine is one of the early Mirage 2000C-S3 aircraft, with improved RDM radar.

Right: EC 1/2 began operations in 1985, and included in its 15-aircraft complement three Mirage 2000B two-seaters. Two of these were passed to EC 2/2 when the second squadron formed as the OCU.

Above: EC 1/2 is known as the 'Cigognes' (stork) squadron. On the starboard side is carried the badge of SPA103, which was René Fonck's unit. Fonck was France's highest-scoring ace.

Above: A different stork insignia on the port side of the EC 1/2 tail is for SPA3, the original unit of Georges Guynemer, France's second highest-scoring ace of World War I, who amassed 54 victories.

Escadron de Chasse 2/2 'Côte d'Or'

1e Escadrille: SPA65 insignia – *Chimera* (Dragon)
2e Escadrille: SPA57 insignia – *Mouette* (Seagull)
3e Escadrille: SPA94 insignia – *Mort qui fauche* (The Grim Reaper)
Codes: 2-FA to 2-FZ (radio call FUGFA/FUGFZ)

Third Mirage 2000 squadron to convert, EC 2/2 is the OCU for Mirage 2000C pilots and type conversion unit for those destined to fly the 2000N. The unit's first aircraft (No. 509) was transferred from EC 3/2 on 27 June 1986, and on 4 July 1986 its Mirage IIIs were passed to EC 13 to allow conversion to proceed unhindered. The 3rd Flight stood

down on 27 June, but was later re-established. 'Côte d'Or' relieved its two companion squadrons of the Mirage 2000Bs they had been using since conversion and gained additional aircraft directly from Dassault. Issue of 2000Bs to ECs 1/2 and 3/2 had been a non-standard measure, as CAFDA and FATac policy was then to concentrate all two-seat versions of the Mirage III and Mirage F1 within single units. EC 2/2's complement is currently 11 two-seat aircraft (Nos 502 and 505-514) and one

Escadron de Chasse 2/2 is named 'Côte d'Or', and is the principal operational conversion unit for the Mirage 2000C.

Above: As originally presented, the badge of SPA57 (EC 2/2's 2^e Escadrille) was superimposed on a yellow flash.

Above: EC 2/2 is almost entirely equipped with Mirage 2000Bs, with only one 2000C on charge at present. This aircraft carries a Magic 2 acquisition round.

2000C-S3, but authorised establishment is 12 and three. Unable to conform to the usual pattern of applying badges, EC 2/2 paints the same insignia on both sides of an aircraft's fin in rotation through the squadron: 2-FA, FD, FG, FJ and FL wear SPA65 markings; 2-FB, FE, FH and FK are SPA57; and 2-FC, FF, FI and FL are SPA94. Flying a Mirage 2000B, Captain Laurent Fournier won the Sir Douglas Bader Trophy for the best aerobatic display in the 1991 International Air Tattoo at Fairford, UK.

'Côte d'Or' is no longer entirely responsible for pilot training, as it was in Mirage III days, and in order to maintain an operational capability it assigns some of the training to its companions, ECs 1/2 and 3/2. For newly-qualified pilots fresh from the flying training system (Epsilon or Magister, followed by Alpha Jet), the Mirage 2000C course lasts 12 months and involves 180

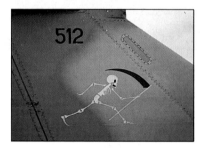

Below: EC 2/2 maintains the traditions of three World War I squadrons. The Grim Reaper badge is for SPA94, with the French name 'Mort qui fauche'.

hours of flying. The airframe conversion stage of 40 hours in three months consists of one month with the OCU and two months at one of the other squadrons. Systems conversion takes 80 hours in six

Below: EC 2/2 aircraft have the same badge on both sides of the fin. The dragon badge is for SPA65 'Chimera', the escadron's 1^e Escadrille.

months, of which only two weeks are spent with EC 2/2. Finally, the air defence training phase of 60 hours in three months sees the student with EC 2/2 for only one month. Instruction is assisted by a Thomson

Below: The 'Mouette' seagull badge of SPA57 adorns the fins of some EC 2/2 aircraft. Each escadrille badge is carried on four of the unit's aircraft.

simulator (which 'flew' its 10,000th hour in September 1990) and a weapons system trainer for head-up and head-down displays known as DAISY (Dispositif d'Animation d'Images Synthétiques).

Escadron de Chasse 3/2 'Alsace'

Insignia: Arms of Alsace (port and starboard)
Codes: 2-LA to 2-LZ (radio call FUGLA/FUGLZ)

Second of the three EC 2 squadrons to receive Mirage 2000s, 'Alsace' retired its Mirage IIIEs on 19 July 1985, by which time conversion of pilots was well under way. Six personnel reported to Mont-de-Marsan early in 1985 for a fortnight of initial training, including the DAISY mission simulator, before joining EC 1/2 to start their flying. The first of three trainers, No. 507 2-LC, was delivered from Dassault on 12 March 1985 (and decorated on the fin with the arms of nearby Savigny-les-Beaunes), followed on 26 April by 2000C No. 19 2-LA, the aircraft of CO Commandant Simon. An initial public appearance of an EC 3/2 aircraft was a brief affair on 31 May 1985 when a flypast of five EC 2 Mirage 2000s to herald the opening of the Paris air show included 2-LA. On completion of training, the squadron was declared operational in March 1986. Having no adopted World War I insignia, the wing decorates both sides of its aircrafts' fins with the arms of Alsace (a red shield containing a gold bend and six gold crowns). It is divided into two flights, but these have geographical names, 'Strasbourg' and 'Mulhouse' for the 1^e and 2^e Escadrilles respectively. The trainers – eventually numbering four – were passed to EC 2/2 in mid-1986, but a single aircraft of this type was added in June 1990.

Right: Like EC 1/2, EC 3/2 originally received a number of two-seaters, but this has been reduced to just one. Both units augment EC 2/2 in the conversion role.

Above and right: Although Escadron de Chasse 3/2 has two escadrilles, 'Strasbourg' and 'Mulhouse', the squadron's aircraft only wear the red and yellow arms of Alsace, this being carried on both sides of the fin.

3e Escadre de Chasse

Destined to be a wing of conventionally-armed Mirage 2000Ds, EC3 has begun re-equipping with late production 2000Ns as the second escadre with strike/attack versions of the Mirage 2000. It is stationed at Base Aérienne 133, Nancy/Ochey, and retains two squadrons of Mirage IIIEs for the moment. Primary role of the latter aircraft is defence suppression with MATRA AJ37 MARTEL anti-radar missiles. First Mirage 2000Ds are expected for ECs 1/3 and 3/3 in 1993.

Escadron de Chasse 1/3 'Navarre'

1e Escadrille: SPA95 insignia – *Oriflamme et Martinet* (Pennant and martlet – port)
2e Escadrille: SPA153 insignia – *Gypaète* (Egyptian falcon – starboard)
Codes: 3-IA to 3-IZ (radio call FUGIA/FUGIZ)

Currently equipped with Mirage IIIEs.

Escadron de Chasse 2/3 'Champagne'

1e Escadrille: SPA67 insignia – *Cigogne* (Stork – port)
2e Escadrille: SPA75 insignia – *Charognard* (Vulture – starboard)
Codes: 3-JA to 3-JZ (radio call FUGJA/FUGJZ)

EC 2/3 was selected as the first of its wing to convert to Mirage 2000Ns and accordingly flew its final Mirage IIIE sortie on 18 December 1990. Working up was undertaken at Luxeuil on K2-standard aircraft temporarily on charge to EC 1/4 and EC 2/4. On 30 August 1991, 'Champagne' became operational at Nancy.

EC 2/3's fin badges are SPA67 'Cigognes' (top, port) for the 1e Escadrille and SPA75 'Charognard' for the 2e Escadrille (right, starboard).

Escadron de Chasse 3/3 'Ardennes'

1e Escadrille: insignia – *Sanglier/barre azur* (Wild boar and blue bar – port)
2e Escadrille: insignia – *Sanglier/barre gueles* (Wild boar and red bar – starboard)
Codes: 3-XA to 3-XV (radio call FUGXA/FUGXZ)

EC 3/3 is currently equipped with Mirage IIIEs.

Above: As the first Mirage 2000 squadron in EC 3, 'Champagne' has adopted the 2000N in a non-nuclear role.

EC 3 is intended to be a Mirage 2000D wing when re-equipment is complete. The other two escadrons currently fly Mirage IIIEs.

4e Escadre de Chasse

Aircraft: Mirage 2000N
The second wing to begin equipment with Mirage 2000s was also the first in the strike/attack role – known in France as 'pre-strategic' nuclear strike. EC 4 was a wing of two squadrons equipped with Mirage IIIEs carrying the AN 52 free-fall nuclear weapon for FATac. After converting both components to Mirage 2000Ns armed with ASMP, it added a third squadron formerly with Jaguars. On 1 September 1991, EC 4 was transferred from FATac to the Strategic Air Forces (Forces Aériennes Stratégiques), thus coming under the same command as the AA's ASMP-armed Mirage IVPs. The wing is resident at Base Aérienne 116, Luxeuil/St Sauveur.

Aircrew for the Mirage 2000N come from separate training streams. Pilots receive conversion to the Mirage 2000 airframe on the 2000Bs of EC 2 at Dijon, but for obvious reasons do not take the full air defence course. WSOs attend Groupement Ecole 316 at Toulouse for navigation experience on Jodels and Nord 262s and a brief fast-jet introduction via the Alpha Jet. Tactical training for two-man crews is the responsibility of Centre d'Instruction Tactique (CITac 339) at Luxeuil, where the Mirage IIIE training unit CPIR 339 was renamed on 1 July 1988 and expanded with two-seat Jaguar Es (advanced fast-jet experience) and two Dassault Mystère 20Ns. These two Mystères , No. 483 'WO' and No. 309 'WP', have Mirage 2000N instruments in the starboard front seat and a representative navigator's position in the cabin ('WP' crashed in December 1991). Ground crew training is undertaken by some of the five mobile training units parented by Groupement des Ensembles Mobiles d'Instruction 30/317, which is a part of GI 317 at Rochefort. EMI Mirage 2000N and EMI ASMP are the two main components involved with training for strike/attack, the other three being EMI Mirage 2000DA, EMI Super 530 and EMI Magic. EC 4 flight planning is conducted in an underground

bunker equipped with the Paloma system, comprising a computer and video screen. By moving a cursor over a map projected on the screen, the WSO can record way-points on a micro-disc for insertion in the aircraft's navigation system, which then follows the required route. Each of EC 4's squadrons has 15 aircraft, 18 pilots, 21 WSOs and three escadrilles. Originally with the normal two flights, squadrons added a third, all of which became operational on 1 September 1991. Escadrille badges are now applied on both sides of the fin, the same insignia on every third aircraft (see EC 2/2 for explanation).

Escadron de Chasse 1/4 'Dauphiné'

1e Escadrille: SPA37 insignia – *Charognard* (Vulture)
2e Escadrille: SPA81 insignia – *Lévrier* (Greyhound)
3e Escadrille: SPA92 insignia – *Lion de Belfort* (Lion)
Codes: 4-AA to 4-AZ (radio call FULAA/FULAZ)

Having flown its last Mirage IIIE sortie on 28 August 1987, EC 1/4 temporarily moved to CEAM at Mont-de-Marsan to re-equip with Mirage 2000Ns. The first 11 aircraft, led by the CO, Commandant Jean-Michel Sinoult, were delivered from CEAM to Luxeuil on 30 March 1988 to complete working up, and the squadron re-formed officially on 1 July. It became operational on 12 July, although celebration of the status was delayed until 14 July when a formation from EC 1/4 flew down the Champs Elysées as part of the Bastille Day parade. 'Dauphiné' was at first assigned a block of 16 aircraft (Nos 305-320 5-AA to 5-AP). These and the remaining K1-standard aircraft up to No. 331 were shared with EC 2/4 when it formed in 1989 – even serial numbers to EC 1/4 – but in the spring of 1990 the squadron re-equipped with K2 aircraft and passed its old equipment to EC 3/4. SPA92 was added on 1 July 1991.

Above: The port side of this Mirage 2000N's fin displays the vulture badge of SPA37 for EC 1/4's 1e Escadrille. The unit was the first to operate the strike Mirage.

Below: Originally the aircraft of EC 1/4 'Dauphiné' carried the white greyhound of SPA81 on the fin, but have also recently adopted this new badge for SPA92.

Escadron de Chasse 2/4 'La Fayette'

1e Escadrille: SPA124 insignia – *Tête de Sioux* (Sioux's head)
2e Escadrille: SPA167 insignia – *Cigogne* (Stork – starboard)
3e Escadrille: SPA160 insignia – *Diable rouge* (Red devil)
Codes: 4-BA to 4-BZ (radio call FULBA/FULBZ)

The 'La Fayette' squadron flew its last Mirage IIIE sortie on 10 November 1988 and stood down for conversion to Mirage 2000Ns at its home base. After re-equipment with K1-standard aircraft, it was declared operational on 1 July 1989 with two component flights. SPA160 was added as a third flight on 1 June 1991 and the fin of the squadron CO's aircraft (No. 335 4-BJ) was modified accordingly. EC 4's squadron commanders carry the escadron badge (comprising the two or three flight badges in a single shield) on both sides of the fin. To mark the 75th anniversary of the 'La Fayette' squadron in 1991, No. 336 4-BP was given appropriate artwork, including a large badge under the fuselage.

Right: The famous Sioux badge of SPA124 dates from the formation of the 'La Fayette' squadron within the French air force by US volunteers.

Below: The aircraft of EC 2/4's commanding officer has all three escadrille badges.

Above: The 2e Escadrille of EC 2/4 has another variation on the 'Cigogne' (stork) theme, this time from SPA167.

Above: EC 4's aircraft are employed primarily in the nuclear strike role, armed with the Aérospatiale ASMP missile.

A new sight on the fins of EC 2/4 aircraft is the red devil badge (SPA160) of the escadron's 3e Escadrille.

Escadron de Chasse 3/4 'Limousin'

1e Escadrille: GC I/9-1e insignia – *Aigle* (Eagle)
2e Escadrille: GC I/9-2e insignia – *Fennec* (Desert fox)
3e Escadrille: SPA96 insignia – *Le Gaulois* (Gallic warrior's head)
Codes: 4-CA to 4-CZ

'Limousin' was formerly a Jaguar squadron, the fourth component of EC 7, detached from the wing's main base and located at Istres and armed with AN52. After flying its last Jaguar sortie on 17 July 1989, 'Limousin' disbanded on 31 July and immediately re-formed at Luxeuil as EC 3/4. By February 1990 it had taken over several K1 series Mirage 2000Ns from EC 1/4 and in May these were transferred to Istres to complete the working-up period. EC 3/4 was declared operational on 1 July 1990, equipped, like its two companions, with ASMP. SPA96 was added in 1991.

Below: Marked with the badges of 1e and 2e Escadrilles, this aircraft is assigned to the commanding officer of EC 3/4.

Above: The escadron's second flight has this badge depicting a Fennec fox in a triangle. The badge has no World War I connections.

Above: On the starboard side of the fin was traditionally the black eagle of GC 1/9's first escadrille.

Below: Another new Mirage 2000N badge to appear recently is that of SPA96 on EC 3/4 'Limousin' aircraft.

5e Escadre de Chasse

Aircraft: Mirage 2000C/B

With EC 2 equipped, EC 5 at Base Aérienne 116, Orange/Caritat, was selected as the second Mirage 2000C wing and the first to receive S4-standard aircraft with RDI radar and -P2 versions of M53 powerplant. Shortly before conversion, the wing comprised two squadrons of Mirage F1Cs and an OCU operating two-seat F1Bs, but the latter passed its aircraft and instructional role to EC 30 at Reims on 1 August 1988 and became a regular interceptor squadron with F1Cs.

EC 5 provided the French Mirage 2000 air defence contingent during Operation Daguet – Desert Shield – and the 1991 Gulf War. An initial four Mirage 2000Cs deployed to Al Ahsa, Saudi Arabia, on 3 October 1990 and the detachment soon increased to 14 aircraft, 24 pilots and 80 groundcrew. These were drawn from all three squadrons, then commanded by Commandants Leroux (1/5), Harmand (2/5) and Hendel (3/5). Air defence missions within Saudi airspace were flown from 12 December onwards and by 16 January 1991 the detachment had generated 1,163 hours in 702 training and air defence sorties.

During the early stages of hostilities, which began on 17 January, the French air defence contingent was not used operationally, although it was employed from 6 February onwards as CAP cover for attack missions and reconnaissance. By the end of fighting on 28 February, the Mirage 2000C had accumulated a further 1,416 hours in 508 sorties, the 1,000th hour (366 sorties) being passed on 18 February. Sorties flown during the combat phase – many of them air-refuelled by French C-135FR tankers – included 163 in offensive missions and 326 for air defence. At least 17 individual aircraft passed through the detachment. The first aircraft returned to Orange on 18 March, and the last on 6 May. Operational fit of the Mirage 2000C was the normal centreline tank, two Super 530Ds (inboard wing) and two Magic 2s (outboard wing), plus two internal cannon. External changes were restricted to Alkan chaff/flare dispensers attached externally to the lower rear fuselage, replacing the back portion of the parachute fairing. One aircraft, No. 74 5-OP, was painted in-theatre with upper surfaces (except the radome) in two shades of sand camouflage, and No. 70 5-AO adopted two-tone grey through having its blue areas altered to the same colour as the standard French radome.

In 1991 the Mirage 2000Cs of EC 5 took part in the coalition effort to oust Iraqi forces from Kuwait.

Escadron de Chasse 1/5 'Vendée'

1e Escadrille: SPA26 insignia – *Cigogne de Saint-Galmier* (Stork – starboard)
2e Escadrille: SPA124 insignia – *Jeanne d'Arc* (Joan of Arc – port)
Codes: 5-NA to 5-NZ (radio call FUGNA/ FUGNZ)

The squadron stood down early in 1988 for conversion, most of which was undertaken at Mont-de-Marsan as the runway at Orange was under repair. A first batch of five aircraft flew to their base on 20 July 1988 (including No. 41 5-NA) and the squadron was officially re-formed on 1 September. It was assigned 15 S4 and S4-1 aircraft (Nos 41-55) and four trainers – two of which were passed to EC 2/5 before the last 2000Cs arrived early in 1989. 'Vendée' was declared operational on 1 April 1989 and retained one of its 2000Bs alongside 14 single-seat machines. Some S4-2s were added late in 1990 for deployment to Saudi Arabia, but in mid-1990 the squadron began upgrading to S5s (No. 75 onwards) and completed the transfer of its older aircraft to EC 3/5. Specially marked squadron aircraft include No. 53 5-NN which had a dummy cockpit and large EC 1/5 badge painted on the underside in 1989, and No. 60 5-NF with artwork to mark SPA26's 75th anniversary on 26 August 1989.

Above: EC 1/5's aircraft proudly wear the Joan of Arc badge on the port side of the fin.

Above right: As its initial aircraft EC 1/5 operated the S4 variant (illustrated), but have re-equipped with S5s.

Right: A single two-seat 2000B flies with EC 1/5 to provide continuation training, orientation and check rides.

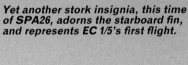

Yet another stork insignia, this time of SPA26, adorns the starboard fin, and represents EC 1/5's first flight.

Escadron de Chasse 2/5 'Ile de France'

Insignia: A cross of Lorraine and three Fleurs-de-lys (port and starboard)
Traditions: No. 340 Squadron, Royal Air Force
Codes: 5-OA to 5-OZ (radio call FUGOA/FUGOZ)

EC 2/5 began conversion early in 1989 with five Mirage 2000Bs and an increasing number of single-seat aircraft, the first of which was No. 57 5-OC, delivered on 18 April 1989. The complement is currently 14 S4-1 and -2 aircraft, plus a single trainer. EC 2/5 became operational on 1 April 1990. The squadron's two un-numbered escadrilles are 'Paris' and 'Versailles'.

Below: This EC 2/5 aircraft has a formal presentation of the Lorraine cross and fleur-de-lys, carried on both sides of the fin.

Above: Originally, EC 2/5 aircraft carried three separate fleur-de-lys, with the Lorraine cross at the fin tip.

Below: An experimental sand scheme was applied to this aircraft for service in the Gulf War. Another aircraft had a new grey scheme.

Above: Special 2000 schemes have included this EC 2/5 aircraft commemorating the 50th anniversary of a Free French unit.

Escadron de Chasse 3/5 'Comtat Venaissin'

1ᵉ Escadrille: ERC571 insignia – *Pirate* (Algerian pirate flag and scimitar – starboard)
2ᵉ Escadrille: SPA171 insignia – *Dragon sable* (Black dragon – port)
Codes: 5-AA to 5-AZ

Having flown its last Mirage F1C sortie on 25 July 1990, EC 3/5 was re-equipped by the transfer of EC 1/5's old equipment, although no 2000Bs were allocated. Apart from a pair of S4-2 aircraft received in early 1991, it operates S4-1-standard Mirages.

SPA171 (above) and ERC571 (left) insignia as carried on the single EC 3/5 aircraft to receive a trial grey camouflage for Gulf service.

Right: Completing EC 5's three-squadron line-up at Orange is Escadron de Chasse 3/5 'Comtat Venaissin'.

12ᵉ Escadre de Chasse

Aircraft: Mirage 2000C/B
The third and last air defence wing to receive Mirage 2000Cs is EC 12 at Base Aérienne 103, Cambrai/Epinoy. All three squadrons of the wing previously operated Mirage F1Cs.

Escadron de Chasse 1/12 'Cambrésis'

1ᵉ Escadrille: SPA162 insignia – *Tigre* (Tiger – starboard)
2ᵉ Escadrille: SPA89 insignia – *Abeille* (Bee – port)
Codes: 12-YA to 12-YZ (radio call FUHYA/FUHYZ)

EC 1/12 became operational with Mirage 2000Cs early in 1992. 2ᵉ Escadrille aircraft are marked with the badge of a wasp (*guêpe*). In a departure from the norm, EC 1/12's pilots have received their radar and weapons training with EC 1/5 at Orange, following Mirage 2000C type conversion at EC 2.

Escadron de Chasse 2/12 'Picardie'

1ᵉ Escadrille: SPA173 insignia – *Oiseau d'azur* (Bluebird – port)
2ᵉ Escadrille: SPA172 insignia – *Perroquet* (Parakeet – starboard)
Codes: 12-KA to 12-KZ

Currently flying Mirage F1Cs.

Escadron de Chasse 3/12 'Cornouaille'

1ᵉ Escadrille: insignia – *Scorpion* (Scorpion – starboard)
2ᵉ Escadrille: insignia – *Dogue d'Ulm* (Bull mastiff – port)
Codes: 12-ZA to 12-ZZ (radio call FUHZA/FUHZZ)

Currently flying Mirage F1Cs.

Right: EC 1/12 'Cambrésis' is the latest Mirage 2000 unit to form, beginning the re-equipment of the entire escadre, which formerly flew the Mirage F1C.

Left: The starboard side of EC 1/12's aircraft carry the SPA162 tiger's head, which qualifies the unit for 'Tiger Squadron' status and a chance to attend the annual 'Tiger Meet' of air force squadrons. The port side carries a wasp badge for SPA89.

Centre d'Expériences Aériennes Militaires

Situated at Base Aérienne 118, Mont-de-Marsan, CEAM 330 is a direct-reporting unit of the AA high command responsible for trials of air force equipment. It includes a fighter [trials] squadron and a training and transport flight. The former was designated Escadron de Chasse 24/118 during the period in which CEAM 330 aircraft were 'owned' by Mont-de-Marsan, but on 15 October 1987 the unit became an aircraft operator in its own right and EC 24/118 was re-designated EC 5/330.

Escadron de Chasse 5/330 'Côte d'Argent'

Insignia: *Tigre pailleux* (Tiger – left, and CEAM – right)
Codes: 330-AA to 330-AZ (radio call FSDAA/FSDAZ)

CEAM personnel regularly evaluate new aircraft at the manufacturer's test site, but the first Mirage 2000 to be semi-permanently assigned to CEAM was 2000C No. 1, which was delivered to Mont-de-Marsan on 27 April 1983 but soon transferred to CEV. Four more permanent deliveries before the end of 1983 were No. 3 118-AV and the next three off the line, together with others destined for the first front-line operator, EC 2/2. EC 24/118 (then an unnamed squadron) oversaw conversion of EC 2/2's pilots and lent some of its aircraft for the latter's commissioning ceremony in July 1984. These included two Mirage 2000Bs taken on charge earlier that year, the first of which was No. 502 118-AZ which had first flown on 11 January 1984. To mark the formation of EC 5/330 in October

1987, No. 3 330-AN was painted an overall 'tiger' colour scheme, which was removed after two days. No. 39 330-AH has worn a large squadron badge under the fuselage.

The first production Mirage 2000N, No. 301, was delivered to CEAM on 19 February 1987, but soon passed to CEV. Nos 302, 303 and 304 were other early arrivals, together with aircraft assigned to EC 1/4 for its working up in the winter of 1987-88. From the outset, Mirage 2000Ns wore codes prefixed 330-, these being applied during the spring of 1987 – i.e. several months before EC 5/330 appeared. The 'Côte d'Argent' badge of a tiger replaced the triangular CEAM badge of a man astride a cog-wheel hurling a dart towards the stars. This badge appeared on both sides of fins prior to the formation of EC 5/330.

Keeping abreast of developments, CEAM is issued with the first aircraft from new production batches as they appear. No. 38 330-AT, the first Mirage 2000C with RDI radar and an M53-P32 turbofan (S4 standard), was delivered in mid-1987, followed by the next two aircraft produced at Bordeaux. During the early months of 1990, the first five S4-2 versions joined CEAM, beginning with No. 64 330-AQ, while in the winter of 1990-91 six early S5 Mirage 2000Cs were received, beginning with No. 80 330-AS. On the strike/attack front, the first four Mirage 2000N-K2s were taken on charge during 1980 (No. 332 330-AR, etc). Older equipment is usually discarded as aircraft of a higher production standard are received, The average holding is around five Mirage 2000Cs, two 2000Bs and three 2000N/Ds. Short-term 'progress checks' are conducted on prototypes still on manufacturer's charge, one of the most recent being undertaken on the prototype Mirage 2000D at Istres between 14 and 27 May 1991.

Above: Another 'tiger' squadron is EC 5/330. This aircraft wears an enlarged version on the fin and suitably-clad nose art.

Right: The starboard side of the EC 5/330 aircraft is more normally adorned with the badge of the Centre d'Expériences Aériennes Militaires.

Below: Prior to becoming EC 5/330, the CEAM was designated EC 24/118, and aircraft wore '118' codes.

Above: The standard tiger badge of the CEAM is depicted here. It is carried on the port side of the fin.

Right: The CEAM operates Mirage 2000Ns and Ds in its fleet. This early 2000N is seen with an ASMP missile under its belly.

Centre d'Essais en Vol

While CEAM concerns itself with military equipment, CEV is an element of the Direction Technique des Constructions Aéronautiques responsible for airworthiness testing and certification. CEV's main base is at Brétigny-sur-Orge, but most Dassault-related testing is conducted at either Istres, where both CEV and the manufacturer have permanent detachments, or Cazaux, which has weapons ranges nearby. Most Mirage 2000 prototypes have been flown by CEV, while production aircraft in long-term use include Mirage 2000C No. 1, 2000B No. 501 and 2000N No. 301. Combat aircraft assigned to CEV are not normally marked with codes or badges.

The CEV test fleet was heavily involved with development of Mirage 2000 avionics during the late 1970s and early 1980s. Aircraft involved include:

Mystère 20:

No. 79	'CT'	RDI radar (Mirage 2000C instrumentation in starboard pilot's position)
No. 86	'CG'	Super 530 missile trials, fitted with modified Cyrano IV radar
No. 104	'CW'	RDI radar and other avionics trials
No. 124	'CC'	ECM trials
No. 131	'CD'	RDM/RDI radar and systems integration
No. 188	'CX'	Systems trials
No. 263	'CY'	Systems trials

Vautour IIN:

No. 304		RDM/Super 530F firing trials
No. 307		RDI/Super 530D firing trials
No. 348		Radar trials
No. 355		Radar and systems evaluation
No. 357		RDM flight trials
No. 358		RDM flight trials

Mirage IIIB-SV:

No. 225		Fly-by-wire development

A handful of Mirage 2000s figure in the CEV's large and disparate fleet of test aircraft. This is an early 2000B, seen at the organisation's main base at Brétigny.

Mirage 2000 Operators

Dassault Aviation

In April 1990, Avions Marcel Dassault-Bréguet Aviation shortened its name to Dassault Aviation. The firm's base for experimental testing is at Istres, while assembly and production flight trials are conducted at Bordeaux/Mérignac. Istres has 12 company pilots and six flight engineers, compared with four and two respectively at Bordeaux. Also at Istres are two anechoic chambers for electromagnetic testing and the flight-test headquarters of the engine manufacturer SNECMA. Aircraft for foreign customers may be flown from Cazaux for weapons qualification. Mirage 2000 prototypes made their first flights at Istres and some have been retained for long-term testing. Production aircraft assigned to

similar roles are frequently given new serial numbers, examples including X34 (Peruvian), H37 (Indian), C2 and X7 (French), BY1 (later BY2) (RDY radar), BX1 (Mirage 2000-3), EG1 (Greece) and EM1 (Egypt). Radio call-signs are in the ranges FZJRA/FZJRZ and FXJTA/FZJTZ. Dassault has marked Mirage 2000s with spurious identities for display at trade events, including 2000N No. 314 as a Mirage 2000S for Paris 1989; No. 327 as a Mirage 2000S coded 'SA' for Farnborough 1990; and No. 350 as a Mirage 2000D for Paris 1991.

Among the aircraft retained by Dassault for trials and demonstrations was this 2000B, coded BX1, which flew as the prototype for the 2000-3 series.

Egypt

Although the first to place an order (worth $890 million), in December 1981, Egypt's air force was the second export Mirage 2000 recipient after India. Requirements were for 16 Mirage 2000EMs (serialled 101-116) and four Mirage 2000BM trainers (201-204), No. 101 making its first flight in December 1985. Deliveries took place between 30 June 1986 and January 1988, the final aircraft delayed as the result of payment difficulties by the customer. Powered by M53-P2 engines, the aircraft have an additional rear-facing ECM antenna towards the top of the fin and RDM radar with an illuminator for Super 530D missiles. Other weapons include Magic AAMs, AS.30L ASMs (and ATLIS designators) and ARMAT ARMs. Colours are medium-grey upper surfaces with light grey below and black radomes. A requirement for 20 more aircraft, including 16 to be assembled at Helwan by AOI, seems unlikely to be met. At least one 2000EM (113 in July 1989) has been lost in an accident.

India

The Bharatiya Vayu Sena signed a memorandum on 8 April 1982 and placed an order in October of the same year for 40 Mirage 2000s worth $500 million. These comprised Mirage 2000Hs KF101 to KF136 and two-seat Mirage 2000THs KF201 to KF204, of which KF101 was the first export Mirage to fly, on 21 September 1984. Deliveries were planned between October 1984 and December 1986, but training did not begin at Mont-de-Marsan until December 1984. When the first batch of pilots had converted, seven Mirages left France on 20 June 1985 and arrived at Maharajpura AFB, Gwalior, on 29 June. At the reception ceremony the Mirage 2000 was named Vajra – loosely translated as 'Thunderbolt' but actually the invincible weapon of the god Indra. Plans to equip two re-formed squadrons, Nos 51 and 52, were changed before delivery and, instead, these units equipped with MiG-21 'Fishbeds' transferred from Gwalior-based No. 7 'Battle Axe' Squadron and No. 1 'The Tigers' Squadron. Mirages equipped the two last-mentioned in that order.

The first 26 single-seat aircraft and all four trainers (delivered from February 1985) were designated 2000H5 and 2000TH5 to signify

Above: Both of India's Mirage squadrons are based at Gwalior. This is the winged battle axe badge of No. 7 Squadron.

Above: The second squadron at Gwalior is No. 1 'Tigers'. This aircraft is from the first batch ordered for the IAF.

that they had the interim M53-5 turbofans until upgrading was carried out in India and the fleet standardised on -P2 versions. A follow-on batch of six Mirage 2000Hs (KF137-KF142) and three 2000THs (KF205-KF207) was ordered in March 1986, with deliveries following rapidly between April 1987 and October 1988. IAF Mirage 2000s have French-style camouflage and black radomes and are equipped with Super 530D and Magic 2 AAMs (both ordered in November 1984 and delivered in 1986). Additionally, the aircraft are available for attack missions with ARMAT missiles, Durandal anti-runway weapons and Belouga cluster bombs. An unconfirmed report alleges that Indian Mirage 2000s have Antilope 5 radar and twin INS, making them similar in essential respects to the Mirage 2000N. One (KF102) was lost in a spectacular crash during a flying display at Palam in October 1989. India originally had plans to build Mirage 2000s locally, HAL being offered a programme of 45 kits and 65 produced mainly from indigenous components. The proportions were later changed to 20 and 90, but India decided in 1984 to buy MiG-29 'Fulcrums' from the USSR.

Left: Despite having black radomes (associated with only the earliest French aircraft), the Indian Air Force aircraft can launch the latest Super 530D missiles. If reports that they have Antilope 5 radar are correct, this may explain the colour.

Peru

Dassault's third customer was Peru's Fuerza Aérea Peruana, which signed an $800-million letter of intent on 15 December 1982 for 14 single-seat Mirage 2000Ps and two 2000DP trainers, and took out an option on a further eight and two respectively. The options were taken up, but Peru's financial problems resulted in the contract being renegotiated in July 1984 and reduced to 12. Of these, 10 were Mirage 2000Ps with the serial numbers 050-054 and 060-064, the remainder being 2000DPs numbered 193 and 195. No. 193 was formally handed over at the Paris air show on 7 June 1985 and began to train pilots in France, while remaining aircraft were accepted from July 1986 onwards. Once training was complete, deliveries to Peru began in December 1986 with the first two aircraft. At Base Aérea

Mariano Melgar, La Joya, Escuadrón 412 was established on 14 August 1987 to operate the Mirage 2000. Its companion unit is Grupo Aéreo 4 (No. 4 Wing), being the Sukhoi Su-22-equipped No. 411 Squadron. FAP aircraft have brown and sand camouflage in the French pattern (brown for blue; sand for grey), pale blue undersides and black radomes. With the standard export RDM radar and M53-P2 turbofan, they are well equipped for attack roles with AS.30L ASMs (and ATLIS designators), 1000-kg (2,205-lb) MATRA laser-guided bombs and smaller bombs carried on CLB-8 and ADP-III adaptors.

Peru's Mirages 2000Ps have a multi-role mission, with AS.30L LGMs among their weaponry.

Abu Dhabi

As leading element in the United Arab Emirates Air Force Abu Dhabi placed a contract on 16 May 1983 for 18 Mirage 2000s and a similar number of options. The first batch was to comprise 12 Mirage 2000EADs, three 2000RAD reconnaissance aircraft and three 2000DAD two-seat trainers, five spare engines, training and support to the total value of $950 million, deliveries to begin in September 1986. During 1985, the option was taken up and a third batch of 18 placed on option – the latter still outstanding. The second batch, valued at $500 million, should have had the same balance of aircraft, but the combined order was altered slightly to comprise 22 Mirage 2000EADs (serialled 731-752), eight 2000RADs (711-718) and six 2000DADs (701-706). Abu Dhabi specified an advanced avionics configuration in addition to M53-P2 engines and RDM radar, this including Elettronica ELT/158 radar warning receivers and ELT/558 jammers in place of standard French internal equipment in at least the second-batch machines. All three variants

have Spirale chaff/flare dispensers and provision for non-French weapons such as AIM-9 Sidewinder AAMs (although Super 530 and Magic capability is retained). Mirage 2000RADs have the ability to carry COR2, SLAR 2000 and Harold pods, and EADs can deploy an Intertechnique 'buddy' refuelling pod. Abu Dhabi also commissioned Signal & Control Group in the USA to develop a 454-kg (1,000-lb) stand-off bomb for the Mirage 2000. A minor change of configuration concerns a Chelton spade aerial in place of the swept blade beneath the forward fuselage.

Dissatisfied with the standard of operational equipment installed, Abu Dhabi refused to take delivery of the Mirage 2000, even after the last was completed in 1987. The dispute was eventually settled and deliveries began to the French base at Dijon in October 1989 for pilot conversion by EC 2. A first batch of six Mirages ferried to Maqatra on 7 November 1989, deliveries ending a year later with the exception of a trainer (704) which crashed at the start of its

delivery flight in January 1990. ADAF Mirages have two colour schemes, both of the same disruptive pattern: trainers are in two-tone grey, while the single-seat aircraft are two-tone sand. Mirages are based at Maqatra (al Dhafra) in two squadrons and flew operational air defence missions during the latter part of Desert Storm, from 19 until 27 February 1991.

Abu Dhabi's order for Mirages included eight to 2000RAD standard, these aircraft being equipped for tactical reconnaissance carrying pod-mounted equipment on the centreline. Among the pods available is the COR2 camera pod, as seen here.

Greece

Greek interest in the Mirage 2000 began with the November 1982 announcement of a requirement for at least 100 combat aircraft which, for political reasons, would be split into purchases from the USA and Europe. In March 1985, the General Dynamics F-16 Fighting Falcon and Mirage 2000 were announced as winners, each to be awarded a contract for 40 aircraft plus an option for 20 more – although only one of the options would be taken up after an interval of three years. The Dassault contract, worth $1,380 million including weapons and equipment, was signed on 20 July 1985 and covered 36 Mirage 2000EGs (serials 211-246) and four 2000BG trainers (201-204), both with RDM3 radar and M53-P2. Industrial offsets are to total 60 per cent over 15 years, including assembly and test of 50 M53-P2 turbofans by HAI at Tanagra from early 1988 onwards.

Greece was unhappy at the low level of the offsets achieved early in the programme and so its officials boycotted the handover of the first four Mirages to the Elliniki Polemiki Aeroporia (Greek Military Aviation) on 21 March 1988. Based with 114ª Pterix Mahis (Combat Wing) at Tanagra, the aircraft are assigned to defence of Athens and fitted with Super 530D and Magic 2 AAMs. The two newly-formed operating squadrons are 331 and 332 Mire Pandos Kairou (All-Weather Fighter Squadrons), of which No. 331 Aegeas has two trainers and the even-numbered 2000EGs, the others serving No. 332 Geraki Squadron.

Following training of eight pilots by EC 2 at Dijon in June 1988, deliveries to Greece began in June 1988, allowing No. 331 to be declared operational on 23 September 1988. The last would have been completed by the end of 1989, but in October of that year deliveries were halted at the 28th aircraft (24 2000EGs and all four trainers) because of Greek

dissatisfaction with RDM radar performance. This difficulty was resolved in 1991, at which time the 20-aircraft option was firmed up in favour of the F-16. No. 332 Mira also acts as the type OCU or Skoli Meteklaidefseos ('Finishing School'), taking only pilots experienced on other types of fighter and providing them with between seven and 10 hours in a simulator, plus 10 hours of familiarisation in the Mirage 2000BG. Greek Mirage 2000s display the French camouflage scheme with grey radomes, but differ in respect of having Spirale chaff/flare systems; an additional pair of small ECM antennas on top of the fin and secondary antennas scabbed to the side of the wingtip Serval receivers; and a spade aerial under the forward fuselage.

Below: Four Mirage 2000BG two-seaters were included in the Greek purchase, split between the two units (332 Mira shown).

Numerous minor details differentiate Greek Mirages, but the most major are the additional radar warning receiver antennas on the fin. The two squadrons of 114 Pterix have the defence of Athens as their primary tasking.

Jordan

On 22 April 1988, 12 Mirage 2000s were ordered by Al Quwwat al Jawwiya al Malakiya al Urduniya in the form of 10 2000EJs and two 2000DJ trainers, and an option taken out on eight more aircraft. The contract, which became effective on 13 July the same year, called for the first to be handed over early in 1991 for training in France, with delivery to Jordan following in May of the same year. Armament was to include Super 530D and Magic 2 missiles, plus Durandal for airfield attack. Including an upgrade for the RJAF's Mirage F1 force, the contract was valued at $840 million, much of it to be paid by Saudi Arabia. The first two aircraft – one of each variant – were flown to Istres in January 1990 for trials. Work on the remaining aircraft was well advanced when Jordan's political support for the Iraqi invasion of Kuwait in August 1990 alienated Saudi Arabia and halted financial support. In August 1991, Jordan formally requested the contract with Dassault to be terminated.

Japan's air force photographed by Peter Steinemann and Robbie Shaw

Japanese Air Self Defence

Main picture: The Bujin-Haniwa (a type of terracotta soldier figure traditionally buried with kings) badge identifies this F-15DJ as belonging to the 202nd Hikotai (squadron), whose Nyutabaru base is close to an ancient burial site known as the 'Saitobaru Kofun'.

Below: The crew of a Kawasaki Vertol KV-107 (the locally manufactured version of the CH-46 Sea Knight) line up for inspection, behind the SAR role equipment their helicopter carries.

Force

The domestic reaction to Japan's part in World War II has been a deep-rooted anti-militarism. Thus, even Japan's military air arm cannot be known as the Japanese Air Force but instead goes under the more cumbersome title Japanese Air Self Defence Force (JASDF). Biased towards the air defence role, the JASDF has built up a tradition of colourful unit markings since its formation in 1952, making it one of the world's most colourful air arms.

Left: Japan's 'Blue Impulse' formation display team flies the indigenously-designed Mitsubishi T-2 advanced trainer, after many years on the F-86 Sabre.

Left: F-15Js form the air defence backbone of the Northern Air Defence Force (2nd Kokudan), the Central Air Defence Force (6th and 7th Kokudan), and the Western Air Defence Force (5th and 8th Kokudan).

Below: The aggressor F-15s wear a variety of colour schemes, with a particular colour (here black) as disruptive camouflage over the normal air defence grey. Several of the aggressor Eagles are two-seaters.

Left: Japan's E-2C Hawkeyes serve with the 601st Hikotai of the 3rd Kokudan at Misawa. Thirteen of these aircraft were delivered from 1983. The sheer size of the airspace patrolled by the JASDF has led to calls for a larger, longer-range AEW & C platform.

Below: Ferocious-looking eagle's heads on the inner and outer faces of this F-15's fins denote the 204th Hikotai, the 7th Kokudan's only F-15 unit. The slender fin-tip projections house indigenous EW equipment. The 204th Hikotai was Japan's third F-15 unit when it transitioned in 1984.

Left: The JASDF received 14 McDonnell-built Eagles and has followed these with 187 aircraft built under licence by Mitsubishi. These will equip seven front-line squadrons and an aggressor unit. The F-15 fighter units are the 201st and 203rd Hikotai of the 2nd Kokudan (wing) at Chitose, the 303rd Hikotai of the 6th Kokudan at Komatsu, the 204th Hikotai of the 7th Kokudan at Hyakuri, the 202nd Hikotai of the 5th Kokudan at Nyutabaru and the 304th Hikotai of the 8th Kokudan at Tsuiki. The aggressor unit is the Hiko Kyodotai, which forms part of the 5th Kokudan. The 305th Hikotai of the 7th Kokudan is due to transition from the F-4 during 1993.

Japanese Air Self Defence Force

Right: Japanese RF-4EJs wear an attractive brown and two-tone green camouflage. The 'Woody Woodpecker' badge is used by the 501st Hikotai, which is based at Hyakuri, which also houses the fighter F-4EJs and F-15Js of the 7th Kokudan.

Below: Like virtually all export RF-4s, Japan's 14 photo Phantoms are RF-4Es, based on the F-4E airframe and licence-built by Mitsubishi.

Bottom: An F-4EJ of the 301st Hikotai, which is co-located beside the F-15-equipped 202nd Hikotai as part of the Nyutabaru-based 5th Kokudan. The frog badge was adopted because of the abundance of these animals at Mount Tsukuba, close to the unit's previous base at Hyakuri.

Right: This F-4EJ is seen taxiing with an underwing target 'dart'. The diving Eagle insignia is used by the 302nd Hikotai, which is based at Naha as part of the Southwest Composite Air Wing. The unit is actually the only aircraft-operating squadron at Naha, the other units being equipped with Nike SAMs. It therefore provides air defence for Okinawa, and fulfils its own target-towing requirements. Surviving Phantoms are being upgraded to F-4EJ Kai configuration with an APG-66 radar and a complete structural rework. Seventeen will be reconfigured as reconnaissance aircraft with a pod-mounted SLAR, to augment the RF-4Es, which are also being re-worked.

Below: The Lockheed T-33 continues to serve in large numbers in the liaison and training roles. Many are attached to front-line squadrons and air defence HQs, like this aircraft which wears the Tengu (a local long-nosed goblin) badge of the 304th Hikotai.

The stylised eagle badge of the 302nd Hikotai spells out 302 (3 being the swept-back wing, 0 being the tail, and 2 being the talons). Japanese Hikotai badges are extremely colourful, and are generally applied very large. Augmenting these unit insignia is a plethora of special camouflage schemes, and individual badges applied for gunnery and other competitions. Cartoon characters and various types of birds of prey are favourites, and range in size from the modest (seen above) to the over-the-top. At least one entire F-4EJ was painted to represent an eagle, with wing feathers on the wings and a vast eagle's head over the forward fuselage.

Above: The reason that this F-4EJ's external fuel tanks have been painted **Dayglo** is unknown, but it was probably to distinguish friend from foe during air combat training between similar types, or perhaps to increase conspicuity during target-towing missions. The dark sea grey upper surfaces are relatively common on Japanese Phantoms.

Right: The Goblin's Nest. The signpost outside the 304th Hikotai crewroom at Tsuiki features the squadron's **Tengu** badge. The **Tengu** is a mythical long-nosed goblin reputed to live on nearby Mount Ehiko. Such outbreaks of squadron spirit are common, and invariably follow **USAF** practice.

Above: Pilot and **WSO** walk from their 305th Hikotai F-4EJ. Both wear high-visibility orange flying suits, designed to aid **SAR** forces in the event of an ejection. Both also wear squadron baseball caps bearing the unit's number.

Right: A line-up of 305th Hikotai F-4EJs at Hyakuri. The squadron badge is a plum flower. The famous Kairakuen plum garden is located in the nearby city of Mito.

Left: Final checks to a 304th Hikotai F-4EJ. The aircraft is configured for a target-towing mission, with a **TDU-25/B** target-towing winch on the centreline. The small dart-like target can be fitted with an **IR** flare or a radar reflector. The 304th Hikotai have since transitioned to the F-15.

Above right: When the F-4EJ Kai modification programme is complete, the Phantoms are likely to be reassigned to close support and anti-shipping tasks, perhaps replacing the indigenous F-1.

Right: Black paint serves to modify the outline of this Mitsubishi T-2 to resemble that of a MiG-21. The 'meatball' national insignia is partially obscured and the aircraft wears the Cobra's head badge of the Hiko Kyodotai aggressor unit.

Above: The Mitsubishi F-1 serves primarily in the anti-ship role, though this is described as anti-landing craft attack to conform with the 'self-defence' ethos of the JASDF. Bearing a close resemblance to the similarly-powered SEPECAT Jaguar, the F-1 was derived from the indigenous T-2 trainer. The aircraft have undergone a structural life extension programme. An aircraft of the Tsuiki-based 8th Kokudan's 6th Hikotai is shown here, with squadron badge of crossed swords and a bow and arrow.

Right: The 3rd Hikotai of the 3rd Kokudan at Misawa uses a Samurai warrior's head as its emblem. It is seen here on the fin of one of the unit's Mitsubishi F-1s.

Below: The Fuji T-3 was developed as a successor to the Beechcraft T-34, from which it was derived. This one serves with the 12th Hiko Kyoikudan at Hofu. The red circles in the badge are taken from the crest of a local clan.

Right: The indigenous Fuji T-1 trainer is now virtually extinct, having been replaced by the Kawasaki T-4. This Orpheus-engined T-1A wears the stylised Japanese numeral '13' representing the 13th Hiko Kyoikudan, which is based at Ashiya. The 1st Flying Training Squadron wears the marking in white, while the second carries it in blue.

Below: A decidedly unofficial 3rd Hikotai marking, featuring a buxom winged devil, stencilled on to the drop-tank of an F-1. Such zaps and unofficial markings are relatively common.

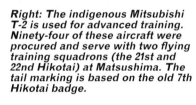

Right: The indigenous Mitsubishi T-2 is used for advanced training. Ninety-four of these aircraft were procured and serve with two flying training squadrons (the 21st and 22nd Hikotai) at Matsushima. The tail marking is based on the old 7th Hikotai badge.

Below: Also based at Matsushima is the T-2-equipped 'Blue Impulse' aerobatic team, which actually comes under the 21st Hikotai. The team re-equipped with the T-2 from the F-86F Sabre in 1982. The team's aircraft wear a striking two-tone blue and white colour scheme.

Right: The aircraft of the Hiko Tenkentai wear red and white checkers on their tailfins as a unit marking. The unit operates in the flight checking and calibration role from Iruma. This Mitsubishi MU-2J serves there alongside YS-11s and T-33s.

Below: The Kawasaki Vertol KV-107 is an indigenous version of the CH-46 Sea Knight. Used in the search and rescue role by the JASDF (and in other roles by the JMSDF and JGSDF), the KV-107 was procured in large numbers. This aircraft serves with the Air Rescue Wing headquartered at Iruma, and with detachments elsewhere.

Above: Thirty-one indigenous Kawasaki C-1s were delivered and these (with a handful of YS-11s) now equip two squadrons: the 402nd and 403rd Hikotai. This aircraft wears the yellow bird badge of the 402nd Hikotai, which represents a stylised figure 2.

Right: The JASDF received 12 NAMC YS-11Ps, YS-11Cs and YS-11PCs (passenger transports, cargo transports and cargo/transport aircraft) and a single dedicated YS-11FC calibration aircraft. Two YS-11E ECM training aircraft were produced by conversion, together with a single navigation training YS-11NT and a single YS-11E (EL) Elint aircraft. The remaining eight transports serve alongside the C-1s with the 402nd and 403rd Hikotai. The aircraft pictured here is a YS-11E, which serves with the Koku Sotai Shireibu Hikotai (Air Defence Headquarters Squadron) at Iruma. The red, yellow and blue flashes represent the JASDF's three Air Defence Forces. The sole YS-11E (EL) is externally very similar.

Above: The Air Development Wing at Gifu incorporates the test pilot training unit, among whose aircraft is this T-33. The Test Pilot Course sign incorporates the intake from an F-104J Starfighter.

Left: Kawasaki converted the 21st C-1 to serve as an ECM training aircraft under the new designation EC-1. Handed over to the Air Proving Wing in January 1985, the aircraft underwent a 100-flight test programme before joining the EW training unit in June 1986. The aircraft carries the indigenous TRDI/Mitsubishi XJ/ALQ-5 ECM system.

Below and below left: Two aircraft used by the Technical Research and Development Institute are this MBB/Kawasaki BK117 and the T-2 modified by Mitsubishi as a CCV testbed (directly below). This aircraft was delivered on 9 August 1983 and underwent a 138-flight test programme by a joint TRDI/Air Proving Wing team between May 1984 and March 1986. Five CCV modes were investigated, including relaxed static stability, direct lift and sideforce control, manoeuvre load control, and control augmentation.

Below: For many years the backbone of the JASDF, the F-104J is now little more than a memory. The last front-line unit, the 207th Hikotai, disbanded during March 1986. The Koku Jikkendan of the Air Development and Test Wing at Gifu was thus the last Japanese Starfighter operator, using the type for training test pilots and for a variety of test and research duties. The unit's fin badge represents a supersonic shock wave and also incorporates a satellite.

Mil Mi-8/14/17
Variant Briefing

The 'Hip' & 'Haze' Family

Backbone of the Warsaw Pact's airmobile assault forces during the Cold War, the basic Mil Mi-8 'Hip' has spawned variants to fulfil every conceivable role, and the family includes the most heavily armed helicopter in the world. Many remain in use all over the globe, continuing to see action in many conflicts.

Above: Wearing Hungary's original Warsaw Pact star insignia, a Mil Mi-8 'Hip-C' clatters along the Danube in Budapest. Hungary remains a major user of the Mil Mi-8 and Mi-17, and has a large maintenance/overhaul centre formerly belonging to the Soviet Union's Southern Group of Forces.

Although official confirmation has not been forthcoming, current estimates indicate that over 10,000 members of the remarkable Mil Mi-8/14/17 family have been built for service all over the world. Despite accusations of obsolescence, new variants keep appearing, and the type remains the backbone of the CIS (USSR) army's helicopter forces. Even today, there are few CIS airfields which do not have at least a small complement of these big helicopters. Had the Cold War ever turned hot, 'Hips' of various types would have spearheaded any Warsaw Pact push, inserting Spetsnaz troops far behind the front line, trucking huge numbers of airborne and other troops, and even attacking NATO tanks and vehicles using the devastating punch of up to 192 unguided 57-mm rocket projectiles, carried in six pods, and up to six guided anti-tank missiles.

And yet, even this does not convey the full story of the versatility of this remarkable helicopter family. As well as armed and unarmed assault helicopters, Mil Mi-8s and -17s would

have performed as airborne command posts, EW platforms and radio relay aircraft, and the dedicated maritime Mil Mi-14's many tasks include sub-hunting, minesweeping and search and rescue. Moreover, the many attributes of the 'Hip' have been demonstrated in active service again and again, in every part of the globe. The 'Hip' can also fulfil many peacetime roles. Virtually every cosmonaut has been recovered by Mil Mi-8s, and 'Hips' have served as crop-sprayers, firefighters, the deliverers of emergency relief, and as air ambulances. Mil Mi-8s can even tow targets on the end of a long horizontal cable, attached to the end of a vertically suspended, weighted cable below the aircraft.

The 'Hip' received its baptism of fire in 1973, when some 100 heavily-armed Mil Mi-8s carried Egyptian commandos across the Suez Canal in one of the most daring and successful helicopter assaults in history. Once landed, the commandos were supported by rocket- and cannon-firing Mil Mi-8s, which also returned to drop bombs and napalm on Israeli forces.

Since then, the 'Hip' has seen active service in Afghanistan against the Mujahideen, in Libya's war with Chad, the long and costly Iran-Iraq conflict, the Ogaden war between Ethiopia and Somalia, and in Angola, Mozambique and Nicaragua. Everywhere it has served, the 'Hip' has won admiration for its ruggedness, simplicity and dependability.

Today, the standard Mil Mi-8 is often thought of as being primitive, under-powered and deficient in range, and by comparison with the very latest Western helicopters such criticisms are fair comment. When judged against its contemporaries, however (few of which remain in use), it is a very different story. When, for example, the British airline BEA evaluated the aircraft, it found it compared very favourably with the Sikorsky S-61, and it was only fears of inadequate spares support which scuttled an order. Other Western operators have been less cautious, and the Mil Mi-8 serves with the Peruvian and Pakistani air forces and with a host of civilian companies from Japan to the USA. When East and

Above: Overall dark sea-grey camouflage and diamond-shaped black, red and gold insignia adorn a Mil Mi-14PL of the East German Volksmarine, water-taxiing near its base at Parow on the Baltic coast.

Below: The Mil Mi-17 is immediately recognisable by the relocation of its tail rotor from starboard to port, and the use of filters in the engine intakes. The latter have only rarely been seen on Mil Mi-8s.

Below: Happy Christmas, Aeroflot style. Aeroflot's fleet retains huge numbers of Mil Mi-8s, some of which have been handed on to the airlines of emerging independent states.

Bottom: KGB Border Guards sprint to their Mil Mi-8 'Hip-C', guard dog in tow. The Border Guards have been a long-standing 'Hip' user, prizing the type's rugged dependability.

West Germany re-unified, most of the former Communist state's Mil Mi-8s were eagerly taken over by the federal Luftwaffe. Service experience in Germany has reportedly won the old workhorse many new admirers.

The Mil Mi-8 began life as a second-generation, turboshaft-powered derivative of, and successor to, the classic Mil Mi-4 'Hound'. Among the many advantages enjoyed by the turboshaft powerplant are a much-improved power-to-weight ratio and the ability to use a wider range of cheaper fuels than traditional piston engines, which run on aviation grade gasoline. Additionally, the small size and compactness of the turboshaft engine allows more flexibility in engine location, in the case of the Mil Mi-8 allowing a position in a streamlined fairing above the cabin, forward of the main rotor hub, which in turn permits a less complex transmission system by comparison with the piston-engined 'Hound', which had its engine in the nose, S-55 fashion.

Comparing the Mil Mi-4 with an early production Mil Mi-8, the later aircraft could seat twice as many passengers (28 rather than 14) while being just under 1247 kg (2,750 lb) heavier and just over 1.2 m (4 ft) longer. The re-location of the engine allowed the cockpit to be moved to the nose, giving a larger, unobstructed cabin. The size of the cabin was clearly a great priority, and nothing was allowed to intrude into it. Thus, the only internal fuel tank is a tiny 371-litre (98-Imp-gal) saddle, behind the main rotor gearbox, which has to be augmented by two permanently carried strap-on tanks on the fuselage sides. These differ in capacity, since the starboard tank (682 litres/150 Imp gal) is shorter than the port (746 litres/164 Imp gal), with a kerosene-burning

heater unit mounted in front of it to supply warm air to the cabin. Extra fuel tanks are often carried in the cabin.

The new cockpit location gave a superb all-round view, which was enhanced by the small size of the two separate instrument panels for captain (in the right-hand seat) and co-pilot, and by the location of many instruments and switches on roof panels. The 'Hip' originally used the same tailboom, tail rotor and main rotor as the Mil Mi-4, although the latter unit was replaced in production aircraft (which appeared in 1964) by a scaled-down version of the Mil Mi-6's remarkable five-bladed rotor.

Engine changes

The first Mil Mi-8 prototype, then designated V-8, featured a single 2,700-shp Soloviev turboshaft engine, and made its first appearance on 3 July 1961 during the annual Tushino air display. This aircraft proved slightly underpowered and in order to remedy this, and to provide greater safety, a switch was made to two less-powerful 1,400-shp Isotov TV2-117 engines in the second prototype, which made its maiden flight on 17 September 1962, and which gained the NATO reporting name 'Hip-B'.

The first production version appeared in 1964 with the five-bladed rotor already mentioned, and with its engines uprated to 1,500 shp and eventually 1,700 shp each. Although famous for its many military roles, the Mil Mi-8 has always had an equally important role as a civilian transport and utility helicopter, and the first variants for the state airline Aeroflot actually preceded the military versions. Similarly, when the aircraft was up-engined with 1,900-shp Isotov TV3-117MTs, the civil Mil Mi-17 appeared

Left: Taxiing at Altenburg, a former World War II Luftwaffe base, is a Mil Mi-8 of the 16th Air Army, the air force of the Soviet Group of Forces in what used to be East Germany. A variety of camouflage schemes are in use.

Above: Armed with rocket pods and (empty) missile launch rails, a pair of Mil Mi-17s (known in the Soviet armed forces as Mi-8TVs) manoeuvres at low level.

Left: A prominent Dayglo fuselage band marks this 'Hip-C' as a SAR aircraft from Kampfhubschraubergeschwader 5 at Basepohl.

Below: An East German 'Hip-F' lets rip with two full cans of 57-mm rockets. The 'Hip-F' could also fire the 'Sagger' anti-tank missile.

Below: Mil Mi-24 'Hind' helicopter gunships hover overhead as a fleet of Mil Mi-8s disgorges squads of troops during a Warsaw Pact exercise. In any war in Europe, this would have been a typical sight.

The Mil Mi-17PP (reportedly nicknamed 'Ping Pong' by its pilots) serves as an ECM jamming platform. The type is identified by huge antenna arrays and underfuselage heat exchangers.

before the military Mil Mi-8M series (the designation Mil Mi-17 should not be applied to military 'Hips').

From the beginning the 'Hip' has featured large clamshell doors at the rear of the cabin, and these can incorporate a built-in airstair. The doors can quickly and easily be removed for activities like parachuting, and hook-on ramps allow light vehicles to be driven aboard. As well as carrying cargo internally, the Mil Mi-8 can lift loads of up to 3000 kg (6,614 lb) using an underslung cargo hook.

Because it was designed to operate under primitive conditions, in all weathers and in all climates, the 'Hip' has a generous array of navigation aids and a four-axis autopilot, providing stabilisation in roll, pitch, yaw and altitude, in normal flight and in the hover. Doppler is often fitted in a box under the tailboom, giving accurate drift and speed information at very low speeds, when the pitot-driven instruments become ineffective. A radio compass, radio altimeter, and even an astro compass (for use in polar regions) are virtually standard equipment. For reliable operation in cold climates the rotor blades are fitted with an ice accretion warning sensor, which can automatically trigger the electro-thermal de-icing system. This also keeps windows and engine intakes clear of ice.

The engine upgrade which resulted in the Mil Mi-17 (and military Mil Mi-8M) revolutionised the 'Hip'. More powerful, the new engines were also much more economical and reliable, and hot and high performance (marginal in some circumstances) was dramatically improved. Cruising

Left: The Mil Mi-14 'Haze' is basically a Mil Mi-17 with a new boat-hulled lower fuselage for amphibious operations. The Mil Mi-14PL is a dedicated ASW aircraft.

speed has been improved by nearly 35 kt (64 km/h; 40 mph), hover ceiling out of ground effect has been more than doubled, and in the event of a single engine failure the remaining engine can produce as much as 2,200 shp. The second-generation 'Hips' incorporate a host of other improvements, including a 'tractor' tail rotor offset to port (instead of a pusher to starboard), a titanium alloy rotor hub, a new gearbox, and various avionics and instrument improvements.

The increased power of the later 'Hip' makes it an even more versatile aircraft than the original, and armed and electronic military variants have already been identified. Scabbed-on armour plating, ECM equipment, chaff and flare dispensers and even large, draggy exhaust suppressors have been added to some military versions of the Mil Mi-17, without an unacceptable degradation of performance.

Although replacement of the Mil Mi-4 in Aeroflot and air force service was initially the top priority, it soon became apparent that the new helicopter could form the basis of an excellent replacement for the many 'Hounds' serving in the land-based ASW and SAR roles with the Soviet navy. In order to improve tactical flexibility it was decided to redesign the lower fuselage of the basic Mil Mi-8 to become a hull suitable for on-the-water operation, with a retractable landing gear and pop-out stabilising floats. Development was protracted, and production has been relatively modest.

Below: East German and Russian Mil Mi-8s accompany Soviet navy hovercraft during an amphibious assault. The firepower and capacious fuselage of the 'Hip' make it a versatile assault/transport tool.

Above: The re-engined Mil Mi-17 is a very much more capable helicopter than its predecessor, with much-enhanced performance and load-carrying capabilities.

Below: An East German Mil Mi-14BT 'Haze-B'. Designed for minesweeping, this Mi-14BT has been converted for SAR duties.

Mil Mi-8/14/17
'Hip' & 'Haze' Variants

The Mil Mi-8 has undergone constant improvements and modifications since it entered production. Derivatives have been produced for a variety of specialised tasks, and even the basic troop transport has been refined and improved. In many cases Design Bureau designations are unknown, as is so often the case with Soviet-built aircraft, and so NATO Air Standards Co-ordinating Committee reporting names are often the only designation known. Where possible we have given both designations for each sub-variant.

Right: A Soviet air force Mil Mi-8, laden with parachutists, kicks up flurries of loose snow as it taxis at Moscow's Tushino airport. The overall dark green colour scheme is typical of many Soviet Mil Mi-8s.

Mil Mi-8 (V-8) 'Hip-A'

The first prototype Mi-8 made its first flight during 1961, and was demonstrated at Tushino on 3 July 1961, and to members of the Soviet government on 25 September 1962. Powered by a single 2,700-shp Ivchenko AI-24V turboshaft, the aircraft featured a four-bladed main rotor (that of the Mil Mi-4) and had distinctive fairings on the main undercarriage units. Other detail differences included the provision of opening doors (with glazed lower panels) on each side of the flight deck. Though the Mi-8 prototype proved an enormous improvement over the Mi-4 that it was designed to replace, it had become clear that a twin-engined helicopter would enjoy important advantages.

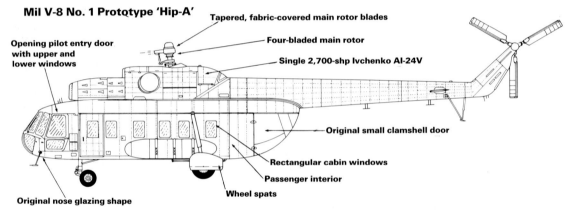

Mil V-8 No. 1 Prototype 'Hip-A'

- Opening pilot entry door with upper and lower windows
- Tapered, fabric-covered main rotor blades
- Four-bladed main rotor
- Single 2,700-shp Ivchenko AI-24V
- Original small clamshell door
- Rectangular cabin windows
- Passenger interior
- Wheel spats
- Original nose glazing shape

Above: The first Mil Mi-8 prototype.

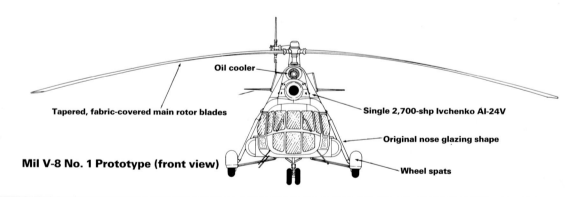

- Oil cooler
- Tapered, fabric-covered main rotor blades
- Single 2,700-shp Ivchenko AI-24V
- Original nose glazing shape
- Wheel spats

Mil V-8 No. 1 Prototype (front view)

Mil Mi-8 (V-?) 'Hip-B'

The second Mi-8 prototype, and subsequent prototypes, were powered by two 1,400-shp Isotov TV2-117 turboshafts, which gave twin-engine safety and provided a useful extra margin of power. The two engines were mounted above the cabin. Although it probably first flew (on 17 September 1962, in the hands of Koloshenko) with a four-bladed rotor (reportedly with constant-chord metal blades in place of the tapered fabric-covered blades fitted

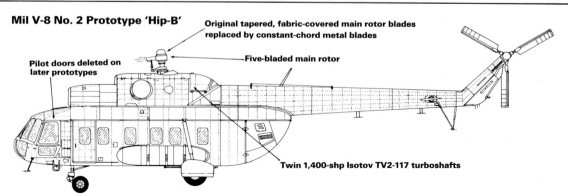

Mil V-8 No. 2 Prototype 'Hip-B'

- Pilot doors deleted on later prototypes
- Original tapered, fabric-covered main rotor blades replaced by constant-chord metal blades
- Five-bladed main rotor
- Twin 1,400-shp Isotov TV2-117 turboshafts

to the V-8), the second prototype was quickly fitted with a five-bladed unit derived from that fitted to the larger Mi-6. The opening doors to the flight deck were also deleted on later prototypes. During flight trials, slightly more powerful 1,500-shp Isotov TV2 turboshafts were installed. With these, the 'Hip' set a speed record of 201 km/h (125 mph) and a distance record of 2464 km (1,532 miles). Early prototypes attended both the 1965 and 1967 Paris air salons, where they were flown by a number of foreign pilots. US test pilots who flew the early aircraft were reportedly astonished by its excellent handling characteristics. The prototypes were configured as passenger/freight utility aircraft, with 24 tip-up seats along the sides of the cabin, and with lashing points on the floor. This basic configuration was seen again in the Mi-8T.

Above: The first twin-engined Mil Mi-8s retained the streamlined wheel spats and pilot entry doors of the V-8.

Right: The twin engines and early nose glazing can clearly be seen in this view of an early Mi-8.

Mil Mi-8P 'Hip-C'

The first production version of the Mil Mi-8, the Mi-8P is a civilian passenger/freight transport, whose seats, bulkheads and passenger amenities can be stripped out to allow freight to be carried. The first examples were delivered to the Azerbaydjan Directorate of Aeroflot during 1967, where they were used to service the oilfields around Baku. Their twin engines and better avionics allowed greater all-weather capability than had been possible with the Mil Mi-4s which

they replaced. The seats are rail mounted, and have armrests, forward-folding backs and tip-up seats. They are usually arranged in seven rows of four, with one pair on each side of the narrow aisle. A lavatory, wardrobe and baggage hold are located aft. Removal of the cupboard allows the installation of another row of four seats. Lightweight luggage racks are provided. Some Mi-8Ps are operated by military users in the transport role.

Right: An early Aeroflot Mi-8P, still with prototype-style wheel spats and an extra window below the co-pilot's sliding window.

Mil Mi-8S (Salon) 'Hip-C'

Designed as a civilian airliner, the Mi-8S is also operated in small numbers by many military users in the VIP role. Externally distinguishable from the standard military 'Hip-C' only by its large rectangular windows, and externally identical to the production Mi-8P, the Mi-8S has between nine and 11 'armchair-style' seats, with tables, and also features a small galley. Six seats are usually ranged along the starboard side of the cabin, facing inwards, with three seats grouped round a table to port. The aircraft has a range of 380 km (236 miles) with 30 minutes' fuel reserves.

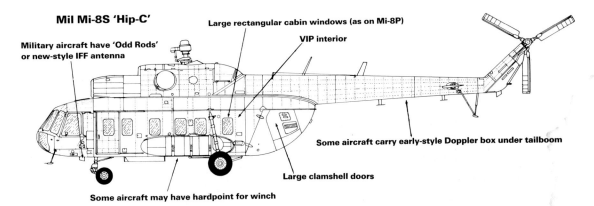

Mil Mi-8S 'Hip-C'
Military aircraft have 'Odd Rods' or new-style IFF antenna
Large rectangular cabin windows (as on Mi-8P)
VIP interior
Some aircraft carry early-style Doppler box under tailboom
Large clamshell doors
Some aircraft may have hardpoint for winch

Left: This East German Mi-8S wears a smart overall glossy-blue colour scheme. The square windows are much larger than the round windows of the Mi-8T.

Above: Many military Mi-8S airframes are used for utility transport duties, and wear the same camouflage as standard Mi-8Ts, like this Czech machine.

Mil Mi-8T 'Hip-C'

The Mi-8T was originally designed as a civil utility transport, and differed from earlier variants in having small round portholes (most of them openable in flight) in place of the original rectangular windows. All seats are rail-mounted, allowing them to be quickly removed for reconfiguration into the cargo or air ambulance roles. In the latter role the Mi-8T (like the Mi-8P) can accommodate 12 stretchers and a number of medical attendants.

A 200-kg (440-lb) winch can be installed inside the Mi-8T to ease the loading of cargo. Initial deliveries were again made to Aeroflot, which used the new variant for passenger, freight and ambulance work, and for patrol and survey duties in the Arctic and Antarctic. For the first time, a 150-kg (331-lb) capacity winch was available above the entry door, making the aircraft suitable for SAR work. Provision was also made for hook-on cargo ramps. There is reportedly a flying-crane version of the Mi-8T, with a glazed gondola in the 'entry hatch' which allows an observer to guide the pilot when moving an underslung load. The aircraft can carry underslung loads of up to 3000 kg (6,614 lb).

The Mi-8T has been built in large numbers for a variety of customers, military and civilian. The military Mi-8T made its first appearance at the Domodedovo Air Display in July 1967. The earliest Mi-8Ts were powered by 1,500-shp engines, but most have the 1,700-shp TV2-117A. Military versions can be fitted with outriggers carrying four pylons (two per side), each of which can carry a UB-16-57 rocket pod (containing 16 S-5 unguided 57-mm rocket projectiles). Many Mi-8Ts have had their outriggers strengthened to carry the larger UB-32-57 pod, or bombs of up to 250 kg (550 lb).

The basic Mi-8T has proved the most widely-built 'Hip', and has been the basis of most of the military versions of this remarkable helicopter.

A number of Mi-8Ts have been locally modified with extra equipment. Egyptian Mi-8s are fitted with British-made dust filters, while Ethiopian and Angolan machines have the PZU filters normally associated with the Mi-17. Finland's Mi-8Ts carry navigation/weather radar in a nose radome, and are also fitted with a powerful searchlight on a small outrigger. Some reports suggest that a handful of Indian Mi-8s was transferred to the Indian Navy, with ASV radar in a nose radome, pending the delivery of British Sea Kings. Mi-8Ts have also served as testbeds. During 1989, for example, one underwent trials with a new fly-by-wire control system and another tested the practicality of propane/butane gas as a fuel. Powered by a pair of 1,500-shp TV2-117TG engines, the aircraft was intended to solve the problems of delivering conventional aviation fuel to remote parts of Siberia, where propane and butane are easily available.

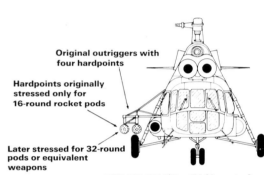

Mil Mi-8T 'Hip-C'

1,700-shp Isotov TV2-117A engines

Small round portholes

Rail-mounted seats

Pilot access doors deleted

'Odd Rods' IFF antenna

Early-style Doppler box sometimes fitted under tailboom

Large production-standard clamshell doors with provision for hook-on cargo ramps

'Odd Rods' IFF antenna

Hardpoint for optional winch

Below: An unarmed Mil Mi-8 'Hip-C' of the East German Luftstreitkräfte und Luftverteidigung der Nationalen Volksarmee. East Germany had two full 'Hip'/'Hind' regiments.

Original outriggers with four hardpoints

Hardpoints originally stressed only for 16-round rocket pods

Later stressed for 32-round pods or equivalent weapons

Mil Mi-8T 'Hip-C' (front view)

Left: A small red, white and green chevron on the tailboom identifies this aircraft as belonging to the Hungarian air force. The new national insignia was adopted after the break-up of the Warsaw Pact. The sliding pilot's windows of the Mil Mi-8 are shown to advantage.

Below: The pilot's station of a Hungarian Mil Mi-8 'Hip-C'. Instrumentation is sparse and entirely conventional, and the pilot and co-pilot enjoy an excellent all-round view. Remaining panels are located on the cabin roof.

Above: The simple yet rugged rotor head of the Mil Mi-8 'Hip-C' allows for simple maintenance.

Above: The distinctive engine exhaust of the standard Mil Mi-8 was re-shaped on the Mi-17.

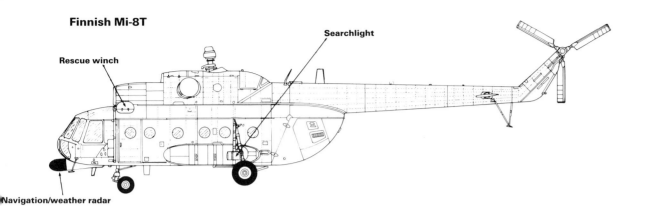

Finnish Mi-8T

Rescue winch

Searchlight

Navigation/weather radar

Egyptian air force Mi-8T

Centrisep dust filters

Some Western avionics

Left: Finland's Mil Mi-8s incorporate various non-standard items of equipment and differ from one another in detail. All have an undernose weather radar, although the mountings vary. Some aircraft also have a pylon-mounted searchlight. Radio antenna fits vary, and at least two aircraft (HS-5 and HS-6) have square windows.

Below: The Egyptian air force has equipped many of its 'Hips' with distinctive squared-off sand filters manufactured by APME (Aircraft Porous Media Equipment) in Britain. These have dramatically increased serviceability and prolonged engine life. Western avionics have also been incorporated.

Right: This is a SAR-configured 'Hip-C' of the East German navy.

Below: An Egyptian 'Hip' as originally delivered. The purpose of the small fittings along the tailboom is unknown.

Another view of an Egyptian air force 'Hip' showing the unidentified fittings along the sides of the tailboom.

Above: The standard rescue winch fitted to early Mil Mi-8s, seen here in the stowed position. This one was on a Hungarian 'Hip-C'.

Mil Mi-8? 'Hip-D'

The CIS air force and Mil designations for this aircraft remain unknown. Distinguished by having rectangular 'canisters' on its Mi-8T-style outriggers, and by extensive antenna arrays above and below the tailboom, the 'Hip-D' is believed to be a communications relay and possibly command and control platform. It is believed that only a handful of 'Hip-Ds' was produced, but it is unknown whether they were newly built or converted from Mi-8Ts.

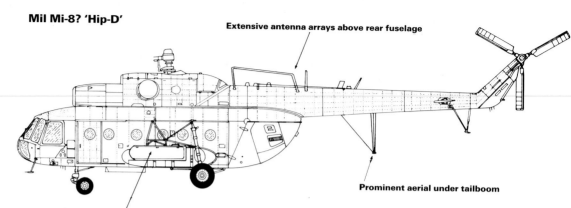

Mil Mi-8? 'Hip-D'

Extensive antenna arrays above rear fuselage

Prominent aerial under tailboom

Outrigger pylons carry unidentified box-like fairings for electronic equipment

Left: 'Hip-Ds' remain in front-line service with the CIS Forces in Germany, where this aircraft was photographed during early 1992. The aircraft is believed to be a communications relay and airborne C³I platform, and has extensive antenna arrays above and below the tailboom, with unusual box fairings on fuselage outriggers.

Mil Mi-8TB 'Hip-E'

The Mi-8TB differs from the standard Mi-8T only in having a flexibly-mounted Afanasayev 12.7-mm machine-gun in the nose, replacing the lowest glazed panel, and in having redesigned outriggers, each capable of carrying up to six rocket pods. They also have provision for the carriage of four 9M17 Falanga (AT-2 'Swatter') radio command line-of-sight guided anti-tank missiles. A gyro-stabilised missile sight is provided for the co-pilot, while the machine-gun in the nose is operated by the flight engineer, who sits on a jump seat between the two pilots. Although a fully armed 'Hip-E' can carry only a handful of troops (14 is thought to be the maximum), it is, in this configuration, the most heavily armed helicopter in the world, with a heavier punch than the dedicated Mi-24.

To improve survivability, some 'Hip-Es' and 'Hip-Cs' have been fitted with scabbed-on armour around the cockpit,

and with various RWRs and IR countermeasures equipment. The latter has included 'hot brick'-type IR jammers and even exhaust diffuser boxes. The latter dramatically increase weight and drag, and are rarely seen outside actual war zones.

Left: Overkill? A Border Guards patrol deplanes from a hovering Mi-8TB. This cannon-armed 'Hip-E' also has three pylons on each outrigger for the carriage of bombs or rockets. 'Overwing' missile launch rails are provided for 'Swatter' anti-tank missiles.

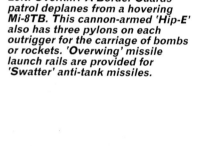

Right: With six 32-round 57-mm rocket pods (192 rockets), and a 12.7-mm machine-gun, the 'Hip-E' packs an impressive punch, even without 'Swatters'.

Mil Mi-8TB 'Hip-E'

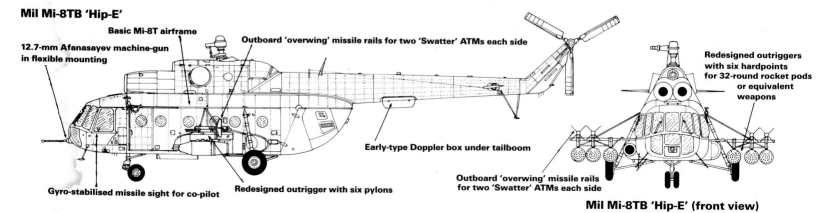

Basic Mi-8T airframe

12.7-mm Afanasayev machine-gun in flexible mounting

Outboard 'overwing' missile rails for two 'Swatter' ATMs each side

Redesigned outriggers with six hardpoints for 32-round rocket pods or equivalent weapons

Early-type Doppler box under tailboom

Gyro-stabilised missile sight for co-pilot

Redesigned outrigger with six pylons

Outboard 'overwing' missile rails for two 'Swatter' ATMs each side

Mil Mi-8TB 'Hip-E' (front view)

Mil Mi-8TBK 'Hip-F'

Before the Mi-8TB and its AT-2 'Swatter' was cleared for export, the former East German air force requested the supply of a similarly armed version. Known officially as the Mi-8TBK, the 'Hip-F' had the same machine-gun and outriggers as the 'Hip-E' but with provision for six of the older 9M14M Malyutka missiles (known to NATO as the AT-3 'Sagger') instead of the four 'Swatters'. The 'Hip-F' made its debut during the Warsaw Pact 'Brotherhood in Arms' exercise of 1980. East Germany seems to have been the only operator of the type, both with the LSK/LV and the navy. Some reports suggest that Yugoslav Mi-8s may have been locally modified to fire the AT-3, which is used by that nation's Gazelle light helicopters.

East Germany, denied the opportunity of obtaining 'Swatter'-armed 'Hips', did the next best thing and took delivery of gun-armed, six-pylon 'Hips' modified to carry six 'Sagger' ATGMs.

Mil Mi-8TBK 'Hip-F'

12.7-mm Afanasayev machine-gun in flexible mounting

Outboard 'overwing' missile rails for three 'Sagger' ATMs each side

No Doppler box

Basic Mi-8T airframe

Redesigned outrigger with six pylons

May have gyro-stabilised missile sight for co-pilot

Outboard 'overwing' missile rails for three 'Sagger' ATMs each side

12.7-mm Afanasayev machine-gun in flexible mounting

Mil Mi-8TBK 'Hip-F' (front view)

Left: The East German armed 'Hips' were designated Mil Mi-8TBK, and assigned the reporting name 'Hip-F'. The Volksmarine took delivery of a handful, painting them dark blue overall. Some former East German 'Hip-Fs' transferred to the Luftwaffe after re-unification.

Mil Mi-9 'Hip-G'

The 'Hip-G' is externally distinguished from a standard Mi-8T by having three 'hockey stick' antennas projecting from the rear of the cabin and from the tailboom. It is believed to be the airborne command post and radio relay platform which replaced the older 'Hip-D'. East Germany, at least, received a handful of these little-known aircraft, and others serve with the CIS air forces in what used to be East Germany, and with the Czech and Slovak air forces.

Mil Mi-9 'Hip-G'

Centre two and rearmost windows effectively obscured by internal equipment

Three 'hockey-stick' antennas under fuselage and tailboom

Underfuselage strakes

Left: Czechoslovakia reportedly operates two airborne command post Mi-9 'Hip-Gs'.

Below left: Equipment in the cabin of the Mi-9 effectively blocks several windows. The other recognition feature of the 'Hip-G' is the three 'hockey stick' antennas under the tailboom and fuselage.

Below: Although former-East German Mi-9s have been transferred to the Luftwaffe, they have been stripped of their mission equipment and operate as utility transports. It is believed that command post Mi-9s have sealed rear-loading clamshell doors.

Mil Mi-17/Mil Mi-8M/TV 'Hip-H'

The Mi-17 made its first flight during 1976, and was revealed to the West at the 1981 Paris air show at Le Bourget. Basically a re-engined, updated Mi-8T, the Mi-17 is powered by a pair of 1,950-shp Isotov TV3-117MT engines, and can be externally identified by the large PZU filters fitted to the intakes and by the relocation of the tail rotor from port to starboard (it rotates in the opposite direction, becoming a tractor, rather than a pusher). In the event of an engine failure, the surviving engine can produce 2,200 shp. Less noticeable externally are a new titanium alloy rotor hub and an all-new gearbox. Maximum underslung and internal loads remain, respectively, 3000 and 4000 kg (6,614 and 8,818 lb), but flight performance is greatly enhanced (cruising speed being increased by 60 km/h; 37 mph, hover ceiling out of ground effect more than doubling), and maximum take-off weight rises from 10000 to 13000 kg (22,046 to 28,660 lb). Fuel consumption is also significantly reduced.

The designation Mi-17 is not used by the CIS air force, which refers to its 'Hip-Hs' officially as Mi-8Ms, Mi-8MTs or Mi-8TVs. Export customers generally use the Mi-17 designation. The operational 'Hip-H' is often fitted with cockpit armour, IR jammer, chaff flare dispensers, 'Slap Shot' IFF and even the bulky EVU exhaust gas diffusers intended to defeat the IR-guided SAM threat, and used operationally in Afghanistan. The Mi-17 carries the same 'six-pylon' outrigger as the Mi-8TB 'Hip-E' and it has been reported that some Mi-17s have been seen with a nose-mounted cannon. This latter report is, however, open to doubt.

Mil Mi-17 'Hip-H'

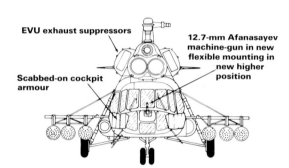

New gearbox · PZU dust filters in intakes · Titanium rotor hub · Twin 1,950-shp Isotov TV3-117MT engines · Tail rotor on port side of boom · Strap-on chaff/flare dispenser · New-style Doppler box

Mil Mi-8TV 'Hip-H' (front view)

EVU exhaust suppressors · 12.7-mm Afanasayev machine-gun in new flexible mounting in new higher position · Scabbed-on cockpit armour

Mil Mi-8TV 'Hip-H'

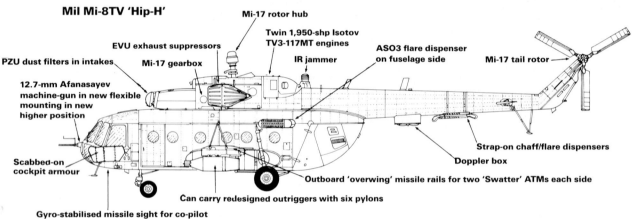

EVU exhaust suppressors · Mi-17 rotor hub · Twin 1,950-shp Isotov TV3-117MT engines · ASO3 flare dispenser on fuselage side · Mi-17 tail rotor · PZU dust filters in intakes · Mi-17 gearbox · IR jammer · 12.7-mm Afanasayev machine-gun in new flexible mounting in new higher position · Scabbed-on cockpit armour · Gyro-stabilised missile sight for co-pilot · Can carry redesigned outriggers with six pylons · Outboard 'overwing' missile rails for two 'Swatter' ATMs each side · Doppler box · Strap-on chaff/flare dispensers

A CIS Mi-8TV in virtually full operational configuration. The only things missing from this military Mil Mi-17 are the prominent exhaust suppressors often fitted in Afghanistan, and the nose-mounted cannon which has sometimes been seen on Soviet Mi-17s. An extra strap-on flare dispenser pack could be carried below the tailboom.

Right: A close-up view of the same CIS 'Hip-H' shows to advantage the scabbed-on armour around the cockpit. Also noteworthy is the triple pack of chaff/flare dispensers mounted on the sides of the rear cabin, just above window level.

Above: Three outrigger configurations commonly seen on Mi-8s and Mi-17s. The top aircraft has two pylons mounted on a tubular support structure which could accommodate three pylons (see bottom picture). The centre aircraft has two pylons, with a guard to prevent parachutes snagging the pylons. None has missile launch rails.

Above: The high-capacity rescue winch fitted to late 'Hips'.

Above left: A gun camera can be fitted close in to the cabin.

Left: Auxiliary fuel tanks, each containing 714 kg, can be carried inside the cabin to extend range. The Mil Mi-17 carries 345 kg in its main tank, and 577 and 527 kg in the port and starboard strap-on tanks.

Mil Mi-17-1 'Hip-H'

As a result of work by the Ulan Ude Aviation Industrial Association to improve the Mi-8 and Mi-17, a new 'Hip' variant emerged in the late 1980s. Designated Mi-171 or Mi-17-1, the new type was powered by two 'high-altitude' 1,900-hp TV2-117VM engines. These allowed the aircraft to carry up to 4000 kg (8,818 lb) of cargo at altitudes of 5000 m (16,404 ft). An 8A-813 airborne weather radar is fitted in a 'chin' radome, and other equipment includes an A-723 long-range navigation system, a Diss-32-90 Doppler, a DAC-DC remote reading star tracker, and a BUV-8A hover control unit. An example was displayed at Redhill's 1990 Helitech exhibition.

Right: The Mil Mi-17-1 which visited Redhill has a weather radar in a chin radome and an improved avionics fit. It wore Aeroflot colours.

Above: The interior of the Mi-17-1, with airline-style forward-facing seats instead of the inward-facing seats of the 'Hip-C'.

Mil Mi-17-1BA 'Hip-H'

Revealed at the Helitech meeting at Redhill, and later demonstrated at the 1989 Paris air salon, the Mi-17-1BA is much more than an air ambulance. More accurately described as a flying hospital, the aircraft has an adjustable operating

table, two recovery bunks, life support equipment and surgical-standard lighting. Two generators and further medical equipment are mounted in the clamshell doors. Produced as a joint venture between Mil and three Hungarian companies, the Mi-17-1BA demonstrator was reportedly used during the Armenian earthquake. Theoretically capable of supporting surgery in flight, it is designed to fly to a disaster area and to act as a ground-based operating theatre.

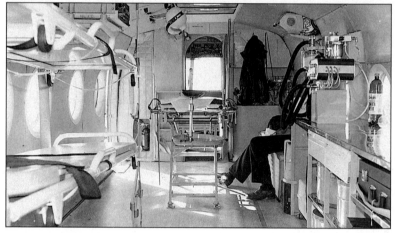

Above right: Externally, the Mi-17-1BA, previewed at Redhill in 1989, looks like a standard 'Hip-H'.

Right: The cabin interior of the Mi-17-1BA is a comprehensively-equipped operating theatre. The normal procedure is for the aircraft to fly to where it is needed, and for operations to be conducted on the ground.

Left: The Mi-17-1BA is optimised for operation in areas where the normal medical infrastructure has been destroyed or dislocated by natural disaster.

Mil Mi-8? 'Hip-J'

No air force or design bureau designation is known for this aircraft, believed to be a radar jamming and ECM platform. A handful may have been converted for, or operated in, the Elint role along the inner German border. Certainly the variant was encountered more often along the border, and over Berlin, than its relatively small numbers would have indicated. The 'Hip-J' was virtually identical to the Mi-8T in external appearance, though with small box-like antennas on the fuselage sides. Outriggers, however, have seldom been noted.

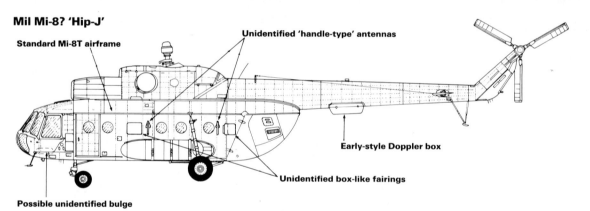

Mil Mi-8? 'Hip-J'

Standard Mi-8T airframe

Unidentified 'handle-type' antennas

Early-style Doppler box

Unidentified box-like fairings

Possible unidentified bulge

Right: This is still the only released picture of 'Hip-J', whose CIS designation remains unknown. The aircraft's recognition features are two small box-type fairings on the cabin sides, together with a number of antennas. Details of the role, equipment fit and deployment of this helicopter remain unknown, although reports indicate that this sub-variant was often seen operating along the old inner German border.

Mil Mi-8P (Mi-8PPA?) 'Hip-K'

Like the 'Hip-J', the 'Hip-K' first appeared in Europe during the early 1980s. Almost certainly tasked with communications jamming (and possibly Elint) the 'Hip-K' carries six cross-dipole antennas on both sides of the rear fuselage and forward part of the tailboom. A large square box projects from the sides of the cabin (immediately below the exhaust) and may be some kind of antenna fairing. Below the fuselage six heat exchangers are mounted side-by-side in a row. A handful has been exported, and Czechoslovakia is one recipient of the type. Czech sources suggest that the designation Mi-8PPA is the correct one.

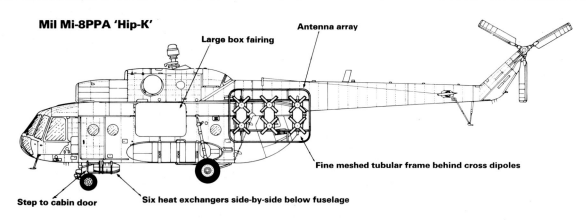

Mil Mi-8PPA 'Hip-K'

Large box fairing

Antenna array

Fine meshed tubular frame behind cross dipoles

Step to cabin door

Six heat exchangers side-by-side below fuselage

Below: A close-up view reveals the cross-dipole antennas fitted to 'Hip-K'. The framework is covered by a fine square mesh.

Above: Czechoslovakia operates a pair of Mil Mi-8PPAs, and is the only known foreign user of this unusual variant.

Mil Mi-17P (Mi-17PP?) 'Hip-K'

The NATO codename for this derivative of the 'Hip-K' remains unknown. Essentially similar to the 'Hip-K' this aircraft is, however, based on the airframe and transmission of the Mi-17. Retaining the same row of heat exchangers and fuselage 'boxes' as the original 'Hip-K', the cross-dipole antennas are replaced by two arrays on each side of the rear fuselage/tailboom intersection, which seem to consist of circular aerials within a slightly concave square fairing. The larger fairing, on the rear fuselage, contains 32 cylinders (in four horizontal rows of eight), with four cylinders in the smaller fairing on the tailboom. At least two of these machines have been delivered to Hungary.

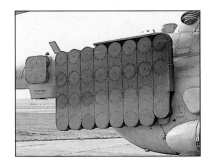

Above: This close-up view concentrates on the antenna arrays fitted to the rear part of the cabin and tailboom of the 'Hip-K2'.

Right: Hungarian ground crew prepare a Mi-17PP for flight. Two of these aircraft serve at Szentkir'alyszabadja.

Mil Mi-17PPA? 'Hip-K2'? (rear view)

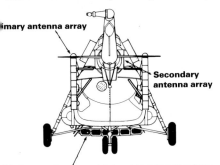

Primary antenna array

Secondary antenna array

Six heat exchangers side-by-side below fuselage

Mil Mi-17PPA? 'Hip-K2'?

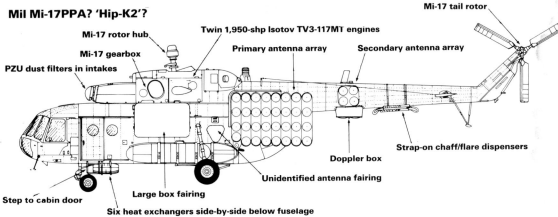

Mi-17 tail rotor

Twin 1,950-shp Isotov TV3-117MT engines

Mi-17 rotor hub

Mi-17 gearbox

Primary antenna array

Secondary antenna array

PZU dust filters in intakes

Strap-on chaff/flare dispensers

Doppler box

Unidentified antenna fairing

Step to cabin door

Large box fairing

Six heat exchangers side-by-side below fuselage

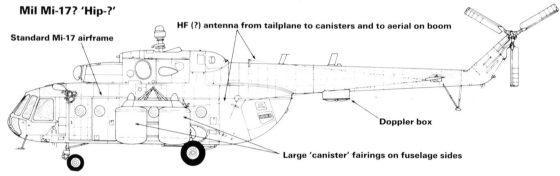

Mil Mi-17? 'Hip-?'

The Czech and Slovak air force is something of a repository for unusual 'Hip' variants, with two Mi-8PPA 'Hip-Ks' on strength, along with at least one Mi-9 'Hip-G' and two hitherto unidentified Mi-17 sub-variants. These carry four huge 'drum'-like canisters mounted in fore and aft pairs beside the cabin, and clearly serve some electronic function. Elint, EW or even AEW are possible roles for this unusual-looking variant, which may be exclusive to Czechoslovakia.

Below: Czechoslovakia uses this unusual and so far unidentified 'Hip' variant. The tandem canister fairings contain some kind of electronic equipment or antenna.

Above: This variant is clearly based on the airframe of the Mil Mi-17 'Hip-H', but no CIS, Czech or NATO designations are known. Two of these aircraft are believed to be in use. Both wear standard camouflage and have large areas of yellow paint on the nose and tailboom.

Large 'canister' fairings on fuselage sides

Mil Mi-17? 'Hip-?' (front view)

Mil Mi-17? 'Hip-?'

Standard Mi-17 airframe

HF (?) antenna from tailplane to canisters and to aerial on boom

Doppler box

Large 'canister' fairings on fuselage sides

Mil Mi-14/V-14 'Haze-A'

Converting the 'Hip' into a maritime helicopter proved far from straightforward, and the programme, begun in 1968, did not yield a flying prototype until 1973. The prototype was basically an Mi-8, with a new lower fuselage incorporating an amphibious 'boat' hull and retractable undercarriage. Pop-out flotation gear was provided, and some operational equipment was fitted.

Mil V-14 'Haze-A'

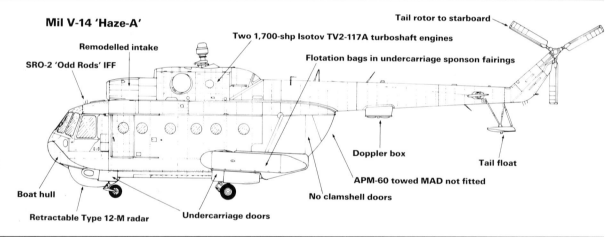

Remodelled intake

SRO-2 'Odd Rods' IFF

Two 1,700-shp Isotov TV2-117A turboshaft engines

Tail rotor to starboard

Flotation bags in undercarriage sponson fairings

Doppler box

Tail float

Boat hull

Retractable Type 12-M radar

Undercarriage doors

No clamshell doors

APM-60 towed MAD not fitted

Mil Mi-14PL 'Haze-A'

The first production Mil Mi-14s retained the same starboard-mounted tail rotor as the prototype, and were powered by the TV2-117 engine. They also retained undercarriage doors for the retractable undercarriage units. From 1982, however, the undercarriage doors were deleted, the weapons bay doors were relocated, and the tail rotor was moved to the port side of the tailfin when the TV3-117 engine was adopted. Naval ASW helicopters spend a disproportionate amount of time in the hover, or flying at very slow speeds. The new, more-powerful engine was adopted because of the need for precise control in the hover and at low speeds (for example when dipping sonar) and to give greater safety margins when in the hover.

A standard production Soviet navy Mil Mi-14 'Haze-A'. Early production aircraft had the tail rotor to port and had a fully-retractable undercarriage with doors.

Mil Mi-14PL 'Haze-A' (early)

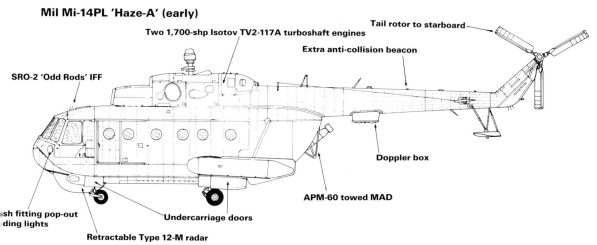

- Two 1,700-shp Isotov TV2-117A turboshaft engines
- Tail rotor to starboard
- Extra anti-collision beacon
- SRO-2 'Odd Rods' IFF
- Doppler box
- APM-60 towed MAD
- sh fitting pop-out ding lights
- Undercarriage doors
- Retractable Type 12-M radar

Above: AV-MF fliers brief in front of their late production 'Haze-A'. The 'Haze' replaced ageing radar-equipped Mil Mi-4 'Hounds' and marked a tremendous rise in ASW capability. Operations are usually conducted from shore bases, since 'Haze' is too large to deploy on most Soviet navy warships.

Mil Mi-14PL 'Haze-A' (late)

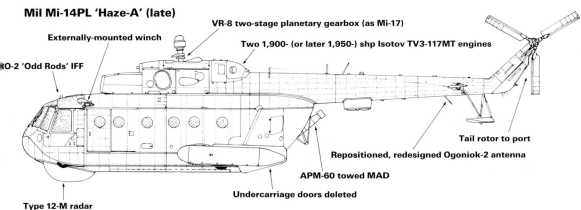

- Externally-mounted winch
- VR-8 two-stage planetary gearbox (as Mi-17)
- Two 1,900- (or later 1,950-) shp Isotov TV3-117MT engines
- O-2 'Odd Rods' IFF
- Tail rotor to port
- Repositioned, redesigned Ogoniok-2 antenna
- APM-60 towed MAD
- Type 12-M radar
- Undercarriage doors deleted

Below: The Mil Mi-14PL has been exported to a number of nations, including East Germany, one of whose 'Haze-As' is seen below. Other operators include Libya, Poland and Yugoslavia.

Mil Mi-14PL 'Haze-A' (underside)

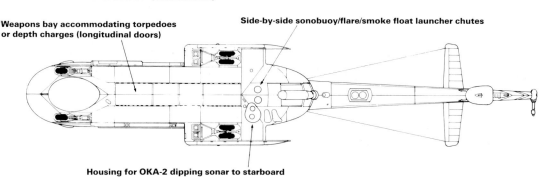

- Weapons bay accommodating torpedoes or depth charges (longitudinal doors)
- Side-by-side sonobuoy/flare/smoke float launcher chutes
- Housing for OKA-2 dipping sonar to starboard

Mil Mi-14PLM 'Haze-A'

Revealed publicly at the 1989 Moscow air show, the Mil Mi-14PLM incorporates a host of minor improvements. Most visible externally is the lower position of the APM-60 magnetic anomaly detector housing. The new sub-type also featured a new 'Parol' or 'Chrom Nickel' IFF system. None is believed to have been exported.

Left: The Mil Mi-14PLM can be identified by the lowered position of its APM-60 magnetic anomaly detector (MAD) bird.

Mil Mi-14PLM 'Haze-A'

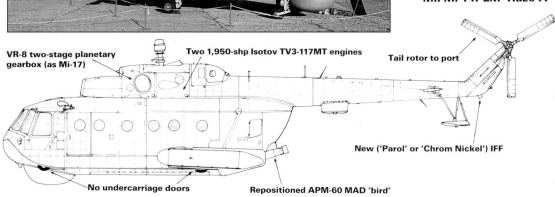

- VR-8 two-stage planetary gearbox (as Mi-17)
- Two 1,950-shp Isotov TV3-117MT engines
- Tail rotor to port
- No undercarriage doors
- Repositioned APM-60 MAD 'bird'
- New ('Parol' or 'Chrom Nickel') IFF

Mil Mi-14BT 'Haze-B'

With the success of the Mil Mi-14PL in the ASW role, and encouraged (if not inspired) by US use of dedicated mine-sweeping helicopters, it became apparent that the new helicopter would also make an ideal mine countermeasures platform, and extensive tests were carried out at Feodosia in the Crimea during 1982 and 1983 . These proved successful and the first Mil Mi-14BTs were deployed aboard Soviet ships participating in multi-national mine-clearing operations during the early 1980s. Operationally, the Mil Mi-14BT (the suffix letters standing for Buksirtralschchik, or 'towing minesweeper'), towed a mine-activating sled behind it while flying at altitudes between 15 and 20 m (50 and 65 ft).

At least three different types of sled can be towed by the Mil Mi-14BT, each optimised for dealing with a different type of mine. For use against magnetic mines, triggered by the close proximity of a large metallic object, an electromagnetic sled is used, towing a system of electric cables. Acoustic mines can be triggered using a noise-generating sled, which incorporates a suitable propeller to exactly simulate the noise made by a target ship. Finally, against contact mines, the sled tows a series of small detonators.

Easily distinguished from the Mil Mi-14PL by its lack of a towed MAD, and by the relocation of the SKW heating and ventilation system from the cabin to a streamlined pod on the starboard side of the fuselage, the aircraft also has a broad strake running back along the starboard side of the fuselage, above the waterline. The aircraft retains the same pilot/co-pilot/flight engineer flight deck crew as the Mil Mi-14PL, but replaces the ASW systems operator with an MCM operator. Used in small numbers (25 are thought to have been delivered) by the CIS navy, the type was also exported to Poland, which is understood to have received four, and to former East Germany, which took delivery of six, along with Mil Mi-14PLs. East German 'Haze-Bs' were converted to SAR duties shortly before re-unification, and as such had their MCM equipment removed. Some Mil Mi-14BTs, at least, had small windows in the extreme rear fuselage, reportedly fitted to allow the MCM operator to watch his sled.

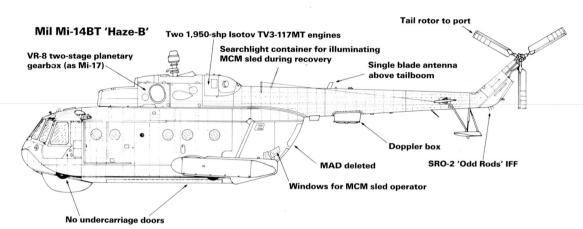

Mil Mi-14BT 'Haze-B'

VR-8 two-stage planetary gearbox (as Mi-17)

Two 1,950-shp Isotov TV3-117MT engines

Searchlight container for illuminating MCM sled during recovery

Tail rotor to port

Single blade antenna above tailboom

Doppler box

SRO-2 'Odd Rods' IFF

MAD deleted

Windows for MCM sled operator

No undercarriage doors

Right: The Mil Mi-14BT featured an SKW heating and ventilation system relocated to a small pod on the starboard fuselage side, just above window level. A cable duct runs along the starboard side lower down, between the windows and undercarriage sponson.

Below: Several East German Mil Mi-14BTs were converted for ASW duties, with mine-clearing equipment deleted and a SAR colour scheme. Windows in the bottom part of the rear fuselage allow an MCM operator to watch his sled.

Mil Mi-14PS 'Haze-C'

Based on the airframe of the Mil Mi-14BT, and with the same fuselage strake and air conditioning/heat-exchanger pod, the Mil Mi-14PS was designed as a general-purpose maritime helicopter, biased heavily towards the SAR role. Thus the 'Haze-C' has a much wider cabin door, with a winch fitted as standard, and more generous provision of searchlights. Equipment fits vary, and some CIS Mil Mi-14PSs are used in the photographic role, with a vertical survey camera mounted in a fairing below the tailboom.

Right: The widened cabin door of the Mil Mi-14PS is the type's main recognition feature.

Above: The Mil Mi-14PS is a dedicated SAR version of the 'Haze', which retains the external heater and cable duct of the Mi-14BT. A Polish aircraft is seen here.

Mil Mi-14PS 'Haze-C'

VR-8 two-stage planetary gearbox (as Mi-17)

Widened cabin entry door

Two 1,950-shp Isotov TV3-117MT engines

Twin blade antennas above tailboom

Tail rotor to port

Doppler box

MAD deleted

SRO-2 'Odd Rods' IFF on export aircraft, 'Parol' or 'Chrom Nickel' IFF on Soviet

Increased capacity winch swings out from inside cabin

Pop-out articulated searchlights in raised fairing

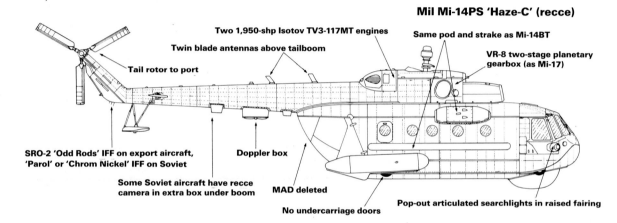

Mil Mi-14PS 'Haze-C' (mod)

Extra light (downwards- and forwards-shining) in nose 'beak'

No undercarriage doors

Widened cabin entry door

Mil Mi-14PS 'Haze-C' (recce)

Two 1,950-shp Isotov TV3-117MT engines

Twin blade antennas above tailboom

Tail rotor to port

Same pod and strake as Mi-14BT

VR-8 two-stage planetary gearbox (as Mi-17)

SRO-2 'Odd Rods' IFF on export aircraft, 'Parol' or 'Chrom Nickel' IFF on Soviet

Doppler box

Some Soviet aircraft have recce camera in extra box under boom

MAD deleted

No undercarriage doors

Pop-out articulated searchlights in raised fairing

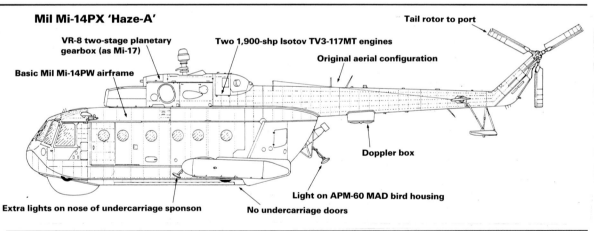

Mil Mi-14PX 'Haze-A'

Poland's No. 40 Squadron uses a single aircraft (1003) for training Mil Mi-14PS aircrew and swimmers. A converted Mi-14PW (as Polish Mi-14PLs are believed to be designated), the aircraft lacks much of the equipment fitted to the Mi-14PS. It is supplied with extra lights on the noses of the undercarriage sponsons and on the APM-60 MAD bird housing.

Mil Mi-14PX 'Haze-A'

VR-8 two-stage planetary gearbox (as Mi-17)

Basic Mil Mi-14PW airframe

Two 1,900-shp Isotov TV3-117MT engines

Tail rotor to port

Original aerial configuration

Doppler box

Extra lights on nose of undercarriage sponson

Light on APM-60 MAD bird housing

No undercarriage doors

Right: Almost certainly a one-off, the Mi-14PX is a converted Mi-14PL used for training SAR aircrew. As such it is fitted with extra searchlights below the tailboom and on the fronts of the undercarriage sponsons. The designation Mi-14PX is a Polish air force designation for what is a local conversion. They also refer to their Mi-14PLs as Mi-14PWs.

Pakistan Border Battles

Between May 1986 and November 1988, the PAF shot down at least eight intruders from Afghanistan, all with the General Dynamics F-16. The first three victims all fell to No. 9 Squadron, the first PAF unit to form on the type.

Since its creation in 1947 the Moslem state of Pakistan has viewed India as the principal threat, and has gone to war several times with its large and powerful neighbour. However, the Soviet invasion of Afghanistan in 1979 forced the nation to turn its attentions westwards, where Soviet and Afghan forces threatened close to the border. Inevitably, aircraft strayed into Pakistani airspace.

The Soviet invasion of Afghanistan in 1979 marked the start of an occupation that was to last for a decade. Throughout this period, Mujahideen rebels continued to harass military forces of the occupying power as well as the Afghan regime that it was supporting, and there is little doubt that heavy casualties were sustained by both sides. In neighbouring Pakistan, the impact of the 1979-89 Afghan War was almost equally far-reaching, for this country was very quickly flooded by hordes of refugees anxious to escape the conflict. In addition, the fact that many of the rebels used Pakistan as a sanctuary from which to stage forays into Afghanistan inevitably resulted in border violations by Soviet and Afghan aircraft that were engaged on 'search and destroy' missions.

For the Pakistan Air Force (PAF) in particular this posed a difficult problem, since it was directly responsible for ensuring the security of national airspace at a time when it was most definitely not at war, but was also far from being at peace. Nowhere was the pressure felt more keenly than at Peshawar, which merited the status of being a 'front-line' base for much of the

time by virtue of its proximity to the Afghan border, which lay barely 15 miles (24 km) – and only a couple of minutes flying time – away. As the ground battles ebbed and flowed on the far side of the border, so too did the amount of corresponding activity at Peshawar, which kept its resident fighter squadrons at various states of readiness throughout the 10 years in question.

At periods of peak alertness, standing combat air patrols (CAPs) were maintained from Peshawar. The slightly lower state of cockpit readiness was also implemented, in addition to many instances of 'hot scrambles' leading to identification passes. However, since the rules of engagement that were in force included stipulations that wreckage must fall inside Pakistan and that only fighter aircraft could be attacked, Peshawar-based units were never actually given clearance to fire. This, of course, gave rise to considerable frustration, an emotion that must have been keenly felt by one pilot who managed to get a transport aircraft in his sights. On requesting clearance to engage, he was denied the chance to open fire by higher authorities, a decision which left him feeling "rather upset", according to a

Pakistan Border Battles

No. 14 Squadron 'Shaheens' scored Pakistan's last five kills, beginning on 16 April 1987.

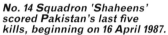

they seldom knew precisely where they were. That, of course, did not in any way lessen the danger, for a bombing or strafing attack is quite as lethal to anyone on the receiving end regardless of intent and irrespective of on which side of the border it occurs. The PAF continued its regime of fatiguing CAPs and scrambles over seven long and fruitless years, for it was not until 1986 that it claimed its first victim.

Throughout those seven years, fighters like the Shenyang F-6 and Mirage rose in hot pursuit on countless occasions, but it was to be a type which was not even in PAF service when these incidents began that would prove its worth in combat. This was the F-16 Fighting Falcon, a type that entered the PAF inventory in January 1983. In anticipation of that eagerly awaited moment, half a dozen pilots and close to 90 technicians had undergone training in the USA during 1982, with aircrew transition being undertaken at Hill AFB, Utah, by the 388th Tactical Fighter Wing's 421st Tactical Fighter Squadron.

Falcons to Pakistan

On completion of pilot conversion, an initial batch of two single-seat F-16As and four two-seat F-16Bs was ferried to Pakistan, this delivery flight beginning at Fort Worth, Texas. Staging via MacDill AFB, Florida, and Lajes in the Azores, they reached Dhahran, Saudi Arabia, where they were officially handed over. From there they were flown to Pakistan by PAF personnel, including Wing Commander Shahid Javed, who was to lead the first unit to equip, No. 11 Squadron at Sargodha.

Subsequent deliveries took the same route and all 40 of the Fighting Falcons – 28 F-16As and 12 F-16Bs – had entered the PAF by mid-1986, permitting two more squadrons to be established. The first was No. 9, which converted in 1984 at Sargodha. It was followed in 1986 by No. 14, which also underwent the conversion process at Sargodha, moving to its operational base at Kamra in October of that year. Today, all three squadrons continue to fly the F-16, with No. 11 having an important additional duty, in that it also functions as an operational conversion unit.

In PAF service, attrition has so far been light, with just two F-16As and one F-16B having been lost, but plans to obtain another 71 Fighting Falcons (60 F-16As and 11 F-16Bs) at a rate of 15 aircraft per year from 1992 onwards now seem unlikely to be realised. The reason behind that is US unhappiness over Pakistan's nuclear policy, which has resulted in the decision to suspend

Even during a high state of tension, the overriding safety factor cannot be ignored, as this sign at Kamra constantly reminds the fliers of No. 14 Squadron.

FMS (Foreign Military Sales) assistance.

In the 1979-89 Afghan War, the F-16 was the only PAF fighter to achieve any success in air combat, five pilots being responsible for seven confirmed 'kills' and one probable 'kill' between May 1986 and November 1988. The first three of those victims (one Su-22, one probable Su-22 and one An-26) fell to two pilots from No. 9 Squadron. No. 14 Squadron wasn't slow in scoring its first success, either, and eventually went

With an armed guard, an F-16 stands alert at Kamra, with a full air defence load-out. Attention to detail minimises the reaction time, including the pre-positioning of cockpit ladder and the removal of safety pins and covers.

on to outdo No. 9 by accounting for the remaining five downed aircraft (two Su-22s, two MiG-23s and one Su-25). In most cases, it was the AIM-9 Sidewinder that was responsible, but at least one Su-22 was engaged by cannon fire.

A number of other incidents are also reported to have taken place, including one on 29 April 1987 when a PAF F-16 allegedly scored a 'kill' in an encounter between two Fighting Falcons and six Afghan Air Force aircraft near Miranshah. However, it appears possible that the victim on this occasion was actually an F-16 'own goal', which fell foul of a missile fired by the leader, although the unfortunate pilot evidently ejected safely. Later reports mentioned an unidentified aircraft being shot down to the west of Peshawar on 20 November 1988 and an 'An-26' which was engaged and crashed near Parachinar with 34 fatalities on 21 November 1988. These two in-

Base Commander, Air Commodore Jamal Hussein.

In discussing that period, the Air Commodore remarked that it was indeed very trying. There was a lot of flying but the minimal reaction time meant that much of the effort – at least as far as Peshawar was concerned – was wasted, since the 'enemy' aircraft very quickly withdrew to the safety of Afghanistan when they became aware that PAF fighters were in the locale. At the time, Air Commodore Jamal Hussein felt a strong sense of futility but, with the benefit of hindsight, his attitude has shifted and he now acknowledges that it provided excellent training value and allowed the PAF to refine and polish its air defence network. No less significantly, it also gave new pilots the opportunity to experience some of the pressures of combat, while being spared much of the attendant risk.

As to the border violations themselves, the PAF assessment is that most were accidental, with Afghan and Soviet aircraft usually operating under strict control from the ground and carrying little in the way of maps and nothing in the way of ground-mapping radar. As a result,

A piece of wreckage from an Afghan air force Sukhoi Su-22 commemorates the first PAF kill, scored by Squadron Leader Hameed Qadri.

cidents were probably one and the same but no mention was made of this during conversation with PAF aircrew in 1991, so it appears unlikely that the PAF was responsible.

No. 9 Squadron's war record

After years of frustration chasing ever-elusive intruding aircraft, Squadron Leader Hameed Qadri finally succeeded in catching up with a pair which lingered just a little too long in the vicinity of Parachinar on 17 May 1986. Precise details of this engagement are not available, but it appears that there is every possibility that Qadri secured a double 'kill'. Of the two Su-22s he attacked, one eventually fell to earth some nine miles (14.5 km) inside Pakistani territory; subsequent analysis of the wreckage revealed the presence of AIM-9L fragments in the empennage, confirming that it was indeed one of Qadri's victims. Today, a fragment of this aircraft displaying an Afghan roundel stands adjacent to one of the Sargodha flight lines. The badly-damaged second Su-22 managed to regain Afghan airspace, although it was apparently on fire and may well have crashed subsequently. Consensus has it that Qadri engaged this machine with gunfire, but in the absence of wreckage it really merits only a 'probable'.

No. 9 Squadron's other successful encounter came on 30 March 1987 when Wing Commander Abdul Razzaq downed an An-26 that may have been on a 'ferret' mission to gather electronic intelligence. Unfortunately, details of the circum-

stances surrounding this incident and the weaponry that was employed are not available.

No. 14 Squadron's war record

Rather more details are available on No. 14's successes in the air combat arena, source material including HUD film and personal interviews with some of the individuals involved. The distinction of opening No. 14's account was claimed by Squadron Leader Badar who destroyed one Su-22 on 16 April 1987. There are reports that this Su-22 had been active strafing villages in Pakistan before it was shot down. The following account is based on HUD film and voice transmissions between GCI (Ground Control Intercept), Badar and his wingman, but it is not known whether this was a standing CAP or a 'hot' scramble mission.

The encounter opens with Badar, who is lead, cruising at about 450 kt at an altitude of 11,000 ft (3353 m) on a heading of 240°. He is advised by GCI that a border violation has occurred and that there are multiple targets almost directly ahead. Badar maintains altitude and heading and is reminded by his wingman of the need to undertake arming procedures. Badar completes the necessary drill and acknowledges that he has done so to his wingman. Moments later GCI informs him that there are four enemy aircraft at a 22-mile (35.4-km) range.

Badar is initially unable to make radar contact but his wingman very quickly reports contact with two 'bogies' at a height of 32,000 ft (9754 m) and a range of 23 miles (37 km). At this point, the pair of F-16s takes up a heading of 270° and Badar then succeeds in obtaining a radar lock on a contact at 21 miles (33.8 km). Within seconds, that contact (possibly a pair) disengages, turns and heads for sanctuary in Afghanistan, leaving Badar unable to pursue without himself violating the border.

Moments later, GCI reports that another enemy aircraft is still inside Pakistani airspace, so Badar rejects the original lock at a range of 16 miles (25.7 km). He changes to a new course of 260° in order to engage the second pair, which is soon confirmed as being 4 miles (6.4 km) inside the border. Badar is now at 16,000 ft (4877 m)

Flight Lieutenant Khalid Mahmood scored three of the PAF's eight kills, the last of which (an Su-22) was gained while flying 84-717 shown below. At the time he was serving with No. 14 Squadron.

and informs GCI that he has four contacts, with a lock-on at 15 miles (24 km). Two of the contacts are high and might be MiG-23s flying 'top cover'. The other two are lower, so Badar opts to pursue these, accelerating to 550 kt as he continues to close.

At a range of 6 miles (9.7 km), the growling tone of an AIM-9 becomes audible. Dynamic launch zone (DLZ) parameters are not yet satisfied so Badar continues to close, until, at a range of 4 miles (6.4 km), the DLZ parameters are achieved. Visual evidence of this is provided by a flashing circle on the HUD.

At 3.4 miles (5.5 km) from the target, while flying at an altitude of 21,500 ft (6553 m) on a heading of 280°, Badar fires his first missile. This appears to come from the port wingtip rail and is almost certainly an AIM-9L. He continues to close and lets go a second missile at 2.9 miles (4.7 km), on the same heading but now at 23,000 ft (7010 m). This comes from the starboard side and is probably an AIM-9P from the underwing stores station.

The second missile has only been in flight for a few moments when a hit is observed at a range of 2.5 miles (4 km), with the target quite clearly flaming and entering a rapid left-hand spiralling descent. Badar watches for a moment or two, before breaking away at 2.1 miles (3.4 km) and initiating a sharp left-hand descending turn as he dives for cover and heads for home. By then, the surviving 'bogie' is at 4 miles (6.4 km) range and running almost as fast in the opposite direction as it hurries to get back across the border.

Almost 16 months elapsed before the next 'kill' was achieved near Miranshah. Squadron Leader Athar Bokhari's success of 4 August 1988 was unique in that it was the only one involving a Su-25 and a Soviet pilot. The mission began with a 'hot' scramble in F-16A 85-725 from Kamra at about 1900 hours, Athar being instructed by GCI to intercept four unidentified radar contacts. By the time he reached the area, however, all four had returned to the safe side of the border, so he began 'CAPping'.

At around 1950 hours, GCI reported the pre-

sence of four more 'bogies', although it is conceivable that this was the original group returning to the scene of the earlier activity. GCI also advised Athar that the contacts were some 23 nm (42 km) away (still 5 miles/8 km on the Afghan side of the border) but that they were heading in an easterly direction, which seemed to indicate that an incursion was imminent.

Athar's initial GCI vector was 300° as he moved to cut off the threat. At a range of 18 nm (33 km) he obtained a radar lock on one aircraft which was heading almost directly towards him. He also noted that there were about 4–6 miles (6–10 km) of lateral separation between the pairs of enemy aircraft.

The range continued to diminish and at 7 nm (13 km) Athar began hearing the familiar growling sound as the infra-red seeker head of a Sidewinder started tracking its target. Thus far, though, DLZ criteria were not satisfied. It was at this range that his adversary started a rapid turn to the right, which was certainly tactically unsound and was eventually to be his downfall. In Athar's own words, "He just came and turned in front of me. . ."

'Go for it'

Athar was then told by GCI to 'go for it', since his target was now about 7 nm (13 km) inside Pakistan with the other three members of the formation about 2–3 nm (4–6 km) inside. At 5 nm (9 km), Athar was abeam the Su-25 and closing fast. He pulled into a left-hand turn which brought him to a heading of about 250–260° and allowed him to take up the almost classic six-o'clock position at a range of about 3 nm (5 km). In just a few moments, DLZ criteria were met, but Athar allowed the HUD circle to flash three or four times before firing his starboard AIM-9L at a range of 2.5 nm (4.6 km). (Earlier he had experienced some difficulty with the port AIM-9L, which would normally be fired first – this resulted in a decision to switch to the starboard weapon.)

At that moment, the target was at 26,000 ft (7925 m) and flying at a speed of about 290–300 kt; Athar was slightly below at 21,000 ft (6401 m) but with a high overtake at 510–520 kt in afterburner as he climbed towards the bandit. Athar was clearly confident in the capability of the Sidewinder, for he fired just once and then waited for a few seconds to observe the fireball before breaking left and dropping to low level. As he egressed the area on a heading of 120°, he looked back and observed what he at first thought to be a number of missiles that had been fired at him. Notifying GCI that he believed himself to be under threat of attack, Athar popped a number of infra-red flares as he departed. It was only later that he reached the conclusion the 'missiles' he had seen were actually infra-red flares launched by other aircraft in the enemy formation.

Within seconds of being hit by Athar's Sidewinder, the Su-25 pilot ejected. He was subsequently captured and interrogated, when it was learned that he was Colonel Alexandrov of the Soviet armed forces. Eventually, he was released into the care of the Soviet authorities, but not before divulging that his initial thought on being hit was that he had a technical problem.

Only later did the pilot realise that he had been shot down, but he remained adamant in his belief

Another successful F-16 pilot was Squadron Leader Athar Bokhari, who downed the only Su-25 'Frogfoot' claimed by the PAF, which was also the only Soviet aircraft hit. He too was with No. 14 at the time.

that he had been hit by a radar-guided missile (either an AIM-7 or an AIM-120) fired from a head-on pass and refused to accept that it was actually an AIM-9L fired from behind that brought about his downfall. He was, however, relieved to be taken into custody by the Pakistan Army rather than Afghan Mujahideen forces, and probably had good reason to feel that way.

A section of wing taken from the wreckage has been placed on display close to the base commander's office at PAF Kamra.

The remaining three kills were all claimed by Flight Lieutenant Khalid Mahmood, who, in the space of just over seven weeks, established himself as 'top man on the totem pole' when it came to the F-16 community. There is every possibility that he could have surpassed Squadron Leader Mohammad Mahmood Alam's celebrated 1965 feat of destroying five aircraft in a single sortie.

Khalid's first success came on 12 September 1988 and opened with an order to scramble from the ADA facility at Kamra at 0700 hours. On getting airborne, Khalid (who was flying as lead in F-16A 85-728) and his wingman were directed by GCI to head north-west towards the border in the vicinity of Nawagai. As they moved towards the designated area, word was passed by GCI that radar revealed the presence of a pair of hostile aircraft at around 32,000 ft (9753 m) on a heading of 90° and behaving in such a way that a violation appeared likely.

To head off this threat, the two F-16s were vec-

tored almost north on a heading of 330°, only to learn that the radar contacts had also turned on to a northerly course and were now flying parallel to the border but remaining inside Afghanistan. At this point, the F-16s swung right to an easterly heading and 'shackled' (performed a cross-over manoeuvre).

Within a few moments of taking up this new course, GCI reported the presence of three more enemy aircraft at about 33,000 ft (10058 m). The two Fighting Falcons performed roughly a 180° turn and headed towards the fresh contacts. Still at 10,000 ft (3048 m), Khalid very quickly brought his own radar into play. This revealed the enemy flight to be four-strong, in echelon starboard with about 3,000 ft (914 m) of separation between each member of the formation. Khalid proceeded to lock up the No. 4 at a range of 16 nm (29 km) and saw that his own heading was 280°. He then engaged afterburner and told GCI that he was accelerating to 550 kt before instructing his wingman to begin climbing.

As they ascended, both aircraft passed through broken cloud at 20,000 ft (6096 m), Khalid then observing a RHAW (Radar Homing And Warn-

Since becoming operational with its first squadron in the mid-1980s, the F-16 has been vital to Pakistan's ability to defend its airspace. Previously, the PAF had to rely on elderly Mirage IIIs and Shenyang F-6s for its interception tasks.

ing) indication which alerted him to the fact that the hostile aircraft were MiG-23s. He notified GCI of this and then succeeded in gaining a visual 'tally' at a range of 7 nm (13 km), subsequently noticing that the four Afghan warplanes were in clean condition (i.e. no drop-tanks or bombs) and that they all featured a basically khaki camouflage colour scheme.

At about the same time, the first two MiGs reversed their course and began heading back towards the F-16s at about 33-34,000 ft (10058-10363 m). It was also apparent that this pair was rapidly overhauling the front four, which would seem to indicate that the latter had decelerated, perhaps in an attempt to place the F-16s under threat. If it were indeed a tactical ploy, it failed dismally to succeed in its objective.

Khalid chose to press on with his pursuit of the larger group and at a range of 1.3 nm (2.4 km), while in an attitude of 135° of bank (i.e. near inverted) at 33,000 ft (10058 m), he launched an AIM-9L at the No. 4 aircraft. Quickly rejecting the lock, he rolled out into level flight and turned to look for the original pair which was now much too close (about 5,000 ft/1524 m away) as they overshot the four-ship.

Since the pair clearly posed no immediate danger, Khalid turned his attention back to the larger group and locked on to the No. 3 from almost directly astern at a distance of about 13,500 ft (4115 m). It was now that Khalid worked out a cunning plan which, if executed correctly, would allow him to kill all six enemy aircraft. Basically, it envisaged using his three remaining Sidewinders (one AIM-9L and two AIM-9Ps) to 'splash' the last three of the four-ship element before disposing of the other two with the Vulcan M61 cannon.

In accordance with that plan, Khalid launched an AIM-9P at the No. 3 aircraft while at 34,000 ft (10363 m) on a heading of 40°, and then began moving towards the No. 2. At this moment, GCI intervened with a warning call to break

right. Khalid responded immediately and in doing so lost his chance of outdoing Alam's earlier achievement. Perhaps the most frustrating thing about this call was that it was subsequently found to be unnecessary and was probably prompted by 'clutter' on the GCI's radar display. Whatever the reason, the manoeuvre cost Khalid precious seconds and even though he attempted to re-engage, by now the remaining enemy aircraft were in a descending left-hand turn and accelerating away towards the sanctuary of Afghanistan.

With regard to the two MiG-23s that Khalid did engage, the Pakistan Army later found wreckage of both. Khalid remains confident that he would have taken all six had he not been distracted by the false call.

Number Three for Khalid

Khalid's and the PAF's last confirmed victory came on 3 November 1988 during the course of a CAP mission near Kohat. On this occasion, Khalid was flying F-16A 84-717 as No. 2 in a two-ship formation. The encounter opened with Khalid and his leader at 10,000 ft (3048 m) when they were informed by GCI that six contacts were heading towards the border, a subsequent message confirming that three of these had violated Pakistani airspace while the other three stayed right on the border line.

On a heading of 280°, the two F-16s moved to engage, the lead very quickly informing GCI that he had radar contact. Khalid obtained a lock on the No. 2 aircraft, which was flying on the southern side of the formation. They continued to close the gap but at a distance of 8 nm (14 km), Nos 2 and 3 of the enemy formation opted for discretion and executed a 180° turn, which very quickly allowed them to regain the security of Afghanistan. Khalid then advised his leader that

his contact had turned tail.

For some reason, the leading Afghan fighter kept coming and at a range of 7 nm (13 km), the F-16 lead pilot obtained a visual tally, with Khalid following suit moments later. At this time, both F-16s were still at 10,000 ft (3048 m) while the bandit – which was confirmed as a Su-22 – was some 7,000 ft (2134 m) higher. Both F-16s then initiated a gradual climb as the Su-22 began turning to depart, the enemy pilot having been advised by his GCI of the presence of the two F-16s. His tardiness in heading for safety was to prove an expensive error.

Khalid's leader elected to press home his attack, but the Su-22 pilot then showed good tactical sense by turning to face the threat. This prevented the first F-16 from getting off a missile, although it later became apparent that its pilot had experienced some difficulty with his Sidewinder which may have prevented him from engaging. In choosing to evade the threat posed by the leading F-16, the Su-22 pilot placed himself at risk of attack by Khalid, who wasted no time in making a hard right turn into the Su-22. He duly launched an AIM-9L from a range of 2.7 nm (5 km) in a head-on pass.

While all that was going on, the lead F-16 began manoeuvring into a position which would enable him to engage the Su-22 with gunfire from a six-o'clock position. He still had some way to go when Khalid's Sidewinder struck home, smoke and panels falling from the damaged fighter, which continued flying about 10 nm (18 km) inside Pakistan.

Khalid realised very quickly that the Su-22 was

PAF F-16s have an important strike role, being fitted with the French ATLIS pod and Paveway laser-guided bombs to permit precision attacks.

\multicolumn{5}{c}{**SUMMARY OF PAF KILLS 1979-89**}
Date	Pilot	Unit	Victim(s)	Weapon
17/5/86	Sqn Ldr Qadri	No. 9 Sqn	Two Su-22s	AIM-9L/gun
30/3/87	Wg Cdr Razzaq	No. 9 Sqn	An-26	??
16/4/87	Sqn Ldr Badar	No. 14 Sqn	Su-22	AIM-9L/P
4/8/88	Sqn Ldr Athar	No. 14 Sqn	Su-25	AIM-9L
12/9/88	Flt Lt Khalid	No. 14 Sqn	Two MiG-23s	AIM-9L/P
3/11/88	Flt Lt Khalid	No. 14 Sqn	Su-22	AIM-9L

damaged. He waited a few more seconds before launching another AIM-9L at an aspect angle of about 150-160°, this barely leaving the rail before the enemy pilot ejected. This missile also scored a direct hit, causing the Su-22 to break in two and head earthwards on fire.

The entire incident was observed from the ground by personnel of the Pakistan Army and by Pathan tribesmen. Khalid was subsequently showered with gifts, including a Kalashnikov and sundry other weapons. Captain Hashim, the luckless Afghan pilot, was captured and revealed under interrogation that all six aircraft were from a squadron at Matun. Three had been tasked with air-to-ground operations while the other three flew top cover, but it seems that the colonel in charge ran away as the strike element crossed the border. In an odd postscript, Hashim also allegedly said that his mother had told him not to fly that day.

For the PAF, that was just about it, although Khalid was to enjoy a further moment of excitement when flying a solo night 'hot' scramble mission in an F-16B on 31 January 1989. On this occasion, he was directed to investigate a border violation near Bannu and he duly headed towards the area at 10,000 ft (3048 m) under GCI direction. Repeated attempts at obtaining an IR lock on the enemy contact (which was down at

2,000 ft/610 m and which was suspected to be engaged on a bombing raid) failed to meet with success.

As Khalid moved closer under GCI control, the aircraft put its lights on and was revealed to be an An-24. Under the rules of engagement then in force, Khalid was directed to let it go, so he pulled up and began flying above it, advising GCI that it looked like the An-24 was planning to

land. Ultimately, the transport made an approach to the River Kuram (a dried-up river bed) and the pilot may have been under the impression that it was a paved runway. Moments after touching down, the An-24 struck a palm tree and cartwheeled before being engulfed in a massive explosion, followed by numerous secondary detonations as the load of ammunition it was carrying 'cooked off' in the intense heat.

General Dynamics F-16

This Fighting Falcon was the mount of Flight Lieutenant Khalid when he downed a Sukhoi 'Fitter' to score the PAF's most recent kill. All Pakistan's machines are from Block 15, the final version of the F-16A/B production.

Markings
Pakistani F-16s wear a unique two-tone grey scheme, with a broad dark band wrapping around the centre of the aircraft and small dark patches on the tailplanes. No squadron markings are carried, the national insignia being presented in toned-down shades of grey. The individual aircraft serial is repeated on the nose.

Service
Three PAF squadrons operate the F-16. Nos 9 and 11 are at Sargodha, the latter also undertaking OCU duties. The third unit is No. 14 Squadron at Kamra.

Armament
In addition to the internal M61A1 20-mm cannon, the Pakistani F-16s carry Sidewinder missiles for the air defence role. Typically four weapons are fitted, a mix of the less-capable AIM-9P and the all-aspect AIM-9L, carried on wingtip rails and outer wing pylons.

Tail
Block 15 F-16s were the first to introduce the big tail (subsequently standard on all aircraft). This increases controllability at high angles of attack.

Fuel
For intercept missions the PAF fits the standard centreline tank to its F-16s. The refuelling receptacle is redundant as the PAF has no tankers.

Powerplant
Virtually all F-16A/Bs are powered by the Pratt & Whitney F100-PW-200 engine, which develops 23,830 lb (106 kN) of thrust.

Radar
The F-16A is fitted with the AN/APG-66 multi-mode radar. Those fitted to Block 15 added a track-while-scan mode for greater air defence capability.

France

Maintaining a clear independence in military matters, France is nevertheless closely tied to the overall defence of Western Europe and is seeking to strengthen its ties with other European neighbours, but not through the NATO framework. A healthy indigenous arms industry provides much of the equipment operated by the air arms, while subsidising this effort with an aggressive export drive.

Central to both the AA's and Aéronavale's future plans is the Dassault Rafale. Here the Rafale A technology demonstrator is seen at the CEV at Brétigny.

L'Armée de l'Air

Western Europe's largest non-NATO air force, the Armée de l'Air (AA), was restructured at its upper levels in 1991 to simplify the command chain of nuclear forces and increase efficiency in air defence. By the end of that year, however, the AA had not announced force reductions of the magnitude of those already begun by the other principal Western nations: Germany, United Kingdom and United States. In part, the reason has been that France retained only a few army units in Germany following its withdrawal from the military structure of NATO in 1966. Instead, Paris initially concentrated on a multi-directional defence of the homeland and maintenance of permanent or earmarked forces for protection of overseas colonies and former possessions in Africa with which friendly relations are maintained.

Reduction in size, accompanied by base closures and unit disbandments, is now in prospect as the implications of recent momentous changes in Eastern Europe are felt in the defence budget. Military re-equipment programmes were under financial pressure throughout the 1980s, but the 1992 defence budget of Fr195.5 billion ($35 billion) reflects a cut of 2.3 per cent after allowance for inflation. Tactical nuclear forces are losing some of their primacy as a result of the changed political situation in Europe, while combat lessons from the Gulf War are prompting modification of some programmes. Most significantly in this respect, the AA now wishes its forthcoming Dassault Rafales to be two-seat, to allow a WSO to be carried. In February 1992 it was revealed that AA front-line strength would be cut from 450 to 390 aircraft.

Since abandoning its multi-directional defence policy in the mid-1970s, France has sought to strengthen ties with (former West) Germany and, in 1984, to re-invigorate the Western European Union defence pact at the expense of what Paris views as the American-dominated NATO. In the mid-1970s France accepted that the only threat to Western Europe was from the Warsaw Pact and accordingly signalled in tacit political language that it was prepared to fight alongside NATO immediately that alliance came under attack. The USA was still kept at arm's length, as a sign of the in-

dependence of French military power. Military collaboration with America, which ended in 1966, was not resumed until 1991 when USAF KC-135 tankers were allowed to fly from a French aerodrome to refuel UK-based B-52s on their way to bomb Iraq.

With the recent collapse of the Warsaw Pact, political moves have again been made to forge a wholly European defence policy, to which end a prototype bi-national Franco-German army unit has been established. While excluded from the NATO Defence Planning Committee and declining membership of the associated Euro-group for planning collective policies, France continues to sit on the civilian North Atlantic Council and participates in the Independent European Programme Group and Conference of National Armament Directors.

Under its Chief of Staff, Général d'Armée Aérienne Vincent Lanata, Air Force Headquarters (Etat Major de l'AA – EMAA) at Boulevard Victor, Paris, directly controls the CEAM flight-test centre and is responsible for two equal levels of administration: Air Regions and Commands. The Regions Aériennes are geographical areas with no direct tactical control of aircraft. Under the Armées 2000 plan implemented on 1 September 1991 the former four RAs have been reduced to three, coinciding with similar divisions within the army and Gendarmerie. The new RAs are:

RA Nord-est (North-East) with HQ at Villacoublay. Centred on the original 1ᵉ RA (12 air bases and 24,000 personnel) but enlarged with the addition of territory south of Belgium formerly in 2ᵉ RA. Now comprises 19 bases and 43,000 personnel, including 25 of the AA's 30 tactical air attack units.

RA Atlantique (Atlantic) with HQ at Bordeaux. Incorporates the former 3ᵉ RA (10 bases, 19,000 personnel) and most of 2ᵉ RA (14 bases, 33,000 personnel). Totals are now 17 bases and 33,000 people.

RA Méditerranée (Mediterranean) with HQ at Aix. The former 4ᵉ RA, with unchanged assets of 12 bases and 20,000 personnel.

Air Regions are responsible for training regulars and reservists, providing their billeting and equipment and organising mobilisation. Personnel totals include some 5,000 civilians and 35,000 conscripts serving one year within the budgeted strength of 91,717.

Apart from two flying units (including

The Mirage 2000N and the 2000D derivative are emerging as the AA's primary strike/attack aircraft. The 2000Ns of EC 4 are now assigned to strategic duties with ASMP missiles.

The Jaguar continues to play a part in the AA's activities, and was the primary attack platform assigned to the war against Iraq as part of Operation Daguet.

The Alpha Jet is the main advanced trainer in AA service, and has also been adopted as the mount of the national formation display team, 'La Patrouille de France'.

In keeping with their USAF counterparts, the 11 surviving C-135F tankers of ERV 93 were re-engined with CFM56 turbofans to become C-135FRs.

THE FRENCH DEFENCE DIMENSION

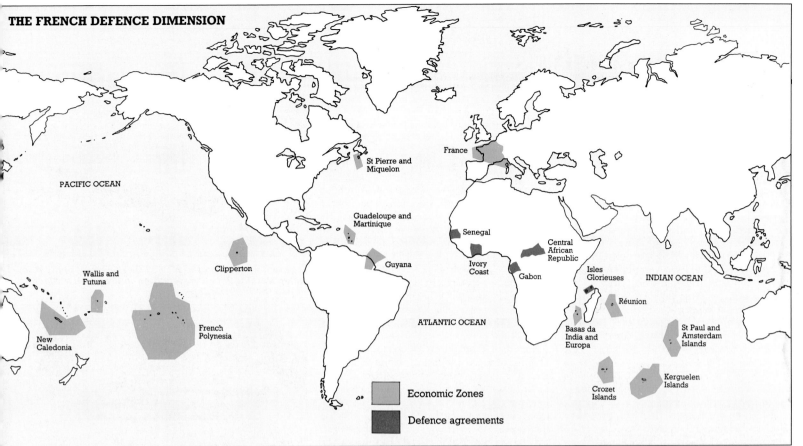

France maintains the vestiges of its colonial empire with far-flung outposts around the world. Djibouti is of great strategic significance, and is the major foreign detachment.

Nuclear strike for the Aéronavale is undertaken by the Dassault Super Etendard, which can carry a single ASMP nuclear stand-off missile.

Of great concern to the Aéronavale is the insufficient capability of the F-8E(FN) Crusader, which still forms the fighter component of the carrier air wing. Replacement by Rafale is a considerable time away.

The ALAT has standardised on the Gazelle as its light helicopter, and operates three main variants in attack, close support and observation roles.

Rapid mobility for French ground forces is provided by the Puma, which equips all the ALAT assault transport units. No heavylift capability is included in the ALAT inventory.

The last vestiges of the Force de Frappe are the two squadrons of Mirage IVPs serving with the strategic air force. Free-fall weapons have been dispensed with in favour of the stand-off ASMP seen here.

CEAM, noted above), control of aircraft is exercised by five Commands organised according to role. Commands are discussed at length elsewhere, but may be briefly summarised as: **FATac** – Tactical Air Force; **CoFAS** – Strategic Air Forces Command; **CAFDA** – Air Defence Forces Command; **CoTAM** – Air Transport Command; and **CEAA** – Air Training Command.

At the same level, but with no aircraft, is Commandement des Transmissions de l'Air (CTAA), or Air Telecommunications Command. Air Construction Command (Commandement du Génie de l'Air – CGA) disbanded on 1 September 1991. Commands concern themselves more with the conduct of operations, as the day-to-day matters of personnel welfare and training are delegated to the Air Regions.

In addition to Air Regions and Commands, the air force has a third level of administration in the form of Central Directorates of personnel, administration, material and infrastructure. The last-mentioned (Direction Centrale de l'Infrastructure Air) absorbed the Génie on 1 September 1991 to become the Cité de l'Air. Only the Direction Centrale de Matériel de l'AA (DCMAA) has direct control of aircraft in the form of 70 Ferry Squadron at Châteaudun. What may loosely be described as 'the French air force' is completed by various administrative Directorates attached to the Ministry of the Armed Forces and the Ministerial Armaments Delegation (the latter being of equal rank to the three armed services).

Military units may be based abroad temporarily (the rapid deployment squadrons included in FATac) or permanently in one of the French possessions – principally groups of islands in the Pacific, Caribbean and off East Africa. These are organised into four tri-service defence Commandements Supérieurs (Com-Sup) corresponding to Overseas Departments of France, each of which is a Zone de Défense (ZD). These are:

ZD Antilles-Guyane (HQ, Fort-de-France) for the French Antilles (St Martin, St Barthélemy, Guadeloupe and Martinique) and French Guyana.

ZD du Sud de l'Ocean Indien et Territoires de l'Antarctique (HQ, La Réunion) for Mayotte, Réunion, Tromelin, l'Europe, Basas da India, Juan de Nova and Antarctic territory (St Paul and Amsterdam, Crozet and Kerguelen Islands).

ZD de la Nouvelle-Calédonie (HQ, Nouméa) for New Caledonia and dependencies and Wallis and Futuna Islands.

ZD de la Polynésie Française (HQ, Tahiti) for Tahiti, Gambier, Windward, Leeward, Marquesas and Clipperton island groups.

At lower levels of command, AA aircraft are organised into numbered wings, squadrons and flights. These are:

Escadre (Wing). Normally located at a single air base, wings are numbered according to their function, those in current use being 1-13 and 30 for Escadres de Chasse (fighter wings); 33 for the Escadre de Reconnaissance; 36 for Escadre de Détection Aéroportée (AEW); 60-65 for Escadres de Transport; 67 for the Escadre d'Hélicoptères; and 90-95 for strategic Escadres de Bombardement, de Ravitaillement

en Vol (flight refuelling) and de Missiles Stratégiques (silo-launched IRBMs). For example, EC 5 is the abbreviation for No. 5 Fighter Wing, correctly expressed as EC00/005 to indicate wing headquarters – which, in many instances, is assigned a training and liaison flight of three or four Fouga Magisters. The flight is variously known as a Section d'Accueil de Liaison et d'Entrainement (SALE – Reception, Training and Liaison Section); or Escadrille d'Entrainement et de Vol Sans Visibilité (EEVSV – Liaison and Blind Flying Section). Magisters were due to be replaced before 1996 by 30 EMBRAER EMB-312 Tucanos – additional to the 50 required by Training Command – but financial constraints appear to preclude this.

Escadron (Squadron). The permanent identity of a squadron is its historic name (usually an area of France), with which is associated one or a pair of badges. Squadrons are numbered as a function of their current wing, but the numbering will change when they move base. Two or three squadrons make a wing. For example, EC 1/5 'Vendée' (EC 01/005) is the first squadron of 5 Wing, partnered by EC 2/5 and EC 3/5. Autonomous squadrons for light transport and various other tasks are numbered between 41 and 59, 70, and (based overseas) 80-88.

Escadrille (Flight). Two and, occasionally, three flights constitute a squadron. Some flights are named, but most take the numbering and insignia of World War I units. In the case of 'Vendée' squadron, the 1e Escadrille is SPA26 (a stork) and 2e Escadrille is SPA124 (Joan of Arc). Appropriate insignia is applied to right and left, respectively, of the fins of squadron aircraft, but a few squadrons reverse the order.

Numbers 100-999 are assigned to air bases, OCUs, maintenance depots, schools, communications units, hospitals, SAM units, HQs and radar sites.

Forces Aériennes Stratégiques

Centre of Operations, Strategic Air Forces (COFAS) is underground at Base Aérienne 921, Taverny, north of Paris, from where are controlled strategic delivery systems and supporting aircraft. Two reserve command posts are COFAS II at Lyon/Mt Verdun and COFAS III at Evreux. On 1 September 1991, FAS was augmented by three squadrons totalling 45 Dassault Mirage 2000Ns of EC 4 transferred from FATac. Its original complement comprised 16 Dassault Mirage IVPs, 11 Boeing C-135FR tankers, seven Dassault Mirage IIIB trainers, four Fouga Magisters and a Dassault Mystère 20SP. FAS now contains all the air force's nuclear delivery systems.

Of the 62 Mirage IVA nuclear bombers which allowed France to leave NATO and provide its own deterrent – colloquially known as the Force de Frappe – 19 were converted during the late 1980s to Mirage IVPs, carrying the Aérospatiale ASMP (Air-Sol Moyenne Portée) stand-off bomb. Fitted with a 300-kilotonne TN81 warhead (which replaced the original 150-kilotonne TN80 in 1987), ASMP has a variable delivery profile between 43 nm (low level at Mach 2) and 135 nm (high level at Mach 3). The two squadrons of 91 Wing have seven Mirage IVPs each, squadrons both having a

A recent addition to the ERV 93 C-135FR fleet is the Adèle radar warning receiver, resulting in the small projection above the flight deck.

The recent restructuring saw the Mirage 2000Ns of EC 4 switched to FAS control. This example is from EC 1/4 'Dauphiné', complete with ASMP missile.

This EC 2/4 Mirage 2000N was specially marked for the 75th anniversary of the 'La Fayette' squadron, which was originally formed with US volunteers.

FATac has now assumed command of the interceptor force previously assigned to CAFDA. Included in the units is EC 2/2 'Côte d'Or' from Dijon.

The new RA N-E has taken over all of the old 1^e RA's territory.

The 'lammergeier' badge of EC 1/3, which flies Mirage IIIEs from Nancy.

detachment in order to spread the force over four bases for additional security from pre-emptive attack. Mirage 2000Ns are also equipped with the ASMP. Nuclear weapons are maintained by a Dépot-Atelier de Munitions Spéciales at each base.

French C-135F tankers were converted between 1985 and 1988 to C-135FR standard with SNECMA/GE CFM56 turbofan engines. Seven are with ERV 1/93 and two each with the remaining pair of squadrons. Hitherto, the tankers have been fitted with a drogue and short length of hose on their US-type 'flying booms' for refuelling probe-equipped aircraft. In mid-1993, however, the fleet will begin receiving a pair of Flight Refuelling Ltd Mk 32 pods under the wings, permitting the boom to revert to its normal form of usage following the delivery of Boeing E-3F AWACS. Boeing is making the first conversion and will then supply 10 kits for incorporation in France.

An OCU, CIFAS 328, has an Escadron d'Instruction with two Mirage IVPs and a Mystère 20 modified with the latter's navigation and attack avionics for training WSOs. The Training Squadron (Escadron d'Entrainement) has a few Mirage IIIB-2s for delta-wing conversion and refuelling training – the B-2 (or B-RV) having a dummy receiver probe in the nose. Two Magisters are also attached, as are two borrowed Alpha Jets to give future navigators fast-jet experience.

The unmanned component of the AA's strategic forces is contained in 18 silos on the Plateau d'Albion, each with a single Aérospatiale S-3 IRBM having a 1.2-megatonne warhead. 1er GMS was to have converted to S-4.5 weapons from 1996 onwards, comprising 18 underground and 18 in surface shelters, but the programme was indefinitely suspended in 1991. Studies are continuing of an 'S-5', based on the submarine-launched M-5 missile, for possible use by the AA.

Dassault Mirage IVP of EB 1/91 'Gascogne' formates on a C-135FR tanker, carrying a Barem ECM pod on the wing pylon. Based at Mont-de-Marsan, the escadron also maintains a detachment at Orange, part of the FAS force dispersal policy to maximise the deterrence value of the small Mirage IV force.

The third Mirage 2000N escadron assigned to FAS is EC 3/4 'Limousin', which is at Istres. The other two escadrons of the escadre are based at Luxeuil.

CIFAS 328 'Aquitaine' is at Bordeaux with a variety of types for instruction of FAS crews. A pair of Mirage IVPs is used.

The latest Mirage 2000N escadron to form is EC 2/3 'Champagne', which is currently the only such unit assigned to FATac. It is based at Nancy.

EC 3/3 'Ardennes' is at Nancy with the Mirage IIIE. This aircraft carries a Martel anti-radiation missile.

EC 5 was the second escadre to equip with the Mirage 2000C for fighter duties. This aircraft is from EC 3/5 'Comtat Venaissin' at Orange.

A small number of Mirage 2000Bs are assigned as continuation trainers, this example flying with EC 1/5.

Forces Aériennes Stratégiques

UNIT	EQUIPMENT
4e Escadre de Chasse (Base Aérienne 116, Luxeuil/St Sauveur)	
00/004 SALE	Magister
EC 1/4 'Dauphiné' (SPA37, SPA81)	Mirage 2000N
EC 2/4 'La Fayette' (N124, SPA167, SPA92 & SPA160)	Mirage 2000N
	Mirage 2000N
EC 3/4 'Limousin' (GC I/9-1e, GC I/9-2e & SPA96)	Mirage 2000N (at Base Aérienne 125, Istres/le Tubé)
91e Escadre de Bombardement (Base Aérienne 118, Mont-de-Marsan)	
EB 1/91 'Gascogne' (SAL28/SPA79) (Detachment at Base Aérienne 115, Orange/Caritat)	Mirage IVP
EB 2/91 Brétagne (GB II/20) (Detachment at Base Aérienne 125, Istres/le Tubé)	Mirage IVP
93e Escadre de Ravitaillement en Vol (Base Aérienne 125, Istres/le Tubé)	
ERV 1/93 'Aunis' (SAL277 & SAL10)	C-135FR
ERV 2/93 'Sologne' (BR44 & BR465)	C-135FR (at Base Aérienne 702, Avord)
ERV 3/93 'Landes' (SPA54 & SAL22)	C-135FR (at Base Aérienne 118, Mont-de-Marsan)
1e Groupement de Missiles Stratégiques (Base Aérienne 200, Apt/St Christol)	
Escadron MS 1/95 'Luberon' (VB135 & VB137)	
1e Escadrille de Tir	S-3 (at Rustrel)
2e Escadrille de Tir	S-3 (at Reilhannette)

Centre d'Instruction des FAS 328 'Aquitaine' (GB I/25)
(Base Aérienne 106, Bordeaux/Mérignac)

EI 1/328	Mirage IVP & Mystère 20SP
EE 2/328	Mirage IIIB-RV, Magister & (on loan) Alpha Jet

Force Aérienne Tactique

By far the greatest change in the AA order of battle resulting from the Armées 2000 reorganisation on 1 September 1991 was transfer of the manned interceptor force from CAFDA (see below) to the FATac. At the same time, AN52 free-fall nuclear bombs were withdrawn from two squadrons of Jaguars and the three Mirage 2000N squadrons of EC 4 were transferred to the FAS. As a consequence of these changes, FATac became a conventional force only. Duties of FATac as officially laid down include destruction of an enemy air force on the ground; offensive support and protection for friendly ground forces; participation in overseas actions; and gathering intelligence on potential enemy forces. To these are added the CAFDA roles of detection and identification of air movements over and around France; assessment of air threats and alert of appropriate government and military authorities; and the opposition of all violations of French airspace.

The 'old' FATac comprised 322 aircraft on established strength (i.e. discounting those in reserve or on overhaul), of which 45 went to the FAS, leaving 15 Mirage 2000Ns, 87 SEPECAT Jaguar As, 18 Jaguar E trainers, 45 Mirage IIIEs, 12 Mirage IIIBs, 32 Mirage 5Fs, 45 Dassault Mirage F1CRs, 20 Magisters, two Transall C.160s and an Aérospatiale SA 330Ba Puma. Assets of CAFDA now incorporated accounted for a further 206 machines: 75 Mirage 2000Cs, 15 Mirage 2000Bs, 86 Mirage F1Cs, 14 Mirage F1Bs and 16 Magisters.

Until September 1991, FATac HQ at Metz was jointly HQ of 1 Air Region. The duties have now been separated, with FATac and North-East Air Region having co-located, but administratively distinct, headquarters. All FATac assets are assigned to 1ᵉ Commandement Aérien Tactique at Metz. Two Jaguar squadrons (EC 4/7 [now 3/4 with Mirage 2000Ns] and EC 4/11) were assigned to the rapid reaction force of 2ᵉ CATac at Nancy until disbandment in 1987. EC 4/11 itself disbanded on 30 June 1992.

It is convenient first to deal with the units of the 'old' FATac. Improved equipment is being received in the form of 75 Mirage 2000Ns and 75 Mirage 2000Ds, of which 75 and 57 respectively had been firmly funded up to the end of 1991. The 2000N is capable of carrying ASMP nuclear missiles, but apart from the 45 aircraft assigned to the strategic force, the aircraft is limited to conventional armament – as is the 2000D, which will become available in 1993. EC 3, which equipped its No. 2 squadron with Mirage 2000Ns in September 1991, is assigned to defence suppression. EC 3 will eventually receive 2000Ds, allowing the surplus 2000Ns to replace strategically-tasked Mirage IVPs. Mirage 2000N/Ds can also employ Aérospatiale AS.30L missiles and MATRA

BGL bombs, both of which are laser-guided.

The Jaguar force has the survivors of 160 Jaguar As and 40 Jaguar Es in two wings. St Dizier's 7 Wing includes EC 1/7 and 3/7, now in conventional attack roles following withdrawal of their AN52s in September 1991. Establishment is 14 As and one E, whereas the Jaguar OCU, EC 2/7, has only five As and one B. Four squadrons at Toul are more diverse: EC 1/11 supporting the 1st Army with 250- and 400-kg bombs, BAP100 anti-runway weapons, AS.30Ls, BGLs and 68-mm rockets; EC 2/11 in the tactical ECM role with Thomson-CSF CT51 pods and Thomson-CSF Barracuda detector pods (plus a secondary attack role with MATRA AJ37 ARMAT anti-radar missiles); and EC 3/11 for attack. Jaguars can also carry an RP36P, which is an RP36 fuel tank containing reconnaissance cameras. All squadrons have 15 aircraft, including one or two trainers. During the Gulf War, Jaguars made precision attacks with AS.30L missiles, self-designating with Thomson-CSF ATLIS pods, and being also cleared to drop 400-kg LGBs. By 2000, the AA expects to have 50 Jaguars on strength at EC 7 and 30 with two squadrons of EC 11.

EC 13 employs the survivors of 50 Mirage 5Fs originally built for Israel as 5Js. These non-radar aircraft – 16 in each of two squadrons – are used for ground attack with bombs and rockets, as are the Mirage F1CTs of EC 1/13. The latter unit flew its final Mirage III sortie (also the last service flight of a IIIB trainer) on 15 January 1992 before passing its IIIB-2s and IIIBEs to EC 2/13 to continue the Mirage IIIE conversion role. Pilots then transferred to Mont-de-Marsan for training on the F1CT. In all, 55 Mirage F1C interceptors are being converted to F1CT tactical attack aircraft at the air force's own workshops (Atelier Industriel de l'Air at Clermont Ferrand/Aulnat), the first returned to service on 13 February 1992. Two prototype F1CTs were converted by Dassault, of which the first was delivered to the CEV trials unit at Istres on 3 May 1991. In 33 Wing, three squadrons each have 15 reconnaissance Mirage F1CRs from 64 delivered, these carrying internal visual-spectrum and IR linescan cameras which may be augmented by a range of centreline pods: Thomson-CSF Raphael-TH SLAR; T-CSF ASTAC emission-locator; FLIR; and TV.

Deliveries of 41 Rafales are expected in 1997-99 to begin re-equipment of EC 11, one squadron of which will have converted by 2000, partnered by two still with Jaguars. These will be interim-standard Rafales, following which 209 full-production machines will be supplied by 2008. That timetable assumes, most optimistically, that there will be no further development delays or defence cuts. In the latter regard, at least, the Rafale is being granted top priority, to the extent that the AA is to forego 24 Mirage 2000s and 30 Mirage 2000Ds to release funds for the Rafale. The AA's share of the 1992 defence budget is Fr40.4 billion ($7.21 billion), of which the lower-than-expected sum of Fr24.3 billion ($4.34 billion) is for procurement of equipment. There are constraints on operating expenses, too, and in 1991 fighter pilots flew an average of only 165 hours – well below the NATO-recommended minimum of 180 hours.

The port fins of EC 1/7's Jaguars wear the Bayard's helmet badge of SPA15.

EC 2/7 Jaguars wear the cockerel of SPA48 on the starboard side.

EC 2/11 'Vosges' uses its Jaguars in a tactical electronic role, carrying the CT51 jamming pod. ARMATs are also carried for defence suppression.

An EC 4/11 'Jura' Jaguar demonstrates the retractable refuelling probe fitted to the type. This is the primary overseas deployment squadron for rapid intervention .

During the war with Iraq, EC 4/11's Jaguars were heavily committed, adopting this sand scheme. This aircraft carries an AS.30L missile and associated ATLIS pod.

EC 12 still has two squadrons of Mirage F1C fighters, but conversion is under way to the Mirage 2000C. This aircraft is from EC 1/12 'Cambrésis'.

Late in the war with Iraq, Mirage F1CRs adopted their secondary bombing role and augmented the main Jaguar attack force. Here a Jaguar A from EC 2/11 and a Mirage from ER 1/33 carry bombs and Barex ECM pods, while the Mirage has additional Magic self-defence missiles.

EC 2/13 'Alpes' at Colmar is one of two squadrons which retain the non-radar Mirage 5F for attack missions. These machines were embargoed from an Israeli order.

EC 1/13 'Artois' acts as OCU for the original Mirage III/5 variants. This is a two-seat Mirage IIIBE.

EC 4/30 'Vexin' is the escadron assigned to Djibouti, where it undertakes a local defence role. Currently assigned are Mirage F1Cs, in this desert camouflage.

The conversion unit for the Mirage F1 force is EC 3/30 'Lorraine', which includes two-seat F1Bs in its fleet.

This ER 3/33 'Moselle' Mirage F1CR carries a Raphael side-looking airborne radar pod under the centreline and Barex ECM pod under the wing.

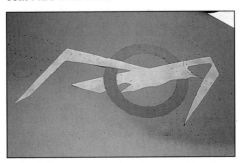

Presented here on a desert camouflage is the SAL6 seagull badge worn on both sides of the fins of ER 2/33 Mirage F1CRs.

Aircrew training is the responsibility of CITac 339, with four Jaguar Es and four Mystère 20s. The Jaguars give WSOs fast-jet experience in conjunction with training aboard one Mystère 20N with Mirage 2000N avionics. Two Mystère 20SNAs (Système de Navigation et d'Ataque) duplicate the Mirage IIIE and a Mystère 20SNR (SN et de Reconnaissance) has Mirage F1CR systems. Tactical forces are completed by an Elint and Comint squadron, EET 54, with two specially converted Transall C.160 Gabriels and a similarly modified Puma.

Air defence elements comprise four wings almost equally divided between Mirage F1Cs and Mirage 2000Cs, these now being separate from the radar, reporting and SAM units which have remained under CAFDA. Mirage F1 receipts totalled 81 F1Cs, 81 air refuelling-capable F1C-200s and 20 F1B trainers, while firm orders for its successor have been 146 2000Cs and 22 two-seat 2000Bs. Planned procurement of a further 24 2000C variants was abandoned in 1991 for financial reasons. Mirage F1s are armed with the infra-red MATRA 550 Magic and radar-guided MATRA Super 530F-1 missiles, while the 2000 has Magic 2 and Super 530D – the latter a more advanced weapon, despite its designation.

Two standards of Mirage 2000C exist, those delivered to EC 2 from 1984 onwards having the Thomson-CSF RDM (Radar Doppler à Modulations) while EC 5 aircraft – beginning 1988 – are equipped with the definitive Dassault Electronique/T-CSF RDI (Radar Doppler à Impulsions). Each squadron has 15 aircraft, but OCU EC 2/2 uses 12 two-seat versions and only three 2000Cs. Next to convert, in 1992, is EC 1/12, which may acquire three or so trainers to expedite the process, as did EC 5.

Six Mirage F1 squadrons have 15 aircraft each, including EC 3/30 with 11 trainers and four single-seat machines as the type OCU. A seventh squadron is EC 4/11 which is permanently detached to Djibouti with 10 aircraft as part of the French force defending this former colony against Somali territorial claims. EC 4/11's aircraft have a sand-coloured camouflage, variations of which have become increasingly common for FATac's Jaguars and Mirage F1CRs, firstly as a result of intervention in Chad during 1983 against Libyan adventurism and secondly for participation in the Gulf War of 1991.

Major bases with a large requirement for communications aircraft may be given their own equipment in the form of a pair of Magisters or Paris. Aircraft are not attached to the resident wing (indeed, the weapons training aerodrome at Solenzara, Corsica, has no permanent residents) but for the bases' own Moyens Opérationelles, for which reason their markings include the Base Aérienne number.

Force Aérienne Tactique

UNIT	EQUIPMENT

1e Commandement Aérienne Tactique

2e Escadre de Chasse* (Base Aérienne 102, Dijon/Longvic)

00/002 EEVSV	Magister
EC 1/2 'Cigognes' (SPA3 & SPA103)	Mirage 2000C
EC 2/2 'Côte d'Or' (SPA65, SPA57 & SPA94)	Mirage 2000B (2000C)
EC 3/2 'Alsace'	Mirage 2000C

3e Escadre de Chasse (Base Aérienne 133, Nancy/Ochey)

00/003 SALE	Magister
EC 1/3 'Navarre' (SPA95 & SPA153)	Mirage IIIE
EC 2/3 'Champagne' (SPA67 & SPA75)	Mirage 2000N
EC 3/3 'Ardennes' (GC III/3)	Mirage IIIE

5e Escadre de Chasse* (Base Aérienne 116, Orange/Caritat)

00/005 EEVSV	Magister
EC 1/5 'Vendée' (SPA26 & SPA124)	Mirage 2000C
EC 2/5 'Ile de France' ('Paris' & 'Versailles')	Mirage 2000C
EC 3/5 'Comtat Venaissin' (ERC571 & SPA171)	Mirage 2000C

7e Escadre de Chasse (Base Aérienne 113, St Dizier/Robinson)

00/007 EEVSV	Magister
EC 1/7 'Provence' (SPA15 & SPA77)	Jaguar A (& E)
EC 2/7 'Argonne' (SPA31 & SPA48)	Jaguar A (& E)
EC 3/7 'Languedoc' (3C-1 & SPA38)	Jaguar A (& E)

11e Escadre de Chasse (Base Aérienne 136, Toul/Rosières)

00/011 EEVSV	Magister
EC 1/11 'Roussillon' (GC III/6-5e & GC III/6-6e)	Jaguar A (& E)
EC 2/11 'Vosges' (SPA91 & SPA97)	Jaguar A (& E)
EC 3/11 'Corse' (SPA88 & SPA69)	Jaguar A (& E)

12e Escadre de Chasse* (Base Aérienne 103, Cambrai/Epinoy)

00/012 EEVSV	Magister
EC 1/12 'Cambrésis' (SPA162 & SPA89)	Mirage 2000C
EC 2/12 'Picardie' (SPA173 & SPA172)	Mirage F1C (& F1B)
EC 3/12 'Cornouaille'	Mirage F1C (& F1B)

13e Escadre de Chasse (Base Aérienne 132, Colmar/Mayenheim)

00/013 SALE	Magister
EC 1/13 'Artois' (SPA83 & SPA100)	Mirage F1CT
EC 2/13 'Alpes'	Mirage 5F, Mirage IIIB-2/IIIBE
EC 3/13 'Auvergne' (SPA85 & GC I/9-3e)	Mirage 5F

30e Escadre de Chasse* (Base Aérienne 112, Reims/Champagne)

00/030 EEVSV	Magister
EC 1/30 'Valois' (SPA84 & SPA93)	Mirage F1C
EC 2/30 'Normandie-Niemen'	Mirage F1C
EC 3/30 'Lorraine' ('Metz', 'Nancy' & SPA62)	Mirage F1B (& F1C)
EC 4/30 'Vexin' (ERC 3/561 & ERC 4/561)	Mirage F1C (at Base Aérienne 188, Djibouti)

33e Escadre de Reconnaissance (Base Aérienne 124, Strasbourg/Entzheim)

00/033 SALE	Magister
ER 1/33 'Belfort' (SAL33)	Mirage F1CR
ER 2/33 'Savoie' (SAL6)	Mirage F1CR
ER 3/33 'Moselle' (BR11)	Mirage F1CR

Escadron Electronique Tactique 54 'Dunkerque' (MF20) (Base Aérienne 123, Orléans/Bricy)

EET 11/54	C-160 Gabriel
EET 21/54 'Goslar'	Puma (at Goslar, Germany)

Centre d'Instruction Tactique 339 (Base Aérienne 116, Luxeuil/St Sauveur)

	Mystère 20SNA/SNR/N & Jaguar E

Base Flights

MO 05/125 (Base Aérienne 125, Istres)	Magister
MO 05/126 (Base Aérienne 126, Solenzara)	Paris
MO 05/128 (Base Aérienne 128, Metz)	Magister

*former CAFDA wing

This grotesque modification of a Transall is a C.160 Gabriel, one of two assigned to EET 54 at Orléans for the signals intelligence role.

CITAC 339 at Luxeuil provides tactical training, including various Mystère 20s in its fleet equipped with fighter radars.

Commandement 'Air' des Forces de Défense Aérienne

CAFDA's four interceptor wings were transferred to the FATac on 1 September 1991, reducing its manned component to a single wing of four new Boeing E-3F Sentry ADAs (Avion de Détection Aéroportée). The first of these aircraft was declared operational on 22 May 1991. On the ground, data from 10 radar sites is passed between units by the STRIDA (Système de Traitement et de Representation des Informations de Défense Aérienne) network which is also linked to the similar NATO NADGE system and exchanges information with it. Headquarters of air defence (Centre Opérationnel de Défense Aérienne – CODA) is underground at Etat Major de Défense Aérienne (EMDA 900), Taverny.

For air defence purposes, France is divided into three Zones Aériennes de Défense corresponding to the Air Regions introduced in September 1991, although the revised arrangements will not be fully implemented until 1993. There are 10 Control and Reporting Centres (Centre de Détection et de Controlle – CDC) of which three are also a primary Sector Operations Centres (Centre Opérationnel de Zone – COZ). The COZ is responsible for the entire zone, although zones are divided equally into two parts, each containing at least one CDC. These are:

3e ZAD Ouest (RA Atlantique) – CDC 07/927 Cinq-Mars-la-Pile (also COZ); CDC 08/927 Brest; and CDC 04/930 Mont-de-Marsan.

1e ZAD Nord-Est (RA Nord-Est) – CDC 05/901 Drachenbronn (also COZ); CDC 05/925 Doullens-Lucheux; CDC 05/914 Romilly-sur-Seine; and CDC 05/902 Contrexeville.

2e ZAD Sud-Est (RA Mediterranée) – CDC 05/942 Lyon/Mt Verdun (also COZ); CDC 05/943 Nice/Mt Agel; and CD Satellite 15/944 at Narbonne.

Short-range air defence of aerodromes is provided by 40-mm cannon and MATRA R.440 Crotale SAM batteries, plus man-portable MATRA Mistral SAMs. There are 11 squadrons of Crotales (Escadron de Défense Sol-Air – EDSA), each with two Sections. A Section comprises two Unites de Tir, each with two four-round launchers and a radar vehicle.

A small number of base flights come under FATac control, equipped with the Paris or Magister. This example of the latter serves at Istres.

This map shows the Zones Aériennes de Défense (black lines) and their headquarters, and the new Régions Aériennes (blue).

Following the recent reshuffle, the only aircraft assets now assigned to **CAFDA** are the four E-3F Sentrys of 36ᵉ Escadre de Détection Aéroportée, based at Avord. The E-3Fs are similar to the E-3Ds of the RAF in being powered by CFM56 turbofans, but do not have wingtip ESM pods.

Several EDSAs are forming with the Mistral SATCP (Sol-Air Très Courte Portée – Ultra-Short-Range SAM).

Commandement 'Air' des Forces de Défense Aérienne

UNIT	EQUIPMENT
36ᵉ Escadre de Détection Aéroportée (Base Ecole 702, Avord)	
EDA 1/36 'Berry' (SAL58 & BR43)	E-3F
EDA 2/36 'Nivernais' (SAL258 & SAL257)	E-3F

UNIT	LOCATION
Crotale squadrons	
EDSA 1/950 'Vaccares'	Mont-de-Marsan
EDSA 2/950 'Sancerre'	Avord
EDSA 3/950 'Lure'	Apt/St Christol
EDSA 4/950 'Servance'	Luxeuil/St Sauveur
EDSA 5/950 'Barrois'	St Dizier/Robinson
EDSA 6/950 'Riquewihr'	Colmar/Mayenheim
EDSA 7/950	Strasbourg/Entzheim
EDSA 8/950	Dijon/Longvic
EDSA 9/950	Cambrai/Epinoy
EDSA 10/950 'Monfort'	Contrexeville
EDSA 11/950	Chateaudun
Mistral SATCP squadrons	
EDSA 12/950	Mont-de-Marsan
EDSA 32/950	Cazaux
EDSA 34/950	Orange

The Franco-German Transall C.160 flies with two escadres and a transport training unit. This ET 61 C.160F features a desert-style camouflage.

The two Transall-equipped escadrons of ET 61 fly the early-generation C.160F variant, distinguished by the lack of probe.

This ET 2/61 Hercules carries the command badge on the fin.

The ET 64 badge incorporates those of its two escadrons.

ET 64 has sole responsibility for the AA's C.160NG fleet, these being new-build Transalls.

The AA's most capable transport is the C-130H Hercules, which serves with ET 2/61. Nine of the 12-strong fleet have been stretched to C-130H-30 standard.

Only three standard-length C-130Hs serve with ET 2/61; the fact that most have been stretched reflects their strategic tasking.

Commandement du Transport Aérienne Militaire

CoTAM has been unaffected by the 1991 changes, apart from administrative transfer of its HQ to the Atlantic Air Region. Duties are the transport support of French armed services throughout the world, for which the command has several units permanently based overseas. SAR and communications are other roles, involving autonomous squadrons and detached flights. The fleet is extremely diverse, comprising 11 types of fixed-wing aircraft and six helicopters, although Alouette IIs are being replaced by Fennecs. Established strength is 136 aeroplanes and 99 helicopters, but the total available is 70 Transall C.160s, 12 Lockheed C-130H Hercules, 23 Nord 262D Frégates, 27 Morane-Saulnier MS.760 Paris, 15 Dassault Mystère 20s, two Mystère 50s, two Falcon 900s, four Sud Aviation Caravelles, four McDonnell Douglas DC-8s, 10 DHC-6 Twin Otters, two Airtech CN.235M-100s, 29 Aérospatiale SA 316 Alouette IIIs, 28 Aérospatiale SA 330Ba Pumas, six Aérospatiale AS 332 Super Pumas (plus four being received in 1991-92), one Aérospatiale AS 365 Dauphin 2, and most of 52 Aérospatiale AS 555 Fennecs (Ecureuil 2s). CoTAM has 4,300 personnel, of whom 1,310 are aircrew, including 545 fixed-wing aircraft pilots and 197 helicopter pilots.

Principal strategic transport is the C.160F, of which 53 were delivered to 61 Wing from 1967, the first and third squadrons currently having 15 and 12, respectively. The new-generation C.160NG has been operated by 64 Wing since 1982 (11 aircraft in each of two squadrons), and of 23 delivered with refuelling probes, 10 have fuel dispensing capability via a hose-drum unit in the port undercarriage pannier. Several C.160Fs have been detached to overseas units since their Noratlases were withdrawn a decade ago. Requirements for additional strategic transport capacity have been met by an order for 12 Hercules, including nine stretched-fuselage C-130H-30s for ET 2/61, the last delivered in 1991. Acquisition of Hercules has relegated the C.160 fleet to mostly tactical duties, but the AA remains short of transports for such major operations as its participation in the Gulf War of 1991. The AA's single airlift capacity is 850 tonnes, compared with 1,800 tonnes for the otherwise comparable Royal Air Force.

At Villacoublay, the 60th Transport Group has a VIP squadron with two Mystère 20s, two Mystère 50s, two Falcon 900s, two Super Pumas (with more awaited) and a Dauphin, but its four DC-8Fs (a -55 and three CFM56-engined -72s) are detached to Roissy Airport and its single Caravelle 10R to Orly. Fixed-wing training is provided by the OCU, CIET 340, at Toulouse with 10 C.160s and three Nord 262s. Belgium has provided instruction for Hercules crews. Long-term AA transport requirements are for three or four military transport versions of the Airbus A340-300, up to eight Airbus AMP340 tanker/transports to be delivered between 1993 and 2005, and from 52 to 70 C.160 replacements. The last-mentioned will be the EuroFLAG (European Future Large Aircraft) being developed for service early in the next century. Long overdue replacement of the Noratlas began in February 1991 when two CN.235s were delivered to CEAM for trials. AA plans to acquire at least 15, of which the first eight are on firm order, to be used by a squadron at Bordeaux from late 1992 onwards.

ET 65 is the main communications wing, operating from Villacoublay, near Paris, with five Nord 262s, 13 MS.760 Paris, five Twin Otters and five Mystère 20s (including two equipped for calibrating navigation aids). A sixth Twin Otter is detached to Tegel, Berlin. Three autonomous transport and training squadrons are No. 41 for use of FATac with two N 262s and three Paris; No. 43 for the Mediterranean Air Region with a pair each of N 262s and Paris; and No. 44 for South-East Region with two EMBRAER EMB-121 Xingus on loan from Training Command and four N 262s.

Three home-based fixed-wing units with a special function include 51 Electronic Squadron at Evreux with a single DC-8-55 SARIGUE (Système Aéroportée de Recueil d'Informations de Guerre Electronique) converted for gathering electronic intelligence – as evidenced by prominent wingtip pods. The 59th Electronic Squadron has four new-generation C.160 ASTARTEs (Avion Station Relais de Transmissions Exceptionelles) fitted with Rockwell-Collins TACAMO (TAke Charge And Move Out) VLF radio equipment for communications with submerged missile-armed submarines of the Force Océanique Stratégique. Finally, 56 Group has three Twin Otters, two Pumas and two loaned C.160Fs for communications and transport on behalf of the Secret Service (Deuxième Bureau).

Six flights of the 67th Wing provide helicopter support and SAR throughout France. Of 52 recently-delivered Fennecs, 44 are the

AS 555AN version with Turboméca TM319 powerplants, but the first eight deliveries were fitted with Allison 250s and designated AS 555F. The first squadron has four Fennecs, three Alouette IIIs and four Pumas for duties including security of the co-located Mirage IVP squadron and nearby Landes missile test area. EH 2/67 uses four Fennecs and five Alouette IIIs on general duties in north-eastern France. Communications in the Paris area are provided by two Alouette IIs, five Alouette IIIs and four AS 555F Fennecs of EH 3/67, this unit also supplying four Fennecs and an Alouette III for overseas detachments. Security of the IRBM force is assigned to EH 4/67 with two Fennecs and two Pumas, while EH 5/67 in the south-east has a large force of three Fennecs, three Alouette IIIs and four Pumas. SAR in Corsica is the duty of two Pumas and a Fennec of EH 6/67. Helicopter training by CIEH 341 at Toulouse employs two Alouette IIIs, three Pumas and eight Fennecs.

Overseas squadrons are assigned to support garrisons in the departments of greater France and protectorates. Off East Africa, Escadron de Transport Outre-Mer (ETOM – Overseas Transport Squadron) 50 has two Alouette IIIs and a pair of loaned C.160Fs, while further north, in the Horn, ETOM 88 uses two Alouette IIs, a III and a C.160F. Senegal is home to ETOM 55 and one each of C.160F, Alouette II and III. The Pacific hosts ETOM 52 (two C.160Fs, two Alouette IIIs and four Pumas) and ETOM 82 with three Caravelle 11Rs, four Super Pumas and three Alouette IIIs – the last-mentioned detached to the nuclear test base (Centre d'Expérience Nucléaires) on Mururoa Atoll, although many of the missions flown by other aircraft are associated with bomb trials. In the Caribbean and South America, ETOM 58 is equipped with two C.160Fs, a Fennec, two Pumas and an Alouette III, and EHOM 68 uses two Pumas and three cannon-armed AS 355F Fennecs. In 1992-93, EHOM 68 will receive AS 555N Fennecs in place of AS 355Fs and gain a third Puma.

Commandement du Transport Aérienne Militaire

UNIT	EQUIPMENT
Strategic and tactical transport units in Europe	
61ᵉ Escadre de Transport (Base Aérienne 123, Orléans/Bricy)	
ET 1/61 'Touraine'	C.160F
ET 2/61 'Franche Comté'	C-130
ET 3/61 'Poitou'	C.160F
64ᵉ Escadre de Transport (Base Aérienne 105, Evreux/Fauville)	
ET 1/64 'Béarn'	C.160NG
ET 2/64 'Anjou'	C.160NG
Centre d'Instruction des Equipages de Transport 340 (Base Aérienne 101, Toulouse/Francazal)	
00/340 'CIET'	C.160F & N 262D
Communications and VIP units	
60ᵉ Escadre de Transport (Base Aérienne 107, Villacoublay/Velizy)	
ET 1/60 'GLAM'	Mystère 20, Mystère 50, Falcon 900, Super Puma & Dauphin
(Groupe de Liaison Aériennes Ministérielles)	
ET 3/60 'Esterel'	DC-8F (at Paris/Roissy) Caravelle 10R (at Paris/Orly)

EE 51 at Evreux operates one aircraft: the DC-8 SARIGUE. This shadowy aircraft is used for strategic reconnaissance missions of an electronic nature.

ET 65 has a wide-ranging communications brief with a variety of types. ET 3/65 employs the Mystère 20, this example being seen at Kuwait City.

ET 65 is known as the Groupe Aérienne d'Entraînement de Liaison.

ETE 41 provides liaison and staff transport duties for FATac.

The Twin Otter is used for various utility transport duties. This ET 65 aircraft wears the badge of ETOM 52 on the nose.

The elderly Nord 262 is still in use with various utility transport units, including ETE 44 which uses the type to support Région Aérienne Méditerranée from Aix.

ET 3/60 'Estérel' is the main long-range passenger transport unit, based at Roissy (Charles de Gaulle airport). Its principal equipment is the DC-8-72.

Augmenting the ET 3/60 DC-8 fleet across the city at Paris-CDG is this single Caravelle 10R, normally based at Orly.

Further VIP/ministerial transport duties are provided by a pair of Mystère 50s, part of the GLAM fleet at Villacoublay.

The AA's transport helicopter fleet is largely concentrated within EH 67, which has six escadrons at various bases. This is an AS 555 Fennec.

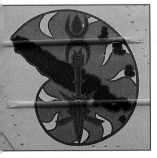

ETOM 52 provides transport for forces in New Caledonia from Tontouta.

ETOM 88's badge is worn on two Alouette IIs, a single Alouette III and a Transall, all based at Djibouti for local transport duties.

ET 1/60 is known as the Groupe de Liaison Aériennes Ministérielles. It has this Falcon 900 on charge.

The mixed GLAM (ET 1/60) fleet includes examples of the Super Puma for ministerial transport.

Completing the GLAM types is the Aérospatiale Dauphin, a single example of which is on charge.

Alouette IIIs continue to serve alongside Fennecs with EH 67. This example is from the Metz-based EH 2/67 'Valmy'.

Among EH 67's equipment is the Puma, although not all of the escadrons have the larger helicopter on strength.

65ᵉ Escadre de Transport (GAEL*) (Base Aérienne 107, Villacoublay/Velizy)

ET 1/65 'Vendôme'	N 262D
ET 2/65 'Rambouillet'	Paris & Twin Otter
ET 3/65 'Commercy'	Mystère 20
DPT 4/65**	Twin Otter (at Base Aérienne 165, Berlin/Tegel)

* Groupe Aérienne d'Entrainement de Liaison
** Détachement Permanent de Transport

41 Escadron de Transport et d'Entrainement (Base Aérienne 128, Metz/Frescaty)

00/041 'Verdun'	N 262D & Paris

43 Escadron de Transport et d'Entrainement (Base Aérienne 106, Bordeaux/Mérignac)

00/043 'Médoc'	N 262D & Paris

44 Escadron de Transport et d'Entrainement (Base Aérienne 114, Aix/les Milles)

00/044 'Mistral'	N 262D & Xingu

Special-role units
Escadron Electronique 51 (Base Aérienne 105, Evreux/Fauville)

00/051 'Aubrac'	DC-8 SARIGUE

Groupe Aérien Mixte 56 (Base Aérienne 106, Evreux/Fauville)

00/056 'Vaucluse'	C-160F, Twin Otter & Puma

Escadron Electronique 59 (Base Aérienne 105, Evreux/Fauville)

00/059 'ASTARTE'	C-160H ASTARTE

Helicopter units in Europe
Escadron d'Hélicoptères 1/67 'Pyrénées' (Base Aérienne 120, Cazaux)

	Fennec, Alouette III & Puma

Escadron d'Hélicoptères 2/67 'Valmy' (Base Aérienne 128, Metz/Frescaty)

	Fennec & Alouette III

Escadron d'Hélicoptères 3/67 'Parisis' (Base Aérienne 107, Villacoublay)

	Fennec & Alouette II/III
	Fennec (at Abidjan, Ivory Coast)
	Alouette III (at Libreville, Gabon)

Escadron d'Hélicoptères 4/67 'Durance' (Base Aérienne 200, Apt)

	Fennec & Puma

Escadron d'Hélicoptères 5/67 'Alpilles' (Base Aérienne 114, Aix/les Milles)

	Fennec, Alouette III & Puma

Escadron d'Hélicoptères 6/67 'Solenzara' (Base Aérienne 126, Solenzara)

	Fennec & Puma

Centre d'Instruction des Equipages d'Hélicoptères 341 (Base Aérienne 101, Toulouse/Francazal)

00/341 'Maurienne'	Alouette III, Puma & Fennec

Overseas units
Groupe Aérien Antilles-Guyane 375 (French Antilles & French Guyana)

ETOM 00/058 'Guadeloupe'	C-160F, Fennec & Puma (at Pointe-à-Pitre, Guadeloupe) Alouette III (at Fort-de-France, Martinique)
EHOM 00/068 'Guyane' (SPA152)	Fennec & Puma (at Cayenne, French Guyana)

Groupe des Forces Aériennes en Nouvelle Caledonie 376 (Base Aérienne Tontouta, New Caledonia)

ETOM 00/052 'La Tontouta'	C-160F, Alouette III & Puma

Détachement Air 160 'Dakar-Ouakam' (Base Aérienne 160, Dakar/Ouakam, Senegambia)

ETOM 00/055 'Ouessant'	C-160F & Alouette II/III

Détachement Air 188 'Colonel Massart' (Base Aérienne 188, Djibouti)

ETOM 00/088	C-160F, Alouette II & III

Escadron de Transport Outre-Mer 50 (Base Aérienne 181, St Denis, Réunion Island)

00/050 'Réunion'	C-160F & Alouette III

Air Power Analysis

Escadron de Transport Outre-Mer 82 (Base Aérienne 190, Faaa, Tahiti)

00/082 'Maine'	Caravelle 11R & Super Puma Alouette III (at Escale Aérienne 195, Mururoa Atoll)

Direction Centrale du Matériel de l'Armée de l'Air

Separate from the Command and Air Region structure of the AA, DCMAA is responsible for administration of maintenance units and other forms of support. A crew ferry and light transport squadron with two Nord 262D Frégates is based at Chateaudun, home of the main MU, Entrepôt de l'Armée de l'Air 601, and Centre de Gestion du Matériel de l'AA 614 (Material Management Centre).

Direction Centrale du Matériel de l'Armée de l'Air

UNIT	EQUIPMENT
Escadron de Convoyage 70 (Base Aérienne 279, Chateaudun)	
00/070	N 262D

Commandement des Ecoles de l'Armée de l'Air

Training for all types of airborne and ground duties is the responsibility of CEAA, which produces some 90 combat pilots and 60 transport and helicopter pilots per year. CEAA has its HQ at Tours and an establishment of 374 aircraft, comprising 104 Dassault-Dornier Alpha Jets, 74 Fouga CM.170 Magisters, 98 Aérospatiale Epsilons, 49 Mudry CAP 10s, five CAP 230s, 14 Jodel D.140 Mousquetaires, 21 EMBRAER EMB-121AA Xingus, three Morane-Saulnier MS.760 Paris, five Nord 262D Frégates and one Dassault Mystère 20. Total holding is considerably larger, deliveries having included 175 Alpha Jets and 150 Epsilons.

Two parallel aircrew training streams are in operation, that for career officers being at the Ecole de l'Air, Salon-de-Provence, where are based 57 Magisters, 12 Alpha Jets, 27 CAP 10Bs, five CAP 230s, five Mousquetaires and a communications Paris. Candidates fly 45 hours on CAP 10s for grading and primary experience prior to a 64-hour Magister course leading to specialisation schools elsewhere. Magisters will have been replaced before the end of 1994 by 50 EMBRAER EMB-312 Tucanos, the first two of which were funded in 1991, followed by 20 in 1992. Also at Salon are the famous 'Patrouille de France' Alpha Jet aerobatic team and the less well known Equipe de Voltige with CAP 230s, plus a recreational gliding section with Jodel D.140R tugs.

Direct entry aircrew spend their first 22-28 weeks at Avord with the Aircrew Initial Training School (Ecole de Formation Initiale du Personnel Navigant) where 20 hours of grading are flown on CAP 10Bs during the first eight weeks. Those selected for navigation duties transfer to Toulouse at this point, but the others spend four weeks of officer training at Evreux, before moving on to Cognac's Basic Flying

School (Ecole de Formation Pilotage de Base) for a 23-week Epsilon course involving 66½ hours. Four Flying Instruction Squadrons (EIV – Escadron d'Instruction en Vol) are partnered by the Instructors School (Ecole des Moniteurs) providing a course of 73 hours. A single Magister is used for liaison. 'Streaming' takes place at the 66½-hour mark, with helicopter pilots then progressing straight to CIEH 341 at Toulouse (see CoTAM section) for a 33-week conversion. Fighter students take 55½ more Epsilon hours in 14 weeks and those destined for transports 21 hours in six weeks before moving to Tours and Avord respectively.

The Fighter School (Ecole de Chasse) at Tours has 55 Alpha Jets (and a pair of communications Paris) on which pilots fly 91 hours in 26 weeks, together with 30 more hours in the simulator, before receiving their 'wings'. In parallel, future transport pilots return to Avord for 29 weeks with Groupement Ecole 319's 21 Xingus, flying 108½ hours to 'wings' standard. These two streams then receive specialist training, the ex-Xingu pilots joining CoTAM's CIET 340 to become (initially) co-pilots of Nord 262s or C.160s. Prospective combat pilots are assigned to the only fighter wing in CEAA, EC 8 at Cazaux. This has 15 Alpha Jets in each of two squadrons, plus an HQ flight with seven Alpha Jets, four communications Magisters and a Mystère 20 target-tug. It plans to re-equip EC 2/8 with some of 30 Alpha Jet As to be bought second-hand from Germany.

Navigators follow their unsuccessful CAP 10 grading with a move to the Ecole des Navigateurs, which has eight Mousquetaires and five Nord 262AENs. The AEN (Avion Ecole de Navigation – Navigation Training Aircraft) is a modified version of the transport aircraft fitted with OMERA ORB-32 radar, Crouzet Omega 600 navigation equipment, TACAN and consoles for four trainees. After a common 181 hours using both aircraft types, courses are split, the transport navigators taking 70 more hours on Nord 262s and those selected for Mirage IVPs or Mirage 2000N/Ds taking 35 hours on borrowed Alpha Jets.

Among other CEAA units, Groupement d'Instruction 317, the Ecole Technique de l'AA at Base Aérienne 721, Rochefort/St Agnant, is of note in having a large number of grounded airframes, some of which are maintained in theoretically airworthy order. There are gliding and air experience sections at several bases, most prominent being the Gliding Centre (Centre Vol à Voile) at Romorantin and Aviation Students' School (Ecole de Pupille de l'Air) at Grenoble/Versoud, both of which have Jodel D.140R Abeilles.

Commandement des Ecoles de l'Armée de l'Air

UNIT	EQUIPMENT
8e Escadre de Chasse (Base Aérienne 120, Cazaux)	
00/008 CDMT	Alpha Jet, Magister & Mystère 20
EC 1/8 'Saintonge' (3C-2 & 4C-1)	Alpha Jet
EC 2/8 'Nice' (SPA73 & SPA78)	Alpha Jet
Ecole de Formation Initiale du Personnel Navigant (Base Aérienne 702, Avord)	
EFIPN 00/307 'Gevaudan'	CAP 10B (Magister & Mousquetaire)

The Alpha Jet fulfils most of the AA's advanced training requirements. Those which serve with EC 8 are used for weapons and tactical training.

GI 312 is the flying unit of the Ecole de l'Air at Salon-de-Provence.

GE 314 is the main advanced training unit, based at Tours.

The Ecole de l'Air gives basic training on the elderly Magister to career officers, before they proceed to further training establishments.

Several AA units have single examples of the Morane-Saulnier MS.760 Paris assigned for communications duties. These aircraft serve GI 312 at Salon-de-Provence.

GE 315 is the basic training unit for direct-entry aircrew, based at Cognac. Four squadrons and an instructor training unit fly the Aérospatiale Epsilon.

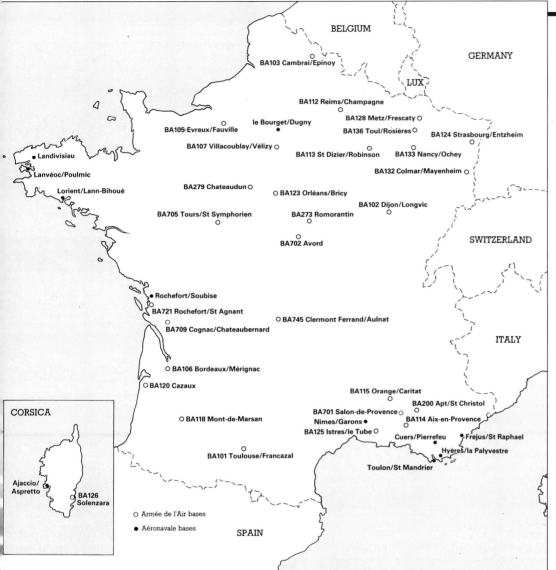

BELGIUM

GERMANY

LUX

BA103 Cambrai/Epinoy

BA112 Reims/Champagne

BA128 Metz/Frescaty

le Bourget/Dugny

BA136 Toul/Rosières

BA124 Strasbourg/Entzheim

BA105 Evreux/Fauville

BA107 Villacoublay/Vélizy

BA113 St Dizier/Robinson

BA133 Nancy/Ochey

BA132 Colmar/Mayenheim

Landivisiau

Lanvéoc/Poulmic

BA279 Chateaudun

BA123 Orléans/Bricy

Lorient/Lann-Bihoué

BA705 Tours/St Symphorien

BA102 Dijon/Longvic

BA273 Romorantin

SWITZERLAND

BA702 Avord

Rochefort/Soubise

BA721 Rochefort/St Agnant

BA745 Clermont Ferrand/Aulnat

BA709 Cognac/Chateaubernard

ITALY

BA106 Bordeaux/Mérignac

BA120 Cazaux

BA115 Orange/Caritat

BA200 Apt/St Christol

BA701 Salon-de-Provence

BA118 Mont-de-Marsan

Nimes/Garons

BA114 Aix-en-Provence

BA125 Istres/le Tube

Cuers/Pierrefeu

Frejus/St Raphael

Hyères/la Palyvestre

BA101 Toulouse/Francazal

Toulon/St Mandrier

CORSICA

Ajaccio/Aspretto

BA126 Solenzara

○ Armée de l'Air bases
● Aéronavale bases

SPAIN

his map shows the principal bases of the Armée de l'Air and the Aéronautique Navale within France ...self. The AA bases are widely spread around the nation, but those of the Aéronavale are necessarily ...ncentrated around the main base areas centred on Brest (Atlantic) and Toulon (Mediterranean).

Ecole de l'Air (Base Aérienne 701, Salon-de-Provence)

Groupement d'Instruction 01/312 — (MS.760 Paris)
Equipes de Présentation de l'AA 02/312
'Patrouille de France' — Alpha Jet
Equipe de Voltige de l'AA — CAP 230
Division des Vols 05/312
Escadrons d'Instruction en Vol:
1 EIV 'Defens' — Magister
2 EIV 'Montmirail' — Magister
3 EIV 'Côte Bleue' — Magister
4 ECS* 'Verdon' — Magister
5 EIA** — CAP 10 & Mousquetaire

* Escadron de Controle et Standardisation (Standards Sqn)
** Escadron d'Initiation Aéronautique

Ecole de Chasse (Base Aérienne 705, Tours/St Symphorien)

Groupement Ecole 00/314 — (MS.760 Paris)
Escadrons d'Instruction:
1 EI 'Jean Lenglet' — Alpha Jet
2 EI 'Henri Jeandet' — Alpha Jet
3 EI 'Henri Arnaud' — Alpha Jet
4 EI 'Marin la Meslée — Alpha Jet
6 ECS* 'Jean Maridor' — Alpha Jet

* Escadron de Controle et Standardisation (Standards Sqn)

Ecole de Formation Pilotage de Base (Base Aérienne 709, Cognac/Chateaubernard)

Groupement Ecole 00/315 — (Magister)
Escadrons d'Instruction en Vol:
1 EIV — Epsilon
2 EIV — Epsilon
3 EIV — Epsilon
4 EIV — Epsilon
Ecole des Moniteurs — Epsilon

Ecole des Navigateurs (Base Aérienne 101, Toulouse/Francazal)

Groupement Ecole 00/316 — N 262AEN & Mousquetaire

Groupement Ecole 319 (Base Aérienne 702, Avord)
00/319 — Xingu

Centre Vol à Voile 55/273 (Base Aérienne 273, Romorantin)
— D.140R Abeille (& sailplanes)

Ecole de Pupille de l'Air 349 (Grenoble/Versoud)
— D.140R Abeille (& sailplanes)

he Jodel D.140 is used for some training duties, notably by E 316 for initial navigation instruction. However, its main ...sk is as a glider tug in its D.140R Abeille form.

In AA use, the EMBRAER Xingu is primarily used to give multi-engine training with GE 319 at Avord.

Etat-Major de l'Armée de l'Air

The CEAM trials establishment is controlled directly by the General Staff and is responsible for assessment and ongoing development of military aircraft, avionics, weapons and even vehicles. An operational squadron is equipped with around 15 Mirage F1s and Mirage 2000s of various sub-types, its duties including training personnel of the first FAS or FATac squadron to receive a new type of equipment. A transport and training squadron has two CN.235M-100s, 10 Magisters, two Xingus, two Alpha Jets, four Paris, two Ecureuil 2s, and a Puma. CEAM maintains three out-stations: two at the CEV bases of Istres (Annexe CEAM 333) and Brétigny-sur-Orge (Annexe CEAM 332) and the third for weapons training from Base Aérienne 120, Cazaux (Annexe CEAM 331).

Etat-Major de l'Armée de l'Air

ET 6/330 is one of CEAM's two squadrons. Among the ...aried types of transports and trainers assigned is this ...irtech CN.235M, one of two on strength.

CEAM's EC 5/330 'Côte d'Argent' performs fighter trials and evaluation duties. Currently assigned is this Mirage 2000N.

UNIT	EQUIPMENT
Centre d'Expériences Aériennes Militaires 330 (Base Aérienne 118, Mont-de-Marsan)	
Escadron de Chasse 5/330 'Côte d'Argent'	Mirage F1 & Mirage 2000
Escadrille d'Expérimentation et de Transport 6/330 'Albret'	various

Aéronautique Navale

Complementing surface vessels and submarines of the Marine National is a land- and sea-based naval air arm, the Aéronautique Navale – usually abbreviated as Aéronavale. Aviation's role is to assist its parent service in protecting the submarine-launched missile deterrent; maintaining an aero-maritime combat capability in Europe to deny an aggressor use of the seas and ensure safe passage for reinforcements; providing an overseas presence and defence for maritime exclusive economic zones; and facilitation of rapid overseas deployment of an aero-maritime intervention force.

Front-line forces of Aéronavale are operated by 15 squadrons known as flottilles assigned either to Aviation Embarquée (Embarked Aviation) or Aviation de Patrouille Maritime (Maritime Air Patrol). Squadron designations indicate their role: 1 F to 10 F for embarked ASW; 11 F to 20 F for embarked strike/interceptor/reconnaissance; 21 F to 30 F for land-based patrol; and 31 F to 40 F for helicopters. Supporting flights, known as escadrilles de servitude, are responsible for surveillance, training, communications and trials and include some based overseas. The 16 currently operative are numbered in the ranges 1 S to 19 S for fixed-wing transport, communications and SAR; 20 S to 29 S for helicopters; and 50 S to 59 S for training.

Some 370 aircraft are possessed by the navy, including 110 aeroplanes and 70 helicopters rated as front-line. Of these, about 140 are operational at any time, comprising 30 Dassault Super Etendards, 12 Vought F-8E(FN) Crusaders, eight Dassault Etendard IVPs and 18 Dassault-Bréguet Alizés all able to operate from aircraft-carriers; 37 Dassault-Breguet Atlantic 1/Atlantique 2s and five Dassault Gardians for patrol; and 11 Aérospatiale SA 321 Super Frelon, 29 Westland Lynx and three Aérospatiale Alouette III helicopters. Aéronavale has 9,000 personnel, including 700 pilots and 1,100 other aircrew. The three major components of Aéronavale are the Service Central de l'Aéronautique Navale, Aviation de Patrouille Maritime and Aviation Embarquée et le Groupe des Porte-Avions.

Aviation Embarquée et le Groupe des Porte-Avions

Geography divides France's navy into two components: Atlantic Region, with headquarters at Brest, and Mediterranean Region at Toulon. The latter was formerly 3ᵉ Region, while the former is a combination of 1ᵉ Region (English Channel) and 2ᵉ Region (Atlantic/Biscay). Naval air bases are situated close to the two seaboards, but most carrier operations are undertaken in the Mediterranean and points east, so that aircraft often have to cross the country to join their ship. Forces assigned to Commandant of Embarked Aviation and Aircraft-Carrier Group at Toulon comprise 11 flottilles and four escadrilles capable of operating from the two aircraft-carriers and – in the case

of helicopters – other warships and support vessels.

Most powerful elements of the Marine Nationale's surface fleet are the twin aircraft-carriers *Clemenceau* and *Foch*, dating from the early 1960s. Each displaces 32,700 tonnes when fully laden and has a flight deck 166 m (543 ft) long and 30 m (97 ft) wide. A complement of 1,920 men includes 1,030 assigned to the air group, to fly and maintain a maximum complement of 20 Super Etendards for strike/attack; seven Crusaders for air defence; six Alizés to undertake ASW patrols; four Etendard IVPs capable of photo-reconnaissance and 'buddy' tanking; and four Lynx (ASW) or four Super Frelon (transport) helicopters.

Super Etendards serve with two squadrons, following disbandment of 14 F in July 1991. Of 71 aircraft received, 53 were modified by the Atelier Aviation de Cuers (Naval Depot at Cuers) to carry an Aérospatiale ASMP nuclear stand-off missile of the kind also fitted to AA Mirage IVPs and Mirage 2000Ns. A mid-life upgrade for 50 aircraft began when the first of three prototype conversions to be undertaken by Dassault flew on 5 October 1990. The 'Super Etendard Modernisé' will enter service in 1993 and serve until 2005, when replacement by the Dassault Rafale is envisaged. Retaining its conventional attack and nuclear capabilities, the modernised aircraft will be fitted with a new radar (Dassault Electronique Anémone), improved navigation equipment, wide-angle HUD with TV or IR overlay, Thomson-CSF SHERLOC radar warning receivers, HOTAS controls and provision for pilot's night vision goggles.

Government rejection of naval plans to obtain McDonnell Douglas F/A-18 Hornets as a temporary replacement for Crusaders has crippled carrier aviation by rendering it dangerously vulnerable in the face of an enemy air threat. Lacking pulse-Doppler (look-down) radar, the aged Crusader is unable to protect a task group with anything more than short-range AIM-9 Sidewinder or MATRA R.550 Magic IR missiles or the obsolete MATRA R.530 radar-guided weapon. An updating of 17 aircraft (from 19 survivors of 42 delivered) for continued service is under way, with re-deliveries from the Cuers workshops planned between June 1992 and December 1994. Apart from addition of a radar warning receiver, work involves safety features such as rewiring, strengthening and new ejection seats, adding nothing to the aircraft's limited potential.

Projected first deliveries of the eagerly-awaited navalised Rafale M recently have slipped from 1 July 1996 to shortly before the end of that year. Rafale M meets the ACM (Avion de Combat Marine – Naval Combat Aircraft) requirement for 86 fighters to replace Crusaders, Etendard IVPs and, eventually, Super Etendards. Despite a rethink by the AA in favour of two crew members, the Rafale M remains a single-seater, in which configuration the first of two prototypes flew on 13 December 1991. The initial recipient will be a reformed 14 F, allowing the Crusader-equipped 12 F to disband once carrier qualification has been achieved in 1998. By 1999, the navy will have 20 Rafales to the interim S.01 standard, lacking the pilot's helmet-mounted sight, forward-facing

Elderly they may be, but the Aéronavale's Alizés continue t provide sterling service in the ASW role, both from carrier decks and shore bases.

4 Flottille has been at Lann-Bihoué with Alizés since July 1964.

The Mediterranean Alizé unit is 6 F, based at Nîmes-Garons.

The cutting edge of the French carrier air wing is the Super Etendard, of which 20 are usually carried for strike/attack duties, including nuclear missions.

11 F is a Super Etendard flottille based at Landivisiau.

Mediterranean partner for 11 F is 17 F, with Super Etendards at Hyères.

The elderly Etendard IVPs of 16 Flottille are retained at Landivisiau to provide carrierborne detachments for reconnaissance and buddy tanking.

In its heyday one of the finest naval fighters, the Vought Crusader is now woefully insufficient for protecting the carrier battle group from air threats. However, 12 Flottille is forced to continue with the type until Rafale M becomes available for the fighter role in late 1996.

The Westland Lynx helicopter fulfils the carrierborne ASW role, or can operate from frigates and destroyers. A major unit is based on each coast: 31 F and 34 F.

Super Frelons previously undertook ASV and ASW work, but are now used entirely for transport duties.

Donald Duck carrying a blunderbuss is the badge of 12 F, worn by F-8E(FN)s.

The black flamingo badge adorns the Etendard IVPs of 16 Flottille.

Alouette IIIs are used by Aéronavale units for a variety of general transport and rescue duties.

32 Flottille is the Atlantic Super Frelon unit, based at Lanvéoc-Poulmic.

Mediterranean helicopters fly from Saint Mandrier, including those of 34 F.

23 S at Saint Mandrier has recently acquired Dauphins for the plane-guard and rescue roles in the Mediterranean.

electro-optics, automatic defensive sub-systems, ASMP capability and other features. There will then be no further deliveries until 2005-2009, during which period the remaining 66 are to be received to full S.02 (or later) configuration.

Related to the Rafale M programme are two nuclear-powered aircraft-carriers, *Charles de Gaulle* and *Richelieu*, of which only the former is currently under construction, for operational service from 1998 as a replacement for *Clemenceau*. The second vessel was due to supplant *Foch* in 2004 but may be deferred for up to five years. Each will displace 35,000 tonnes fully loaded and accommodate 35-40 aircraft, of which 23 can be stored below deck. Overall flight-deck size is 262 m (858 ft) by 64 m (211 ft), the angled portion 195 m (640 ft) long. To complete their air groups, the Aéronavale is examining the possibility of obtaining some four Grumman E-2C Hawkeye AEW aircraft, a category of air power also urgently required by the fleet.

Embarked patrol duties are assigned to Alizés, two squadrons of which (4 F and 6 F with an operational establishment of nine each) also undertake shore-based surveillance. During the early 1980s, 28 of the 75 originally received were updated to Br 1050M standard with new Thomson-CSF Iguane radar and ARAR 12 passive ESM, and 24 of these are being further upgraded with a datalink and improved decoy system for service until 1998. 4 F is assigned to Atlantic operations and 6 F to the Mediterranean, the offensive capability including 68-mm rocket pods, Mk 44 torpedoes and Aérospatiale AS.12 wire-guided missiles. 6 F has been responsible since September 1989 for Alizé deck-landing training and role conversion, for which it has an extra three aircraft. Of equal age to the Alizé, Dassault's Etendard IVP serves with one reconnaissance squadron, the attack-configured Etendard IVM having been withdrawn from training (with 59 S) on 1 July 1991. Retirement of IVPs is expected in 1995.

Helicopters fly from a larger number of vessels, but only those with hangars have a permanent allocation – and not always the maximum complement possible. Ships are:
Jeanne d'Arc (13,270 tonnes) helicopter-carrier with hangarage for eight (rarely fully embarked).
Colbert command cruiser (11,300 tonnes); pad for one helicopter.
Three 'Tourville'-class (F67) anti-submarine frigates (5,885 tonnes); hangarage for two Lynx. Vessels are *Tourville, Duguay-Trouin* and *de Grasse*.
Seven 'Georges Leygues'-class (C70 ASW/F70) ASW destroyers; hangarage for two Lynx. Vessels are *Georges Leygues, Dupleix, Montcalm, Jean de Vienne, Primauguet, La Motte-Picquet* and *La Touche-Treville*.
Two 'Cassard'-class (C70 AA) anti-aircraft frigates (4,300 tonnes); hangarage for one Lynx. *Cassard* and *Jean Bart*. Two deferred until 1994 (*Courbet* and *Chevalier Paul*).
Eight 'Commandant Rivière'-class frigates; pad for one helicopter. Vessels are *Victor Schoelcher, Commandant Bory, Amiral Charner, Doudart de Lagrée, Balny, Commandant Bourdais, Protet* and *Enseign de Vaisseau Henry.*
Foudre landing ship; hangar for four large

helicopters. Two more postponed until late 1990s.

Two 'Ouragan'-class landing ships; platform for three large or 10 small helicopters. *Ouragan* and *Orage*.

Four 'Champlain'-class landing ships; pad for one helicopter. Vessels are *Champlain, Francis Garnier, Dumont d'Urville* and *Jacques Cartier*.

Four 'Meuse'-class replenishment ships; pad for one helicopter. Vessels are *Meuse, Var, Durance* and *Marne*.

Trieux landing ship; pad for two small helicopters.

Jules Verne repair ship; hangarage for two helicopters.

Four 'Rhin'-class support ships; various facilities for small helicopters: *Rhin* hangar for one; *Loire* pad only; *Rance* hangar for three; *Rhone* pad only.

Three research ships: *Henri Poincaré*, with hangar for two large or five small helicopters; *Commandant Rivière* pad for one; and *Triton* pad for one.

Main frigate helicopter is the Lynx, deliveries having comprised two prototypes, 26 HAS.Mk 2(FN)s and 14 HAS.Mk 4(FN)s with uprated engines. Equipment includes French avionics (OMERA ORB 31W radar and Alcatel HS/DUAV-4 dipping sonar), Mk 46 homing torpedoes or Aérospatiale AS.12 wire-guided anti-ship missiles. The BAe Sea Skua used by Royal Navy Lynx would be more effective in view of the Lynx's 50-per cent dedication of anti-surface vessel missions, but the planned 1990s upgrade for the helicopters does not appear to include a newer missile. Lynx of 31 F are assigned to 'Leygues'-class and 'Cassard'-class ships; those of 34 F to 'Tourville'-class. Three Aérospatiale AS 365F Dauphins were delivered to 23 S in February 1990 to replace 'pedro' plane-guard Lynx aboard the aircraft-carriers, and a further 12 will be ordered to complete replacement of the unit's remaining eight Alouette IIs and IIIs, which are also assigned to SAR, instrument training and communications in the Mediterranean Region.

Alouettes of 22 S – including wheeled-undercarriage Alouette IIs – provide a similar service in the Atlantic Region, the unit being also the Ecole de Spécialisation sur Hélicoptères Embarqués, providing deck-landing training to pilots trained on helicopters by the army. 35 F is based aboard the *Jeanne d'Arc* during exercises, the vessel's peacetime role being training cruises for naval officer cadets. The SA 321G Super Frelon formerly possessed an anti-ship capability with Aérospatiale Exocet missiles, but the 20 survivors are now relegated to commando transport, vertical replenishment of ships at sea and civilian support duties such as SAR. On retirement of the Super Frelon in 2001, the navy plans to begin standardisation of its helicopter fleet with up to 60 NFH-90 navalised versions of the European-built NH-90.

Carrier conversion is undertaken only after pilots have completed jet training with the Armée de l'Air. 59 S has a dozen carrier-capable Fouga CM.175 Zephyr versions of the Magister for initial experience of deck landing and catapult take-offs, its advanced course being undertaken since July 1991 on Super Etendards transferred from the disbanded 14 F. Up to 30 replacements for the Zephyr are required, for

which Dassault is proposing a navalised Alpha Jet. 57 S has four Mystère 10MERs (Marine Entrainement Radar) for radar training and eight MS.760 Paris continuation training and communications aircraft, its supplementary duties including simulation of radar targets for ships' air defence training.

Embarked aviation currently employs 1,600 personnel, including 317 pilots and 140 other aircrew.

Aviation Embarquée et le Groupe des Porte-Avions

UNIT	EQUIPMENT	BASE
4 Flottille	Alizé	Lann-Bihoué
6 Flottille	Alizé	Nîmes/Garons
11 Flottille	Super Etendard	Landivisiau
12 Flottille	Crusader	Landivisiau
16 Flottille	Etendard IVP	Landivisiau
17 Flottille	Super Etendard	Hyères
31 Flottille	Lynx	Saint Mandrier
32 Flottille	Super Frelon	Lanvéoc-Poulmic
33 Flottille	Super Frelon	Saint Mandrier
34 Flottille	Lynx	Lanvéoc-Poulmic
35 Flottille	Alouette III	Lanvéoc-Poulmic
22 Escadrille	Alouette II/III	Lanvéoc-Poulmic
23 Escadrille	Alouette III & Dauphin	Saint Mandrier
57 Escadrille	Mystère 10MER & Paris	Landivisiau
59 Escadrille	Super Etendard & Zephyr	Hyères

Aviation de Patrouille Maritime

Four squadrons of Atlantic/Atlantique long-range, twin-turboprop patrol aircraft, two flights of overseas-based medium-range Gardian twin-jets and three training/communications squadrons are controlled by the Maritime Patrol Aviation Command, which has its HQ at le Bourget/Dugny. As replacements for the original 41 Atlantic 1s and five attrition replacements bought from the Netherlands in 1985, Dassault is producing 30 Atlantique 2s, the last to be completed in 1998. The two west coast squadrons have priority, resulting in 23 F being declared operational with three of its planned eight Atlantique 2s on 1 February 1991. Co-located 24 F begins equipping in 1992, to be followed by the two Mediterranean squadrons: 21 F from 1994 and 22 F. The new Atlantique has better corrosion protection, improved avionics and the ability to launch AM39 Exocet anti-ship missiles instead of the AJ37 Martels fitted to Atlantic 1s. Not all the older aircraft will be retired immediately, as some will be retained for surveillance tasks abroad, perpetuating the detachments already established at Djibouti, Dakar (Senegambia), Réunion and in the Antilles. In the absence of more suitable aircraft, Atlantics were used for overland reconnaissance during the French intervention in the Chad civil war during the early 1980s.

For patrol and SAR within French territorial economic zones in the Pacific, two Mystère 20H Gardians are assigned to 9 S at Tontouta, New Caledonia, and three to 12 S at Faaa, Tahiti. The latter's aircraft, complemented by an Alouette III, are additionally responsible for communications for the nuclear test centre at Mururoa.

Pilots destined to fly twin-engined aircraft are first trained by the air force, career officers

56 S at Nîmes-Garons has a training function for patrol aircrew.

57 S has Mystère 10MERs for radar training and simulating targets.

Mystère 10MERs of 57 Escadrille de Servitude fly from Landivisiau on a variety of support duties for the fleet. Some transport duties are undertaken.

57 S also has examples of the MS.760 Paris, these flying on target simulation, communications and training duties, the latter mainly for desk-bound officers.

59 S is based at Hyères for carrier training, equipped with the hook-equipped CM.175 Zéphyr for initial work. Students then proceed to the Super Etendard.

A specialist Mystère 20 variant for the Aéronavale is the Gardian, characterised by the extra-large observation window. Two overseas patrol units operate the type.

with an Atlantic squadron before receiving the co-pilot's brevet.

56 S trains navigators and flight engineers on its fleet of seven Nord 262Es and two Piper PA-31 Navajos. From 26 N 262s (mostly 262As) delivered to the Navy, 12 were modified to 262E standard in the early 1980s with underfuselage OMERA ORB 32 radar and training consoles in the cabin, plus ARAR 12 ESM and Crouzet Omega 501 navigation equipment.

Aviation de Patrouille Maritime

UNIT	EQUIPMENT	BASE
21 Flottille	Atlantic	Nimes/Garons
22 Flottille	Atlantic	Nimes/Garons
23 Flottille	Atlantic	Lann-Bihoué
24 Flottille	Atlantic	Lann-Bihoué
9 Escadrille	Gardien	Tontouta
12 Escadrille	Gardien	Faaa
52 Escadrille	Xingu	Lann-Bihoué
55 Escadrille	Nord 262A	Aspretto
56 Escadrille	Nord 262E & Navajo	Nimes/Garons

Escadrilles de Soutien Régionales

Seven Escadrilles de Servitude and a ferry flight complete the Aéronavale's flying units. In the Atlantic Naval Region, 2 S has a fleet of six Nord 262s and four (of the navy's 12) Piper PA-31 Navajos for communications and light transport, although three of the Nords are radar-equipped 262Es for inshore surveillance. Similarly, for the Mediterranean Region, 3 S operates two 262As, two 262Es, five Navajos and two Mystère 10MERs – the last-mentioned for radar/instrument training as well as VIP flights. Deliveries of the 10MER totalled seven, of which six survive.

Naval headquarters in Paris is served by 11 S at Le Bourget with three Xingus and two Nord 262s. A Xingu is also operated by the Escadrille de Réception et de Convoyage as a crew ferry for the Cuers naval workshops, augmented as required by Rallyes and Navajos on loan. Experimental work is undertaken by 10 S (aeroplanes) and 20 S (helicopters).

Two light aircraft units include 50 S with four SOCATA Rallyes to give informal flying training to students of the Ecole Navale (Naval College). Apart from one loaned to ERC, the remaining 12 Rallyes are with 51 S alongside eight Mudry CAP 10s, their role being provision of 20 hours' grading of NCO students at the St Raphael Naval School before progression to the air force for Epsilon training.

Escadrilles de Soutien Régionales

UNIT	EQUIPMENT	BASE
2 Escadrille	Nord 262A/E	Lann-Bihoué
3 Escadrille	Nord 262A/E, Navajo & Mystère 10MER	Hyères
10 Escadrille	Xingu, Nord 262A & Alizé	Saint Raphael
11 Escadrille	Xingu & Nord 262A	Le Bourget/Dugny
20 Escadrille	Alouette II/III, Super Frelon & Lynx	Saint Raphael
50 Escadrille	Rallye	Lanvéoc/Poulmic
51 Escadrille	CAP10	Rochefort/Soubise
Escadrille de Réception et de Convoyage	Xingu, Navajo & Rallye	Cuers

For land-based maritime patrol the Aéronavale leans heavily on the Atlantic/Atlantique, this example being one of the latter new-build aircraft. Improved avionics and weapons fit are the main difference, the later aircraft being equipped to fire the Exocet anti-ship missile.

Escadrille de Servitude is at Lann-Bihoué with Nord 262s. Some are used for transport/communications work, while others are radar-equipped for coastal patrol.

Aéronavale Xingus are used for multi-engine training with 52 S, liaison (11 S), trials (10 S) and as crew ferries (ERC).

Piper PA-31 Navajos are used for a variety of tasks, including communications (2 S and 3 S), crew ferrying (ERC) and training (56 S).

The SOCATA Rallye flies on initial grading duties for prospective students, and for general instruction for non-aircrew.

51 S operates the Aéronavale's fleet of CAP 10s, these performing the task (alongside Rallyes) of grading Aéronavale students prior to training with the AA.

with the Ecole de l'Air on Magisters before transferring to 52 S, the Ecole de Spécialisation Multimoteurs, for a 90-hour twin-conversion course using half the navy's 16 EMBRAER EMB-121AN Xingus. Next, the tactics of Maritime Patrol are learned at 55 S, the Ecole de Perfectionnement sur Multimoteurs, with 25 hours on Nord 262s. Qualification is as an Atlantic/Atlantique co-pilot, in which role some 700 more hours are required with a squadron before promotion to aircraft captain. NCO pilots train with air force Epsilons at Cognac, then spending 34 weeks at 52 S flying 120 Xingu hours and a short, 30-hour course at 55 S. They must then serve a further 300 hours

Aviation Légère de l'Armée de Terre

Army Light Aviation (Aviation Légère de l'Armée de Terre – ALAT) is a force of 710 helicopters and 7,200 personnel (including 650 officers and 3,000 NCOs, of whom 1,100 are pilots) tasked with provision of supporting services to the Armée de Terre ([Land] Army). Principal tasks are anti-tank missions with guided missiles; armed escort; reconnaissance (scouting); communications; and liaison. In overall command is a general (three-star) whose HQ, the Commandement de l'ALAT, is at Villacoublay and responsible for organisation, training and management of the aviation budget. Indicating the importance of the last-mentioned, ALAT represents only 4 per cent of the army, yet takes 15 per cent of its equipment funding.

As with all army aviation forces, ALAT is based close to the ground elements it will support in wartime. For an understanding of its organisation, it is necessary to look briefly at the deployment of the Armée de Terre. Principal ground fighting units are 12 Divisions, of which eight are assigned to the 1re Armée and four to the Force d'Action Rapide (Rapid Reaction Force).

1re Armée (Metz)

2e Corps d'Armée (Baden-Oos, Germany): 1r, 3e and 5e Armoured Divisions; 15e Infantry Division.

3e Corps d'Armée (Lille): 2e, 7e and 10e Armoured Divisions; 8e Infantry Division.

Force d'Action Rapide (Maisons-Laffitte):

6e Light Armoured Division; 9e Marine Infantry Division; 11e Parachute Division; 27e Alpine Division. Total 47,000 men.

Under the Armées 2000 restructuring plan, 1 Corps disbanded on 1 July 1990 and transferred its two armoured divisions (7 and 10) to 3 Corps. Units returning from Germany before 1994 are to disband and pass their equipment to existing formations.

The two training divisions (12 and 14 Light Armoured), formerly within 1 Corps, were re-allocated to a second level of army structure, the Forces de Défense du Territoire (or Forces Régionales). Originally based on six defence zones, this was reduced to three by 1992, the boundaries of which are identical to the three Air Regions. Largely comprising reservist personnel, forces in the zones are assigned to the defence of static installations and borders.

Administration of units at levels below ComALAT is via two geographical sub-divisions: ComALAT Nord at Lille and ComALAT Sud at Aix. Management of the interface between land and air units is handled by Commandement d'Aviation Légère de Corps de l'Armée 2 (Army Corps Light Aviation Command 2) at Baden-Oos for 2 Corps; COMALCA 3 at Camp des Loges, San Germain-en-Laye for 3 Corps; Etat-major de la Division Aéromobile at Nancy for the FAR; Groupement ALAT 103 at Versailles for Territorial Defence Forces in the north; and GALAT 104 at Aix for those in the south.

Five types of Aérospatiale-built helicopter form almost the complete strength of ALAT: Alouette II, Alouette III, Gazelle, Puma and Cougar (Super Puma). Most numerous is the Gazelle, which is used in several roles with appropriate equipment. From 170 SA 341F versions received in 1973-77, 67 were converted to Canon standard with a GIAT M621 20-mm cannon mounted externally on the starboard side of the cabin for armed escort of transport helicopter formations. A further 40 received an interim fitment of the Euromissile HOT anti-tank missile and APX M397 rooftop sight under the designation SA 341M, although their performance is limited by an all-up weight of 1900 kg (4,189 lb). Other SA 341s are used for scouting with the M334 Athos magnifying sight – a simplified M397, lacking missile guidance equipment – and an extra VHF/FM radio.

ALAT has now taken delivery of 200 SA 342M Gazelles, a second-generation variant dedicated to anti-tank missions and fitted with an uprated version of the Astazou turboshaft which increases its maximum combat weight to 2100 kg (4,630 lb). When deployed to an operational theatre, the Gazelle can be fitted rapidly with an upturned engine exhaust to reduce the infra-red signature. With a range of 4000 m (13,123 ft) the four HOTs carried by the SA 342M are currently day-capable only, but that will be rectified in 1993 when deliveries begin for about 70 Gazelles of the SFIM VIVIANE sight, which includes a thermal imaging camera. In 1990, ALAT also took delivery of 18 SA 342Ls built for China, but not delivered, and marked as 342Ms.

A further extension of SA 342M capabilities concerns addition of an anti-helicopter capability with the MATRA ATAM – an air-launched version of the Mistral AATCP (Air-Air Très Courte Portée) infantry SAM. Four Mistrals, each with a range in excess of 4500 m (14,764 ft), and a T2000 sight will be carried in place of HOT on 30 helicopters, although the installation was pre-empted in 1990 in preparation for the Gulf War. As the 'Gazelle Celtic', helicopters were rapidly modified with just two Mistrals on the port pylon (two HOTs to starboard) and an SFOM 80 sight as fitted to cannon-armed SA 341Fs.

Replacement of the Gazelle is planned through a considerably delayed Franco-German programme undertaken by Eurocopter, first fruits of which will be seen in 1999 with service entry of the Gerfaut HAP (Hélicoptère d'Appui et Protection – Support and Protection Helicopter). As a follow-on to the Gazelle/Canon, Gerfaut will mount Mistrals, rocket pods and a turret-mounted 30-mm cannon. ALAT requires 75 Gerfauts, of which 40 will be assigned to the FAR. Early next century, deliveries are planned of 140 of a second version, the Tigre HAC (Hélicoptère Anti-Char – Anti-Tank Helicopter), with a mast-mounted sight (TV, FLIR, tracker and laser), four Mistrals and eight of either HOT or the forthcoming AC3G (multi-national TriGAT).

The above-mentioned improvements correspond to ALAT's four priorities for the 1990s, which are: (**1**) extension of operational capability through addition of night vision equipment; (**2**) reduction of helicopter vulnerability

Replacement for the Gazelle is expected in the form of the Eurocopter Tigre/Gerfaut, the former being an anti-tank version and the latter for general gunship duties.

1 RHC at Phalsbourg has three flights equipped with the SA 342M Gazelle/HOT, and is assigned to the Force d'Action Rapide.

Another 1 RHC Gazelle in scout configuration. No offensive armament is fitted, but the aircraft retains the roof-mounted sight for aiming HOT missiles.

The Puma is useful for moving large objects around the battlefield, as demonstrated here by this example seen depositing a slung artillery piece.

The Puma is the ALAT's primary assault helicopter, and is often deployed overseas, with many aircraft wearing a desert scheme.

This SA 342M Gazelle/HOT serves with one of two escadrilles of 7 RHCCA, based at Nancy as part of 1re Armée. Note the empty HOT rails.

Different armament in the shape of the GIAT M621 20-mm cannon characterises the SA 341F Gazelle/Canon, which are distributed through the ALAT with one flight per regiment.

A large-scale ALAT exercise involves many Gazelles. In the foreground are HOT-armed SA 342Ms for anti-armour work, while waiting to the rear are Gazelle/Athos scouts, which are equipped with roof-mounted sights but no armament.

The FAR's 4 RHCM is basically a transport unit, and was deployed to Kuwait/Iraq during the 1991 war. This example is seen wearing the coalition identification stripes.

Also part of the FAR is the 3 RHC at Etain. This has a single flight of SA 330B Pumas which wear this smart three-tone camouflage scheme.

Two flights of the 4 RHCM now operate the AS 532UL Cougar, a vastly improved version of the Puma with far greater load-carrying ability.

by passive means such as exhaust diffusion and chaff/flare dispensers, and by active means including escort helicopters armed with cannon and Mistrals; (**3**) augmenting anti-tank efficiency by introducing the fire-and-forget AC3G and mast-mounted sight, both of which reduce helicopter exposure to enemy countermeasures; and (**4**) reduction of training costs through use of 10 Aérospatiale AS 555UN Fennec instrument training helicopters and greater reliance on simulation.

In this last regard, a simulator will be delivered in 1993 for ALAT's second most numerous helicopter, the Puma/Cougar. Beginning in 1969, the service received 132 SA 330B Pumas, to which were later added 15 SA 332Ba versions (equivalent to the 330L) and a few attrition replacements bought from the Romanian production line. The current fleet stands at 135, each of which can lift up to 15 fully-equipped troops, or 2 tonnes internally or 2.5 tonnes underslung. The FAR has recently been equipped with 22 AS 532UL Cougars, which have a seating capacity of 25 and the ability to lift 4.5 tonnes. Plans to obtain a further 20 Cougars equipped with the Orchidée (Observatoire Radar Cohérent Héliporté d'Investigation des Eléments Ennemis) battlefield surveillance radar were abandoned in 1990 but reinstated in the following year after the demonstration Puma took part in the Gulf War. To cut costs, ALAT will receive a simplified version known as HORIZon (Hélicoptère d'Observation Radar et d'Investigation sur Zone), deliveries to begin in about 1997.

Replacing the Puma will be the multinational NH-90 in its TTH-90 (Tactical Transport Helicopter) guise. Combining Aérospatiale, Agusta, DASA and Fokker design and manufacturing, NH Industries SARL has its HQ at Aix-en-Provence, France, and expects to make initial deliveries in 1998. ALAT has a requirement for 150 TTH-90s, each with accommodation for 20 equipped troops or over 2 tonnes of freight. The French version will have a rear ramp for loading vehicles.

Now assigned to the regional defence units and training organisation are 140 remaining SE 3130 and SA 318C Alouette IIs and 60 SA 316B Alouette IIIs. As the Tigre/Gerfaut is a tandem-seat helicopter, configured for the battlefield, replacement of liaison and training helicopters will be by Ecureuils. Some 80 AS 550Us and 20 twin-engined AS 555URs are required, although economies will almost certainly reduce the total purchased. Completing the ALAT inventory are the unique SA 361H Dauphin I helicopter testbed and five aeroplanes: three Cessna O-1E Bird Dogs for liaison, and two Reims/Cessna F406 Caravan IIs. The latter are fitted for towing sleeve targets on up to 7000 m (22,965 ft) of cable or can carry nine passengers in the liaison role. Employment of the various ALAT helicopters is detailed below.

Force d'Action Rapide

Formed in July 1985, the FAR is unofficially regarded as a NATO reserve, capable of rapid movement to reinforce a threatened position or to exploit an enemy's weakness. It is also able to respond to overseas events, either in French colonies, in countries with which France has a defence agreement, or on behalf of the United Nations, as was the case in the Kuwait crisis of 1990-91.

Air component of the FAR is ALAT's 4e Division Aéromobile, comprising an HQ at Nancy/Essey and 241 helicopters in five major units. Three of these are designated RHC (Régiment d'Hélicoptères de Combat – Combat Helicopter Regiment) and a fourth is the unique RHCM (Régiment d'Hélicoptères de Commandement et de Manoeuvre – Command and Transport Helicopter Regiment).

Completing the FAR is a much smaller GHL (Groupe d'Hélicoptères Légers – Light Helicopter Group) in the form of 5 GHL at Lyon. Regiments comprise up to six flights, designated according to their duties and equipment, while a group has up to three flights. These are: **EHAC** Escadrille d'Hélicoptères Anti-Char (Anti-Tank Helicopter Flight) with 10 SA 342Ms and HOT missiles; **EHAP** Escadrille d'Hélicoptères d'Appui et de Protection (Support and Escort Helicopter Flight) with 10 SA 341F/Canon, although 1ᵉ RHC was re-structured in 1990 with a mixture of 341F/Cs and 342M(L)s; **EHC** Escadrille d'Hélicoptères de Commandement (Command Helicopter Flight) with 10 SA 341Fs equipped with Athos scouting sights; **EHLR** Escadrille d'Hélicoptères Légers de Reconnaissance (Light Reconnaissance Helicopter Flight) with 10 SA 341Fs carrying Athos scouting sights. Since 1990, the EHLRs of both 1ᵉ and 3ᵉ RHCs have been partly or wholly equipped with SA 342M(L)s; **EHL** Escadrille d'Hélicoptères Légers (Light Helicopter Flight) with eight Alouette IIs or IIIs; **EHM** Escadrille d'Hélicoptères de Manoeuvre (Transport Helicopter Flight) with nine or 10 Pumas or Cougars; **EHS** Escadrille d'Hélicoptères de Soutien (Support Helicopter Flight) with nine Pumas.

The FAR's three RHCs (1ᵉ, 3ᵉ and 5ᵉ) each have three flights of anti-tank Gazelles, plus one flight for scouting, one for protection and one of Pumas for support. The 4ᵉ RHCM is primarily a transport force attached to the FAR HQ, for which reason it has six Puma/Cougar flights and one liaison flight of Gazelles. Furthermore, the transport flights include one permanently detached to the 5ᵉ RHC at Pau and two which would form only in wartime, using helicopters of the training school, Ecole d'Application. The three flights of 4ᵉ RHCM, which are detached to Phalsbourg, operate 15 Pumas and 16 Cougars. All RHCs and the RHCM additionally possess two non-flying flights: Escadrille de Commandement et de Service and Escadrille de Soutien et de Ravitaillement. In addition to these, RHCs have 900 men and 350 vehicles.

Finally, 5ᵉ GHL at Lyon has one flight of eight Alouette IIs at its home base and one of eight Alouette IIIs at Gap – of which two are detached to Luc/Le Cannet and one to Ajaccio, Corsica. One specialist task of the unit is provision of training in mountain flying, for which pilots already experienced in helicopter work first attend a 14-week/44-hour course at the advanced flying school, the Ecole de Spécialisation. They then transfer to Gap for a further 18 weeks, during which 91 hours are flown in the Alps.

Force d'Action Rapide

UNIT	EQUIPMENT
1ᵉ Régiment d'Hélicoptères de Combat (Phalsbourg)	
1ᵉ EHLR	SA 342L1 Gazelle/Athos
2ᵉ EHAP	SA 341F Gazelle/Canon
3ᵉ EHAC	SA 342M Gazelle/HOT
4ᵉ EHAC	SA 342M Gazelle/HOT
5ᵉ EHAC	SA 342M Gazelle/HOT
6ᵉ EHS	Puma

UNIT	EQUIPMENT
3ᵉ Régiment d'Hélicoptères de Combat (Etain/Rouvres)	
1ᵉ EHAP	SA 341F Gazelle/Canon
2ᵉ EHLR	
SA 342L1 Gazelle/Athos	
3ᵉ EHAC	SA 342M Gazelle/HOT
4ᵉ EHAC	SA 342M Gazelle/HOT
5ᵉ EHAC	SA 342M Gazelle/HOT
6ᵉ EHS	Puma

UNIT	EQUIPMENT
4ᵉ Régiment d'Hélicoptères de Commandement et de Manoeuvre (Nancy/Essey)	
1ᵉ EHC	SA 341F Gazelle/Athos
2ᵉ EHM	Puma (at Phalsbourg)
3ᵉ EHM	Cougar (at Phalsbourg)
4ᵉ EHM	Puma (at Pau)
5ᵉ EHM	Cougar (at Phalsbourg)
6ᵉ EHM*	
7ᵉ EHM*	
* to form in wartime from Pumas of Ecole d'Application	

UNIT	EQUIPMENT
5ᵉ Régiment d'Hélicoptères de Combat (Pau/Uzein)	
1ᵉ EHAP	SA 341F Gazelle/Canon
2ᵉ EHLR	SA 342L1 Gazelle/Athos
3ᵉ EHAC	SA 342M Gazelle/HOT
4ᵉ EHAC	SA 342M Gazelle/HOT
5ᵉ EHAC	SA 342M Gazelle/HOT
6ᵉ EHS	Puma

UNIT	EQUIPMENT
5ᵉ Groupement d'Hélicoptères Légers (Lyon/Corbas)	
1ᵉ EHL	Alouette II
3ᵉ EHL	Alouette III (at Gap with detachments at Luc/Le Cannet des Maures and Ajaccio)

1ʳᵉ Armée

In addition to its small communications flight of three Gazelles and three Alouettes at Trier, Germany, the 1st Army has three RHCs and one GHL attached to its two remaining corps. The former are designated RHC de Corps d'Armée (2ᵉ, 6ᵉ and 7ᵉ) to indicate their affiliation and the fact that they are considerably smaller than the similarly-named units in the FAR. In the case of an RHCCA, only four or five flights are operational in peacetime, each with just eight helicopters. All have at least two anti-tank flights and one of Pumas, but only two possess canon-armed Gazelles, the 7ᵉ RHCCA having to manage with Alouette IIIs and its anti-tank force diluted with SA 341Ms. Each would add at least a Gazelle/HOT flight taken from training units in the event of war. Duties of 6ᵉ RHC include VIP flying to augment the air force's 60ᵉ Escadre de Transport.

Similarly, of three notional GHLs, two would only appear for hostilities, equipped with training Alouette IIs for liaison and communications. Only 12ᵉ GHLCA is a permanent unit, serving 2 Corps from Baden, Germany, with 10 Alouette IIIs and ALAT's last three O-1E Bird Dogs – these assigned to the HQ French Forces in Germany (Commandement Centrale des Forces Français Allemandes – CCFFA). GHLCAs have the tasks of artillery spotting, liaison, light transport and forward observation post, for which their six Alouette II light helicopters would form an Escadrille d'Hélicoptères Légers, backed by six Alouette IIIs in an Escadrille d'Hélicoptères Légers de Reconnaissance. Finally, 3 Corps and the old 2 Zone HQ have their own attachment of 10 Alouette IIIs at Lille/Lesquin 'parented' by 6ᵉ RHCCA at Compiègne.

The view from above provides an excellent display of the mounting for the four Euromissile HOT weapons carried by the SA 342M.

An SA 341F Gazelle/Canon in action, firing the M621 weapon installed on the starboard side. These will be replaced by the Gerfaut with anti-helicopter capability.

Many Alouette IIIs are retained by ALAT units for regional defence and training duties. In time of war they could be formed into offensive units.

5 GHL's Alouette IIIs are part of the FAR, but are used primarily for training crews in specialist mountain work. For this they are based at Gap with detachments.

The *Orchidée* stand-off radar surveillance platform is seen in flight with the radar fully deployed. The system proved a significant success during an evaluation in the Gulf.

Force d'Action Rapide: areas and divisional HQs
2ᵉ Corps d'Armée: areas and divisional HQs
3ᵉ Corps d'Armée: areas and divisional HQs

When stowed, the *Orchidée* radar rotates to lie under the tail boom of the Puma carrier. The aircraft has identification stripes for Gulf War participation.

Alouette IIs are retained for training and liaison work, notably with the Forces de Défense du Territoire. This example, however, serves with 5 GHL at Lyon.

2 GHLCA operates the last three Cessna O-1E Bird Dogs left in ALAT service, these being based in Germany at Baden and used for liaison.

A pair of Cessna F406 Caravan IIs serves with 3 GHL at Rennes, flying as target-tugs for anti-aircraft artillery training.

1ʳᵉ Armée

UNIT	EQUIPMENT
2ᵉ Régiment d'Hélicoptères de Combat de Corps d'Armée (Phalsbourg –2 Corps)	
1ᵉ EHAP	SA 341F Gazelle/Canon
2ᵉ EHAC	SA 342M Gazelle/HOT
3ᵉ EHAC	SA 342M Gazelle/HOT
4ᵉ EHM	Puma
EHAC*	
EHLR*****	
6ᵉ Régiment d'Hélicoptères de Combat de Corps d'Armée (Compiègne – 3 Corps)	
2ᵉ EHL	Alouette III (at Lille)
3ᵉ EHAP	SA 341F Gazelle/Canon
4ᵉ EHAC	SA 342M Gazelle/HOT
5ᵉ EHAC	SA 342M Gazelle/HOT
6ᵉ EHM	Puma
EHAC*	
7ᵉ Régiment d'Hélicoptères de Combat de Corps d'Armée (Nancy/Essey – General Reserve)	
1ᵉ EHL	Alouette III
3ᵉ EHAC	SA 342M Gazelle/HOT
4ᵉ EHAC	SA 342M Gazelle/HOT
6ᵉ EHM	Puma
2ᵉ EHAP****	
5ᵉ EHAC*	
11ᵉ Groupe d'Hélicoptères Légers de Corps d'Armée (Nancy/Essey – 2 Corps)	
EHL**	
EHLR***	
12ᵉ Groupe d'Hélicoptères Légers de Corps d'Armée (Baden – 2 Corps)	
EHLR	Alouette III
Esc CCFFA	O-1E Bird Dog
EHL*	
13ᵉ Groupe d'Hélicoptères Légers de Corps d'Armée (Compiègne – 3 Corps)	
EHL**	
EHLR***	
Escadrille 1ᵉ Corps d'Armée (Trier)	
	Alouette III & SA 341F Gazelle
Détachment ALAT (Lille/Lesquin)	Alouette III (for HQ 3ᵉ Corps d'Armée)

* to form in wartime with SA 342M Gazelle/HOTs
** to form in wartime with Alouette IIs
*** to form in wartime with Alouette IIIs
**** to form in wartime with SA 341F Gazelle/Canons
***** to form in wartime with SA 341F Gazelle from the Ecole de Spécialisation

Forces de Défense du Territoire

Regional defence forces possess a small number of aircraft for communications and other second-line duties. 1ᵉ GHL at les Mureaux has five each of Alouette IIs, Alouette IIIs and Gazelles for use by the High Command in Paris and the former 1 Zone; 3ᵉ GHL has two target-towing Cessna Caravan IIs and 10 Alouette IIs previously used by 3 Zone; and 4ᵉ GHL at Bordeaux (4 Zone) has 10 Alouette IIs, plus two at Montauban. Some reorganisation of these units is expected as a result of the change from six to three military zones.

Aircrew attached to GHLs require different skills to those employed on anti-tank and transport helicopters, as they will be involved with work for the civil authorities, such as mountain rescue, accidents and forest fires.

Forces de Défense du Territoire

UNIT	EQUIPMENT
1ᵉ Groupe d'Hélicoptères Légers (les Mureaux)	
1ᵉ EHL	SA 341F Gazelle
2ᵉ EHL	Alouette II
3ᵉ EHL	Alouette III
3ᵉ Groupe d'Hélicoptères Légers (Rennes/St Jacques)	
EHL	Alouette III
EA	Caravan II
(Escadrille d'Avions)	
4ᵉ Groupe d'Hélicoptères Légers (Bordeaux/Souge)	
1ᵉ EHL	Alouette II (Detachment at Montauban)

Other Units

Instructional, overseas and experimental units are the final category of ALAT aircraft operators. Helicopters have recently served in the Middle East during the Gulf War and its aftermath, but the sole permanently based units abroad are Détachement ALAT 188 at the AA's

Base Aérienne 188, Djibouti, and the Détachement ALAT in Chad.

Training is undertaken at two schools, that for basic flying being the Ecole de Spécialisation d'ALAT (ESALAT) at Dax, where students from ALAT (70 per cent), the Aéronavale (20 per cent), Gendarmerie (6 per cent), Sécurité Civile and abroad are instructed. A fleet of 56 Alouette IIs, including four provided by the navy, gives prospective pilots 106 hours of flying in their first 22 weeks, completed by 15 more hours in three weeks on 18 Gazelles. ALAT personnel then go to the Ecole d'Application d'ALAT (EAALAT) at Luc for tactical flying with 14 Alouette IIs, 17 SA 341F Gazelle/Canons, 15 SA 341M/342M Gazelle/HOTs, 20 Pumas and two Cougars. EAALAT trains some 800 personnel per year, including those returning for more advanced instruction after gaining experience with an operational unit. Among the many courses offered are cannon (Gazelle and Puma) and missile (Gazelle) firing; anti-tank helicopter captain (two months); Puma captain (2½ months); anti-tank flight leader (3½ months); Puma flight leader (2½ months); use of night-vision goggles (one month) and Puma flight engineer (three weeks). Instructors are also trained at Luc. A detachment of Pumas is based at Aix as the Groupe de Manoeuvre de l'Ecole d'Application (GMEA) while HOT missile firing is undertaken at Canjuers. The four AS 555UN Fennecs recently ordered by ALAT are expected to be based at Luc for training with NVGs.

Main trials unit is the Groupement Aéromobilité de la Section Technique de l'Armée de Terre (GASTAT), where some 311 military personnel and 20 helicopters are based for work on all aspects of army aviation. Communications flights of two Alouette IIs are operated by the Commandement ALAT at Villacoublay and ComALAT Sud at Aix, while the Escadrille attached to the Bourges maintenance unit of Direction Central du Matériel has two Alouette IIIs and one each of the Puma, Gazelle and Alouette II.

Other Units

UNIT	EQUIPMENT
Ecole de Spécialisation de l'ALAT (Dax)	Alouette II & SA 341F Gazelle
Ecole d'Application de l'ALAT (Luc/Le Cannet des Maures)	Alouette II, SA 341F Gazelle/Canon, SA 341M/342M Gazelle/HOT, Puma & Cougar (detachment of Pumas at Aix)
Détachement ALAT 188 (Djibouti)	Puma
Détachement ALAT (Chad)	SA 341F Gazelle, SA 342M Gazelle/HOT & Puma
Commandement ALAT (Villacoublay)	Alouette II
Commandement ALAT Sud (Aix)	Alouette II
Groupement Aéromobilité de la Section Technique de l'Armée de Terre (Valence/Chabeuil)	all helicopters, plus SA 361H
Escadrille de Direction Centrale du Matériel (Bourges)	all helicopters

Other Agencies

Several French government agencies operate aircraft which are essentially civilian in nature, these including the Sécurité Civile (SAR, coastguard, firefighting), Douanes (customs), Police Nationale, Centre Nationale d'Etudes des Télécommunications and Ecole Nationale Supérieure d'Aéronautique et l'Espace (aeronautical engineers school).

Those with closer military ties are discussed below.

Gendarmerie Nationale

A military police force which undertakes civilian roles in peacetime, the Gendarmerie has 3,650 territorial brigades and permanent stations throughout rural France. Manpower comprises 55,000 in the Gendarmerie Départmentale; 17,000 in the Gendarmerie Mobile; and 5,000 attached to smaller units. Personnel are conscripted into the force (about 6,800 serving at any time) in the same manner as with the other armed services.

The Departmental force includes an air element, the Groupement Central des Formations Aériennes de la Gendarmerie at Villacoublay. Following retirement of the last Alouette II in May 1990, this now has a home-based force of 30 AS 350B Ecureuil 1s, 11 Alouette IIIs and six Cessna U206Fs. These are identified by a three-letter code in the same manner as ALAT aircraft.

Operating units are organised on regional networks, at the hub of which is a Section Aérienne. Sections can maintain up to three permanent Détachements Aériennes and up to two Détachements Saisonniers – the latter manned during holiday seasons, winter or summer. There are currently nine Sections, 11 permanent Detachments and six Seasonal Detachments.

Gendarmerie Nationale

SECTION AERIENNE	DETS AERIENNES	DETS SAISONNIERS
Amiens	nil	Abbeville
Rennes	St Nazaire	nil
Villacoublay	Tours	nil
Metz	nil	Gérardmer
Dijon	nil	Mouthe
Lyon	Megève	Modane
	Chamonix	
La Teste	Limoges	Royan
	Egletons	Mimizan
	Bayonne	
Hyères	Briançon	nil
	Montpellier	
	Ajaccio	
Toulouse	Tarbes	nil

Overseas units in the French possessions

Fort de France (Martinique)	Cayenne (French Guyana)	nil
	Pointe-à-Pitre (Guadeloupe)	
Noumea (New Caledonia)	nil	nil
St Denis (Réunion)	Comores (Comoros Islands)	nil
-	Libreville (Gabon)	nil

One of several quasi-military services which operate aircraft is the Douanes Françaises (French customs) which flies this Cessna F406 Caravan II.

The Gendarmerie operates the Aérospatiale AS 350B Ecureuil as its principal equipment. These are used for general police work and for rescue duties.

The CEV maintains a large and disparate trials fleet. Included are five CASA 212-300 Aviocars, two of which are flown by the test pilot school.

Mirage IIIBs are used for a variety of duties by the CEV. Among the more important is the training of future test pilots undertaken by the EPNER.

One of the CEV's two assigned Caravelles is used to provide zero-g for astronaut experience in association with the Centre National d'Etudes Spatiales.

A small fixed-wing fleet for the Gendarmerie consists of six Cessna U206Fs. These perform general surveillance work on police matters.

Partnering the Ecureuil in the Gendarmerie rotary-wing force is the Alouette III. The once-widespread Alouette II has now been completely retired.

The Gendarmerie badge depicts an Alouette II over mountains.

The CEV badge has a stylised representation of the unit's initials.

Among the French military aircraft unique to the Centre d'Essais en Vol is the Pilatus PC-7. Five were bought for general trials duties.

A small communications fleet serves the DCAN, the naval dockyards and weapons board. This single MH.1521 Broussard flies alongside Robin HR.100s and Wassmer Guépards.

GENDARMERIE AVIATION

■ Sections Aériennes
● Détachements Aériennes
▲ Détachements Saisonniers
  lines of command

Centre d'Essais en Vol

CEV is a pure research establishment, one role of which is to evaluate for issue of a type certificate all civil and military aircraft operated by the government. Tasks assigned to CEV tend more towards military applications, and the establishment is administered by the Direction des Constructions Aéronautiques – part of the Délégation Générale pour l'Armement (a Ministry of Defence department of rank equal to the three armed services). CEV has a staff of 2,400 – of whom 55 are pilots – and a fleet of over 100 aircraft which fly some 8,000 hours per year. There are three bases, each with specialist sections: Brétigny-sur-Orge – prototype testing, aircraft equipment, radar and radio; Istres – prototypes, helicopters, powerplants, simulators and test pilots' school; Cazaux – armament.

The permanent test and transport support fleet of some 35 aircraft includes one or more examples of the Mirage 2000B/C/N, Mirage F1, Mirage IIIB/R, Jaguar A/E, Alpha Jet and Mystère 20 (several avionics testbeds), plus five Pilatus PC-7s, two Caravelles, a Transall C.160, five CASA C.212 Aviocars, two Nord 262s, two Pumas, an Alouette II, four Alouette IIIs and four SA 365N Dauphin IIs. CEV is lavishly supplied with liaison and communications aircraft in the form of 10 MS.760 Paris, four Cessna 411s, one Cessna 337, 14 Cessna 310s, one Jodel D.140R, 13 Robin HR.100s, 16 Wassmer CE.43 Guépards and a CAP 10.

Ecole du Personnel Navigant d'Essais et de Réception

As part of the CEV, the Ecole du Personnel Navigant d'Essais et de Réception is a school for test pilots and flight engineers who will progress to either prototype testing or acceptance flying. Based at Istres, it has call on the CEV fleet as required, but the typical allocation of aircraft (taken from those listed above) is three Alpha Jets, three Mirage IIIB-1s, one Mystère 20, the CAP 10, one Nord 262, two Aviocars, three Alouette IIIs and two Dauphin IIs. Courses available include test pilot (10 months), light aircraft test pilot (four months), acceptance test pilot (four months), flight-trials engineer (10 months), flight-trials mechanic (10 months) and flight-acceptance mechanic (four months).

Direction des Constructions et Armes Navales

DCAN – the Board of Naval Dockyards and Weapons – has a small communications fleet based at Hyères and Cuers. The aircraft, which use Aéronavale callsigns, are two Robin HR.100/250s, two Guépards and a Max Holste MH.1521 Broussard.

INDEX

Page numbers in **bold** refer to an illustration

158

159

357th FS: 14
358th FS: 14
421st TFS 'Black Widows': 131
428th F-BS: 45
428th FS 'Buccaneers': 44-46
428th TFS 'Buccaneers': 45
428th TFTS: 45
492nd FS: 11, 12
493rd FS: 12
494th FS: 11, 12
495th FS: 12
522nd F-BS: 46
522nd FES: 46
522nd FS 'Fireballs': 44-47
522nd SFS: 46
522nd TFS: 46, 47
523rd FES: 48
523rd FS 'Crusaders': 44, 45, 48
523rd SFS: 48
523rd TFS: 48
524th FES: 50
524th FS 'Hounds': 44, 45, 50, 51
524th TFS: 50
524th TFTS: 50
909th ARS: 14
961st ACS: 14
962nd ACS: 14
Wings
3rd TFW: 14
3rd Wg: 14
4th Wg: 14
18th TFW: 14

18th Wg: 14
19th Wg: 12
21st FW: 14
23rd FW: 14
23rd Wg: 14
27th FW: 12, 44-51
27th TFW: 44, 46, 48
37th FW: 12
37th TFW: 12
48th FW: 11, 12
49th FW: 12
55th Wg: 12
57th FWW: 11
89th AW: 12
89th MAW: 12
92nd Wg: 12
100th ARW: 14
306th Wg: 14
317th AW: 14
343rd TFW: 14
343rd Wg: 14
353rd SOW: 14
355th FW: 14
376th SW: 14
388th TFW: 131
405th TFW: 48
434th Wg: 15
474th TFW: 45
502nd ACW: 11
509th Wg: 15
513th ACCW: 14
552nd ACW: 14
602nd ACW: 14

Army: 10, 11, 34, 37, 43
Army Air Force
Group
474th FG: 45
Squadrons
11th RS: 50
17th BS (Light): 48
91st BS: 50
522nd F-BS: 46
823rd F-BS: 48
524th F-BS: 50
Army National Guard (ArNG): 9
Coastguard: 13, 41, 42
Federal Aviation Administration: 43
Marine Corps: 4, 10, 15, 28, 33, 35-39, 42, 43
Air Reserve: 31
Squadrons
HMX-1: 43
VMFA-333 'Shamrocks': 15
VMFA-531 'Grey Ghosts': 15
VMFA(AW)-225 'Vagabonds': 15
National Aeronautics & Space
Administration (NASA): 13
Navy: 4, 8, 11, 16, 28-31, 34, 36-43, 47
Carrier Air Wings
CVW-5: 28
CVW-6: 15
Pacific Fleet: 28
Squadrons
VC-5 'Checkertails': 28-31
VF-11 'Red Rippers': 15
VF-31 'Tomcatters': 15
VF-124 'Gunfighters': 15

V

W-22 Ground Test Vehicle (see Bell-
Boeing)
V-22 Osprey (see Bell-Boeing)
Var: 150
**VC-5 'Checkertails' & Mount
Pinatubo**: 28-31, **28-31**
VC10 tanker/transport (see Vickers)
Venezuela
Air Force (Fuerza Aérea Venezolana): 10,
11
Vertol VZ-2: 34
VFW-614 (see Fokker)
Vickers VC10 tanker transport: 8
Victor Schoelcher: 149
Viking, S-3 (see Lockheed)
Voodoo, F-101 (see McDonnell)
Vought A-7 Corsair II: 11, 32
Vought F-8E(FN) Crusader: **137**, 148,
149
VZ-2 (see Vertol)

W

Warrior, SF.260 (see SIAI-Marchetti)
Warsaw Pact: 110
Wasp, USS (LHD-1): 33, 36, **36**, 40, **42**
Wassmer CE.43 Guépard: 157
WC-135 (see Boeing)
Wessex (see Westland)
Westland

Lynx: **6**, 8, 148-150, **149**
Sea King: 8, 118
Super Lynx: **8**
Wessex: 8

X
XV-3 (see Bell)
XV-15 (see Bell)

Y
Yakovlev
Yak-44: 24
Yak-141 'Freestyle': 19
YE-8B (see Boeing)
YF-22 (see Lockheed/Boeing/General
Dynamics)
YS-11 (see NAMC)
YT-45 (see McDonnell Douglas/BAe)
Yugoslavia
Air Force (Jugoslovensko Ratno
Vazduhoplovstvo): 9

Z
Z.43 (see Zlin)
Zephyr, CM-175 (see Fouga)
Zlin Z.43: 5

Picture credits